BIOLOGICAL METHODS FOR THE ASSESSMENT OF WATER QUALITY

A symposium
presented at the
Seventy-fifth Annual Meeting
AMERICAN SOCIETY FOR
TESTING AND MATERIALS

ASTM SPECIAL TECHNICAL PUBLICATION 528
John Cairns, Jr. and K. L. Dickson, editors
Virginia Polytechnic Institute and State University

List price $16.25
04-528000-16

AMERICAN SOCIETY FOR TESTING AND MATERIALS
1916 Race Street, Philadelphia, Pa. 19103

NOTE

The Society is not responsible, as a body,
for the statements and opinions
advanced in this publication.

Printed in Baltimore, Md.
Second Printing, December 1973

Foreword

The Symposium on Biological Methods for the Assessment of Water Quality was presented at the Seventy-fifth Annual Meeting of ASTM held in Los Angeles, Calif., 26–29 June 1972. The symposium was sponsored by Committee D-19 on Water, and was designed to form Subcommittee D-19.01 on Biological Monitoring. John Cairns, Jr. and K. L. Dickson, Virginia Polytechnic Institute and State University, presided as cochairmen.

Related
ASTM Publications

ASTM Manual on Water, STP 442 (1969), $16.50
Microorganic Matter in Water, STP 448 (1969), $9.50

Contents

Introduction

It is probable that in the near future many industries will be required to maintain a continuous environmental quality assessment program to demonstrate what biological impact the materials they produce, both products and waste products, have upon ecological systems. We have found that environmental management groups (industrial and governmental) have suddenly and, in some cases, unexpectedly faced environmental crises, but often know very little about the biological aspects of water pollution.

This volume is intended to be a management tool to apprise the reader of the types of considerations involved in making biological assessments of water quality, developing water pollution monitoring programs, and assessing the effects of potentially deleterious waste discharges in the aquatic environment. Also, it provides information which would enable a non-biologist to get a state-of-the-art view of the existing techniques available, as well as some historic perspective.

Papers by world authorities on the use of fish, algae, aquatic invertebrates, and bacteria in the assessment of pollution, in addition to bioassays for evaluating the toxicity of products or waste effluents, are included. Futuristic methods for continuous biological monitoring of industrial effluents are presented, as well as a possible alternative to the much belabored Biochemical Oxygen Demand. Obviously, no book covering such a vast array of subjects can cover any one in sufficient detail, therefore, papers in the volume contain excellent bibliographies.

The Symposium on Biological Methods for the Assessment of Water Quality held at the ASTM Annual Meeting 26–29 June 1972 in Los Angeles was designed to form Subcommittee D-19.01 on Biological Monitoring of Committee D-19 on Water, and was intended to be a springboard from which ASTM methods for the biological assessment of water quality will develop.

We feel that the authors have done an excellent job of keeping technical terms to a minimum and have directed their efforts toward making biological monitoring useful and understandable to all readers. In short, we feel that this publication offers to the nonbiologist and biologist excellent resource material essential in developing a biological monitoring program.

John Cairns, Jr.
K. L. Dickson

Virginia Polytechnic Institute and State University, Blacksburg, Va.
symposium cochairmen

W. W. Eckenfelder, Jr.[1]

Interaction of Engineers and Biologists in Water Quality Management

REFERENCE: Eckenfelder, W. W., Jr., **"Interaction of Engineers and Biologists in Water Quality Management,"** *Biological Methods for the Assessment of Water Quality, ASTM STP 528,* American Society for Testing and Materials, 1973, pp. 3–5.

ABSTRACT: This paper discusses the need for a closer interaction between the biologist and engineer in water quality management. Various interdisciplinary programs are reviewed which include the academic scene and the technical literature. The author gives an example of how the two disciplines need to work closely in order to meet the requirements to maintain and preserve the aquatic environment.

KEY WORDS: water pollution, aquatic biology, environmental surveys

Until recently aquatic biologists engaged primarily in research in government and academic institutions involving studies on lakes and rivers. Probably the most famous study of this type has been that involving Lake Mendota in Wisconsin. During this same period, sanitary engineers were primarily concerned with stereotype designs of wastewater treatment plants for the removal of BOD and suspended solids. The primary concern as reflected in regulatory requirements was the maintenance of prescribed dissolved oxygen levels in the receiving waters. In the educational area, most environmental engineers fell under traditional civil engineering programs, while the aquatic biologist was an integral part of the science program areas. If the two disciplines met, it was usually unrelated to professional interests or activities. In fact, even the professional societies drew certain disciplinary lines which minimized or discouraged professional intercourse between the engineer and the biologist.

[1] Professor of Environmental and Water Resources Engineering, Vanderbilt University, Nashville, Tenn. 37235.

In the past few years, however, this picture has undergone a substantial change. This can be attributed in large measure to an awareness of environmental effects other than BOD or dissolved oxygen on receiving waters. New and pending legislation is cognizant of other pollutants such as nitrogen, phosphorous, COD, etc., and their effects on the aquatic environment. An increasing number of industries and regulatory agencies are relating pollutional discharges to the overall effect on the aquatic environment, rather than restricted specific effects. This fact has led to a professional linkage between the engineer responsible for removing or modifying the pollutant and biologist responsible for defining its effect on the environment. Since the realistic requirements must consider both the establishment of criteria which will fully protect the water for its intended use and the economic and technical feasibility of achieving these levels, the two disciplines need to work closely in accord with each other.

The present relationship between the engineer and the biologist is also being reflected on the academic scene. An increasing number of interdisciplinary programs now exist in this country. For example, at Vanderbilt University only a few years ago, all of our graduate students in Environmental and Water Resources Engineering came from a civil engineering or chemical engineering background. At the present time, 30 percent of the students in this program have a basic background in biology or chemistry. The graduate program at Vanderbilt is being modified to fully accommodate students with both interest and background in engineering to fulfill the environmental needs in the field.

A number of interdisciplinary journals are now available, such as *Water Research,* which links the engineer and the biologist through the technical literature. International and regional conferences such as those sponsored by the International Association on Water Pollution Research and the International Association of Limnology has interdisciplinary sessions to encourage dialogue and interchange between the engineer and the biologist.

The engineer must have knowledge of the effects of pollutants on the aquatic environment in order to have a better understanding of treatment methodology to achieve these levels or modifications to industrial processes to eliminate or change the deleterious substances. The biologist must develop an understanding of the technology and economics of water pollution control in order to assist with an effective water quality management program. How can this be done? Students presently in environmental programs at most of our universities are exposed to interdisciplinary-type programs, and in general develop the broadness of knowledge and understanding required. Practitioners in the field, however, still suffer from the earlier disciplinary guidelines of a decade ago. The author submits that a series of seminars interrelating biology and engineering using field experience and practice could be one possible approach. This is presently being considered by the International Association on Water Pollution Research, among other groups.

I can cite an example of the interrelationship between the biologist and the engineer at the present time. A chemical plant in the Southwest was required to develop a water quality management program, including wastewater treatment to meet specified effluent qualities, and to establish a program which would insure that the aquatic environment was not damaged. In order to achieve these results, biological surveys of the receiving water above and below the plant were instituted prior to the industrial plants being constructed and waste treatment facilities installed. These surveys were conducted on a seasonal basis. Pilot plant studies were then conducted to determine the type and degree of treatment that would be required to maintain and preserve the aquatic environment. The effluents from the pilot plant studies were subjected to biological analyses, including species diversity indices, in order to determine what level of treatment would be required for preservation of the environment. These conjunctive studies between the wastewater treatment and the biological effects provided the primary basis for wastewater treatment plant design. At the construction of the plant, biological surveys were continued on a seasonal basis which, in turn, were related to the effluent from the wastewater treatment plant. It is the author's opinion that this is the approach of the future, and that this integration between the biological effects on the aquatic environment and the engineering inputs required to meet water quality requirements become an integral part of all industrial water quality management programs in the future.

J. B. Sprague [1]

The ABC's of Pollutant Bioassay Using Fish

REFERENCE: Sprague, J. B., **"The ABC's of Pollutant Bioassay Using Fish,"** *Biological Methods for the Assessment of Water Quality, ASTM STP 528,* American Society for Testing and Materials, 1973, pp. 6–30.

ABSTRACT: This is a recommended method for tests of acute toxicity of pollutants to fish. Improved procedures are recommended: chiefly, more frequent observations of mortality and simple statistical treatment. The four-day lethal concentration or the lethal threshold concentration should be used as the final expression of the test result. Toxicity curves should be constructed as the experiment progresses, for the information of the investigator. Tests should provide at least two liters, and preferably three liters of test water per gram of fish per day, whether the test is static or continuous-flow. Tests should not be aerated. Standard species such as rainbow trout are recommended.

Effects of mixtures should be assessed by adding toxicant concentrations which have been expressed as fractions of the lethal concentration. Some suggestions are made for using the standard bioassay technique in experiments on sublethal and chronic effects.

KEY WORDS: water pollution, tests, fishes, bioassay, toxicity

A series of three papers about fish bioassays is included in this publication. This paper deals with the specific details of how to conduct a simple lethal test with fish, while the paper by Brungs [2] emphasizes long-term or sublethal tests, and the paper by Stephan and Mount [3] shows how to use such test results in practical problems of pollution control.

The following methods are taken from two sources: the first is the standard bioassay method of the American Public Health Association et al[*1*], [4]

---

[1] Associate professor, Department of Zoology, University of Guelph, Guelph, Ontario, Canada.

[2] See p. 117.

[3] See p. 164.

[4] The italic numbers in brackets refer to the list of references appended to this paper.

which is based on a paper by Doudoroff et al[2]; the second source is the series of review articles which were written by the author[3], giving detailed substantiation of the points described here.

Purposes of a short-term bioassay of a waste are usually to answer one or more of the following questions.

Is it toxic?

How toxic?

Does it vary in toxicity?

Which fraction of the waste is most toxic?

Is available dilution sufficient to protect fish?

How effective are treatment methods in reducing toxicity?

Basically, fish are used to answer these questions by means of the bioassay. No assumptions need be made concerning the chemical structure or form of the pollutant, although naturally, the more that is known about this, the more revealing the assay can be.

Terminology

A bioassay may be defined as "a test in which the quantity or strength of material is determined by the reaction of a living organism to it" (modified from Quayle[4]). That definition would cover the usual pharmacological tests of drugs and also the toxicity tests of which we speak here.

The median lethal concentration is the usual method of reporting results. The current trend is to use the symbol LC50 (lethal concentration for 50 percent of the individuals), a notation which is used in most fields of biological testing. The symbol TL50 (formerly TLm) or median tolerance limit, has been commonly used by United States fisheries workers. The two terms have the same numerical value. A time period must always be specified (for example, 96-h LC50). The LC50 is merely a convenient reference point for expressing the acute lethal toxicity of a given pollutant to the average or typical fish. Obviously, the "safe" concentration which permits successful reproduction, growth, and all other normal life processes in the fish's natural habitat, is lower than the LC50, usually much lower. The term median lethal dose (LD50) is seldom valid for work with fish, since it means the amount of drug or toxicant which is actually received inside the body, for example, by injection or by eating.

Toxic effects may be divided into a number of overlapping categories. Acutely lethal toxicity would be considered that which causes severe and rapid damage to the organism by the fastest acting mechanism of poisoning, fatal unless the organism escapes the toxic environment at an early stage[3]. However, no single definition clearly separates acutely lethal action from other kinds. Most toxic effects could be described accurately by using one or two of the following terms, which are sometimes also used to describe the type of experiment which is being conducted.

Acute—involving a stimulus, severe enough to bring about a response speedily, usually within four days for fish.

Subacute—involving a stimulus which is less severe than an acute stimulus, which produces a response in a longer time, and may become chronic.

Chronic—involving a stimulus which is lingering or continues for a long time; often signifies periods of about one tenth of the life span or more.

Lethal—causing death, or sufficient to cause it, by direct action.

Sublethal—below the level which directly causes death.

Cumulative—brought about, or increased in strength, by successive additions at different times or in different ways.

Delayed—symptoms do not appear until an appreciable time after exposure; often the response is triggered by the occurrence of some other stress.

Long-term—chronic but more indefinite.

Short-term—acute but more indefinite.

Broadly speaking, we may distinguish two categories of effects[5], acute toxicity which is usually lethal, and chronic toxicity which may be lethal or sublethal.

The Basic Method

The method described here is primarily one for testing chemicals or industrial effluents in a laboratory. However, many of the items are also desirable for field tests, especially the techniques for analysis of results.

Procedures for bioassay with fish are now standardized on generally advantageous methods. Almost without exception, modern tests use:

(1) a series of test tanks, each with a different but constant concentration of the toxicant;

(2) a group of similar fish, usually ten, in each container;

(3) observations on fish mortality during exposures which usually last four days; and

(4) final results expressed as the concentration which is lethal to the median or "average" fish.

Two types of assays are in general use: (1) the static bioassay with fish in a tank of standing testwater, which may or may not be changed during the period of test; and (2) the continuous-flow or flow-through bioassay in which the test solution is renewed continually or by frequent periodic additions. The difference between the two types need not be great, and either type can be meaningful or useless, depending on how well or poorly it is designed.

Sometimes one type of assay has clear advantages over the other. The continuous-flow test is not necessarily greatly superior to a well-done static test, but it has some clear advantages and is the method of choice for high-quality work. There is no need to disturb the fish by changing the water, even in a test which runs for a week or more. This is desirable since it may take fish one day to recover from laboratory diuresis after handling. There is little fluctuation in concentration of the test material—it may be lower than the intended concentration because of sorption or volatilization, but there is no reason for it to fluctuate. In cases of unstable toxicant the total volume of the test tank can be smaller, with a turnover of test water several times a day. These advantages occur only if there is adequate flow and replacement of test water as recommended in the section on volume of test water.

For bioassays which are infrequent, exploratory, or carried out in the field, proper static tests may yield an equally valid result as continuous-flow tests, yet provide speedier answers at less cost, because the expenses and considerable set-up time of continuous-flow layouts are avoided. If a waste is sticky, lumpy, or has components which coagulate or settle out, it may not work satisfactorily in a continuous-flow device. A static test, with dilutions of known accuracy, could be superior to a continuous-flow test of uncertain concentrations.

There are many individual items which make for good practice, and these are summarized in the following sections.

Fish

Species—There is a trend towards the use of standard species of fish, although no single species is satisfactory from all points of view. For example, the rainbow trout (*Salmo gairdneri* Richardson) is attaining world-wide use to represent the cool-water salmonid family. In the United States, the fathead minnow (*Pimephales promelas* Rafinesque) is rapidly becoming a standard fish, mainly because it is readily used for sublethal bioassays involving reproduction in the laboratory. However, this species is not native to the region west of the Rockies, and perhaps should not be introduced into laboratories of that region. The bluegill (*Lepomis macrochirus* Raf.) has been widely used in the United States. The goldfish (*Carassius auratus* (L.)), although an exotic, shows promise as a standard, easily available species. A high quality source of supply would be required, especially with regard to undesirably strong prophylactic treatment of the fish. Finally, a small tropical fish such as the flagfish (*Jordanella floridae* Goode and Bean) or the comon guppy (*Poecilia reticulata* Peters) would have real advantages of size and fast easy breeding in the laboratory. Whether either of these species adequately represents the response of native species is an open question at the moment.

However, in general, the tendency to use standard species seems to be a good one, inasmuch as results may be fairly representative of the reactions of a broad spectrum of fish. Differences between species in susceptibility to a toxicant are generally less than might be expected—sometimes no greater than the variability within a single species tested in different types of water. For example, several coarse fish and trout are about equally resistant to ammonia in four-day tests which give the "coarse" species time to react[6], and even for zinc, the coarse fish resisted no more than 3.8 times the concentration resisted by trout[7]. There are some important exceptions to this generalization; for example, heavy metals and insecticides are especially damaging to certain invertebrates or plants. Enough knowledge exists to predict these situations.

An alternative good principle is to select a sensitive game or pan fish which is locally important. The species should be adaptable to healthy life in the laboratory for some weeks, readily available in number, and from a common source with similar past history. A list of suggested species prepared by D. I. Mount, has been published by Cairns[8].

Size—Fish should be small, preferably less than 8 cm or 5 g. It is a good rule that the longest fish in a set of tests should not be more than 1.5 times the length of the shortest[1].

Holding Facilities—Fish tanks and accessories should be of nontoxic material. Often used today are cylindrical fiberglass tanks with large bottom areas. The best tanks have a central drain and standpipe so that the lowest layers of water are removed, and a bottom which is slightly funnelled towards the drain, to assist the exit of waste food and faeces. A mild circular water current is desirable to assist this process and to provide exercise for the fish. The tanks should be located away from any serious visual or mechanical disturbance. They should be exposed to the ordinary local sequence of darkness and light, either from natural daylight or room lighting, unless some other photoperiod is desired. Flowing water is desirable for holding native fish. Ideally, at least one liter per minute should be provided for every kilogram of fish being held, to carry away metabolic wastes (equals 1.44 liter/g of fish per day). Vigorous aeration with oil-free compressed air should also be provided. The fish should not be overcrowded, and so the volume of water in the tank should be a liter of water or more for every 10 g of fish. Another good guideline would be to have the volume of water in the tank equal to total flow during 2 or 3 h, which would mean 90 percent replacement of water in 4.5 or 7 h (Fig. 1). Fish can certainly be kept with less water than described, but there is no question that healthier fish result when crowding is reduced and water flow is increased.

Acclimation of the fish to the dilution water and to the temperature

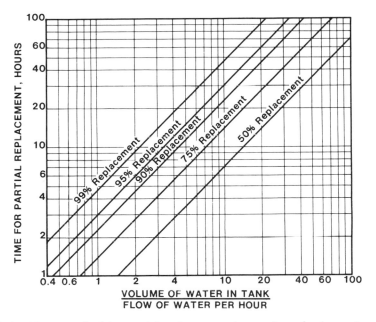

FIG. 1—*Times required for partial replacement of water in tanks, for various sizes of tanks with constant inflows. Example: for a tank containing 60 liters of water with an inflow of 20 liters/h, the ratio for the horizontal axis would be three. The graph indicates there would be 90 percent replacement of water in 7 h. Any units can be used, as long as a single unit of time and a single unit of capacity are used throughout a given calculation. From information supplied by Alfred A. Heusner.*

that will be used in the tests, seems to require at least two weeks. Abrupt changes in quality of holding water must be avoided, especially extreme temperature changes. Fish take much longer to acclimate downwards on the temperature scale to a winter temperature, and probably at least a month should be allowed if such acclimation becomes necessary.

Feeding during holding is important. The most desirable food is usually a specially designed and balanced fish food, for example, in the form of moist frozen pellets. Other foods may be acceptable, but it is best to depend on the judgement of someone with professional knowledge of fish nutrition. Daily feeding during the five-day work week is usually satisfactory, but very small fish may require several feedings of small quantities of food every day.

Disease should be virtually absent, and mortality should be negligible, if a stock of fish is to be considered suitable for bioassays. Weak fish will of course prejudice the assay so that the toxicant will appear to be more dangerous. Specifically, it is a good guideline that mortality should be less than 5 percent during the four-day period preceding the bioassay[1]. There are several suitable publications on culture of fish, their diseases, and treatments[9–11].

Dilution Water

A dependable supply of clean, nontoxic water is essential for holding and testing. The best supply may be water from a well, which is aerated, possibly filtered, but not chlorinated. Surface water which is known to be clean may also be good. "Tap-water" is often poisonous to fish. In particular, it is becoming evident that even small traces of chlorine, such as those remaining after filtration through carbon, may cause morbidity in fish, and mortality after long exposure. Copper or galvanized plumbing, brass fittings, or the plasticisers from some molded fittings will also cause toxicity and must be completely avoided.

Another alternative is to prepare synthetic dilution waters; for this purpose suitable formulae for both hard and soft fresh waters[8] and for sea water[47] have been published.

The sources of clean dilution water previously mentioned are suitable for obtaining absolute values of the LC50 for pure compounds, or "standard" values for a certain waste. However, if the bioassay is being performed to answer an immediate question of local waste disposal, then the toxicant should be tested in the natural water which will receive the waste. In this way all modifying factors and joint toxicity will be automatically included.

Variations in natural qualities of water, such as mineral content, pH, and temperature, may affect toxicity. Therefore, if a clean "standard" water is to be used, it is desirable to use a common, comparable type. Total hardness of water is one good distinguishing characteristic, since this is usually related to many other general qualities of the water. There seems to be a trend to standardize on a "soft" water with hardness of about 50 mg/liter as $CaCO_3$, and a "hard" water of about 200 mg/liter as $CaCO_3$. The pH of the dilution water should normally be the stable one which prevails when the water is well-aerated. Often this approaches pH 8.3 in natural waters; a pH of 7.8 to 8.3 is desirable for dilution water. Although pH values from 6.5 to 8.5 are not harmful to fish, the toxicity of some materials could vary considerably over this range. Fluctuation should preferably be within 0.5 pH units. Standard temperatures of 15°C for cool-water fishes and 25°C for warm-water fishes seem to be developing[1] and should be used if there is no specific reason for choosing another temperature. Fluctuation 2 deg above or below such an average is not critical during holding. There is no reason that aeration should not hold dissolved oxygen near saturation during acclimation of fish, and it should not drop more than 1 mg/liter below saturation. A problem which is not easily recognized is supersaturation of the water with nitrogen and other gases, which may cause gas-bubble disease and mortality of fish. The usual cause is warming of water after it reaches the tank.

Test Tanks

The tanks and all plumbing leading into them must be of nontoxic material. Glass is best. Fiberglass or unplasticised polyethylene or polypropylene are good materials, although they may sorb organic materials. Rubbers and many plastics release toxicants.

The test containers should allow fish reasonable scope to swim around freely, but this must be left as a matter for judgement. The best shape for tanks is oval or cylindrical, with perfectly smooth inside surfaces so that fish cannot scrape themselves. Fiberglass tanks of such design have been described[12]. Widemouth 5-gal pickle jars are frequently used for static tests. Like the holding tanks, these test tanks should be in a location free of visual and mechanical disturbance, and subject to the same photoperiod as during acclimation.

Volume of Test Water

This item is of the highest importance. If there is not sufficient test water, the fish may deplete the toxicant, lower the dissolved oxygen, foul the water with wastes, or all three. The amounts of water suggested here are based on the premise that if the respiratory needs of the fish are met, the other two problems will also be successfully solved.

The basic guideline is that there should be at least two liters, and preferably three liters of test water per gram of fish per day. This is a good deal more test water than might be convenient, but it means that without aeration, the oxygen concentration would not be lowered more than about 1.3 mg/liter, based on the oxygen requirements of fingerling trout[3]. Very small fish, for example of guppy size, would require several times as much test water since their respiration rate would be higher per unit of biomass.

In static tests, the water could be supplied by daily changes of the test water, perhaps by transferring the fish to another newly made-up tank of test water. Such daily changes would be desirable if the toxicant tended to volatilize, or be sorbed onto the tank, or appreciably removed by the fish. If the toxicant were stable, it would be preferable to use a larger tank, holding sufficient test water for four days (that is, 8 or 12 liters/g of fish).

In continuous-flow tests, the same numbers should be used, namely, the total daily inflow of new test water should equal two or preferably three liters per gram of fish. However, as an additional requirement, the volume of test water in the tank at any one time should be set so that the volume equals the total flow during 8 h. This would bring about 90 percent replacement of water in about 18 h (Fig. 1), or 95 percent replacement in about 24 h which is comparable to a daily change in a static test and should be regarded as the slowest permissable turnover. However, it would usually be preferable to have a somewhat faster renewal, and 90 percent replacement in 12 h would seem reasonable (that is, volume= total flow during 5 h). If the stability of the waste was in doubt, it would be desirable to have an even faster turnover of water in the tank by reducing the 90 percent replacement time to 8 h (that is, volume=total flow during 3.5 h) or less.

Dosing Apparatus for Continuous-Flow Tests

The best pieces of machinery for continually adding toxicant at a fixed dilution are homemade. They depend on a constant flow of dilution water which periodically fills a container and siphons quickly into the test tank. In doing so, it trips some sort of device for adding a fixed dose of the effluent or material being tested. These apparati are "fail-safe," since if the flow of water is interrupted or slowed down, the effluent addition is slowed down in the same proportion, within reasonable limits.

Excellent dosing apparatus has been described by Brungs and Mount[13] and by McAllister et al [45]. Following either pattern, a doser could be built for each test tank, and thus, the concentration or the kind of toxicant could be changed in each individual tank at any time. Another suitable individual doser based on a different principle is described by Stark[14]. "Diluter" dosers have also been described[15,16,46]. These devices supply a number of tanks with successive dilutions of waste; they would be good for fixed, long-term tests, although they offer less flexibility for starting a new concentration in a given tank once mortality is complete in that tank. Aside from this general deficiency of serial diluters, one system[46] has advantages of greater flexibility in concentration and apparently easier construction, but has a disadvantage of not changing the flow of toxicant in proportion to any change in flow of dilution water. It does shut down safely in case of complete or severe failure of water supply.

Sometimes an effluent is not suitable for use in such dosing apparati. It may be quite satisfactory to make up large batches of the test material at the desired concentrations, and run it through the test tanks in a continuous flow. Problems with some types of effluents may be solved by mixing separate streams of dilution water and test material just ahead of the test tank, each stream regulated by a pump or other device. However, this often leads to unacceptable variability in concentration since each stream can change delivery or even stop, independently of the other.

Physico-Chemical Conditions in the Tests

It may be desirable to mix the test water and exercise the fish by maintaining a rotating current in the tank by means of a shielded propeller or a recycling external loop of test water through a pump.

If the toxicant is known and can be measured, this should be done in each test tank at the beginning and end of the exposure in that tank and, preferably, daily in between these measurements. The measured concentrations, or the average of them, should be used in estimating the LC50. If it is not possible to measure the toxicant, then introduced concentrations may be reported, but it should be realized that actual concentrations in the water may become reduced.

The temperature should be checked daily and the average temperature used to characterize the test. A variation of ±0.5°C cannot be regarded as excessive, but temperatures should be kept within ±1.0°C.

The pH is often a useful measure of changes in the test water, and in most cases it should be measured on the schedule suggested for the toxicant. A variation of ±0.3 pH units would seem reasonable, but greater change than this from the initial pH would justify a search for the cause. For some toxicants such as ammonia or cyanide, small changes such as this are critical for toxicity.

Because aeration or oxidation may degrade or remove the toxicant, there must be no artificial aeration in the test tanks unless it can be proved that this does not reduce the toxicity. The suggestions on test volume and replacement times should provide adequate oxygen in most cases. However, some wastes with an oxygen demand may consume much of the dissolved oxygen from the test water. Initial aeration of the test material is not desirable because this may degrade or remove the toxicant. The best solution is to use a continuous-flow test, mixing the toxicant with well-aerated dilution water just before it reaches the test tank, and arranging a short turnover time in the test tank. In attempting to solve the problem of testing an oxygen-consuming waste, it would sometimes be most realistic to regard the increased toxicity of the waste, caused by lowered oxygen, as a legitimate component of its toxic action.

Dissolved oxygen should, in any case, be measured on the same schedule suggested for toxicant measurement. There is no simple number which can be given as a minimum suitable concentration of dissolved oxygen, and indeed an extensive review[17] has shown that any reduction below saturation places some stress on fish. If the recommendations on amounts of test water are followed, and the waste has no appreciable oxygen demand, there is no reason why dissolved oxygen in the test tanks should drop beyond 2 mg/liter below saturation.

In addition to the important measurements above, a reasonable record of total hardness should be obtained, and also of any other basic characteristic of the water which is likely to be changed by the test material. A fairly complete mineral analysis of the dilution water is desirable, perhaps at the beginning of a series of tests.

Exploratory Tests

A great deal of delay, expense, and frustrating back-tracking may be avoided by doing some preliminary small-scale tests ahead of time. These can be very primitive and need not come anywhere close to the specifications given, since the only object is to get a general idea of the range of concentrations suitable for the full-scale tests. For example, we might put one or two fish into a 3-liter beaker of test water and check mortality over one or two days. The important thing is to use a wide range of concentrations over intervals of an order-of-magnitude, such as 1 ml/liter, 1 percent, 10 percent, and 100 percent.

Setting Up Tests

The usual principles of good scientific investigation apply. A control test must be run for each series. All the test tanks should have identical conditions, except for the toxicant. Furthermore, all such conditions should be measured as required for adequate description, and the measuring tools should be checked for accuracy against known standards. Each system that controls test conditions (temperature, water flow) should have a standby system and a warning signal to call attention to any breakdown.

Concentrations—These must be chosen to span a range from that causing zero mortality to that causing complete mortality. Geometric or logarithmic series of concentrations are efficient to use. Any such series would serve, but the one given in Ref *1* is recommended. The first full tests following the exploratory ones should be selected from the series 0.1, 0.32, 1.0, 3.2, 10, 32, etc. The series runs upwards and downwards in the same way, with only a change in decimal point. Any unit of concentration may be fitted to the series. Usually, it would be sufficient to start four or five tests from the series. After partial or complete results have been obtained, another test one step higher or lower in the series could be started. Sometimes, if reactions are very sharply dependent on concentration, it may be desirable to get a finer gradation by selecting an intermediate concentration from the same series, split one step further on an equal logarithmic basis: 1.0, 1.8, 3.2, 5.6, 10, 18, 32, 56, etc. A further split is seldom necessary.

Number of fish—It is desirable to have about ten fish at each concentration. If the fish are large, it may be necessary to split them between two or more tanks at the same concentration to get the recommended volumes of water. If test materials or other facilities are in limited supply, it may be satisfactory to reduce the number of fish in each concentration to as low as five. The confidence limits on the final LC50 will become wider as precision is reduced with fewer fish in the test.

Randomization—The selected concentrations should be randomized or judiciously distributed among the available test tanks, in case there is an effect of position, such as different temperature or lighting. Furthermore, the fish should be randomized among the test tanks in case the weakest ones in the holding tank are caught first. At the very least this should be done by a process similar to dealing out a pack of cards. Even better, if there are five tanks to be filled, the first five fish to be caught should be formally randomized among the tanks, then the next five also, until the tanks are filled.

Other Considerations—Handling of the test material should follow normal good practice. It should be stored so as to prevent change in its composition, usually in a cold-room. The same sample of waste should be used to make up all dilutions.

Fish should not be fed during the usual acute bioassays, nor for at least a full day before testing. In tests which last longer than a week, feeding may be carried out, but refuse should be removed, preferably by using continuous-flow tests with an effective self-cleaning tank.

Observations on Mortality

Tests should ordinarily be continued for four days. For most toxicants, acute mortality has either occurred by that time or else has ceased[3]. In some cases, acute lethal action may continue beyond four days, and it may be desirable to continue the tests in order to determine a threshold, as described in the next section on toxicity curves.

Mortality should be recorded frequently during the early part of the tests, then gradually less frequently until observations become daily. A great deal of information is lost if the frequent early observations are not made. The observation times should approximate a logarithmic series, in keeping with the apparent logarithmic nature of biological time. (For example, to a fish which has been exposed for one minute, an additional minute would double his exposure. To a fish exposed for an hour, an additional minute would be insignificant, and doubling his exposure would require another hour.) A convenient set of observation times is given in the following:

$$\text{minutes} = 15, 30, \text{and } 60,$$
$$\text{hours} = 2, 4, 8, 14 \pm 2, 24, 33 \pm 3, \text{and}$$
$$\text{days} = 2, 3, 4, \text{and daily beyond this.}$$

If a test was started in midmorning, almost all these observations could be made during normal daytime working hours. Only one observation, late in the evening of the first day, need be outside such hours. Beyond four days, the daily observations are more for the interest of the observer who would probably be checking the test apparatus in any case. By that point, periods such as weekends could be skipped.

Fish should be considered dead when there is no respiratory or other movement, and no response to gentle prodding. Dead fish should be removed, and the length to the fork of the tail or wet weight (drained but not dried) or both should be recorded.

Mortality in controls should be virtually absent in acute tests. It should not be greater than 10 percent, representing the occasional very weak fish in a group, and anything more than this should be regarded as unsatisfactory. (This is one reason for using ten fish instead of a minimal five.) There is a method of correcting for higher mortality in controls[3], but it really does not solve the problem of probable interaction of stress from the toxicant with whatever stress is causing mortality in the control. The real solution is to improve holding conditions for the fish. Sometimes with tests lasting several weeks, or with some animals such as invertebrates subject to considerable mortality under the best possible conditions, it is feasible to consider the threshold lethal concentration as that in which mortality is equal to mortality in controls.

Plotting Results to Estimate LC50

For each of the observation times, a graph similar to Fig. 2 is constructed. For example, the observations made at 4 h would yield one graph. The mortality observed in each test tank is plotted against the concentration in the same tank. Concentration is on a logarithmic scale, and percent mortality is on a probability or "probit" scale. Such graph paper can be purchased from standard sources. It will be noted that the probit scale never reaches 0 or 100 percent mortality, so any such points must be plotted with an arrow indicating their true position.

A line is next fitted to the points by eye. Most consideration should be given to points between 16 and 84 percent mortality, and an effort made to minimize total vertical deviations of the line from the points. Only one 0 percent and one 100 percent should be utilized, these to be the ones nearest the center of the range of concentrations used. If there is doubt about the placement of the line, it should be rotated to a flatter slope (that is, more horizontal in Fig. 2), since this acknowledges more variability in the data.

The concentration causing 50 percent mortality is read from the fitted line, and this is the LC50 for that exposure time. In our example it would

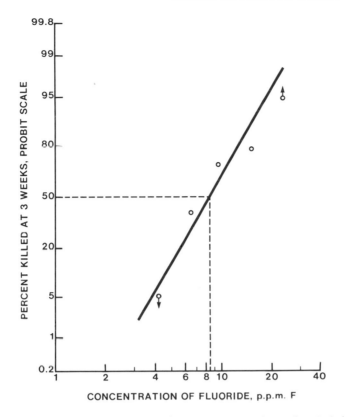

FIG. 2—*The first stage in analysing results. Estimation of the median lethal concentration (LC50) for a given exposure time. The concentration lethal to half the individuals is read from the eye-fitted line. A more common type of log-probit paper has a probit scale running from 2 to 98 percent mortality and is satisfactory. Modified from Herbert and Shurben [40].*

be the "4-h LC50." This signifies the concentration which would kill the "average" or typical fish in 4 h.

Constructing a Toxicity Curve

Each LC50 should be estimated by the steps given above, as the observations of mortality are made for that time period. Then the series of LC50's should be used to construct a "toxicity curve" as the experiment progresses. Examples of toxicity curves are shown in Figs. 3 and 4. The purpose of constructing these curves is to give the experimenter an overall view of what is happening in the tests. For example, if he were plotting the curve for ammonia shown in Fig. 3, the vertical asymptote after about 300 min would tell him that acute mortality was all over, and

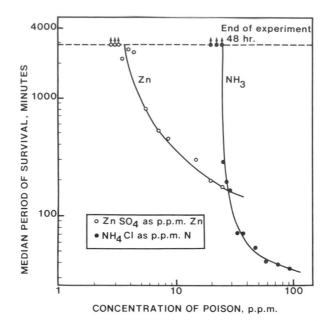

FIG. 3—*The second stage in analysing results. A series of LC50's, estimated as in Fig. 1, is used to draw a toxicity curve, like the two above. This should be done as the experiment progresses. In the examples here for trout, a lethal threshold concentration has obviously been defined for ammonia, but longer tests might have shown additional mortality for zinc* [41].

he might wish to end the experiments earlier than planned. However, if he plotted the Fig. 3 results for zinc, the lack of asymptote at 48 h would tell him that acute mortality was continuing, and he would probably wish to continue the tests to 96 h.

Toxicity curves may assume a variety of shapes. For example, the threshold for mortality may be abrupt, as for copper and zinc in Fig. 4. The curves may be complex, as are some illustrated by Warren[18]. The shape might give some clues about the mode of action or indicate the presence of more than one toxic material. Sometimes straight-line relations have been found, with no evidence of a lethal threshold even at weak concentrations, if exposure is prolonged.

The important thing is that plotting such a toxicity curve as the test progresses, may give the experimenter a number of clues about the action of the material he is testing and will tell him whether it would be advantageous to keep the test tanks going longer than 96 h. It is unfortunate that attempts to provide a numerical guideline for judging the cessation of mortality have so far been somewhat arbitrary, and the matter seems best left to the good judgement of the investigator.

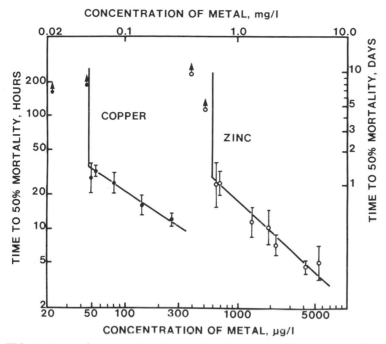

FIG. 4—*Examples of another shape of toxicity curves. These straight-line ones are for salmon. The curves are equivalent to those in Fig. 3, but were constructed as suggested in the secton on alternate methods for research, and hence, confidence limits are indicated for the median survival times* [42].

Final Estimate of LC50 and Confidence Limits

When the experiment has been completed to the satisfaction of the investigator, a more careful estimate should be made of the LC50 for the longest time period used in the test. In routine tests this would usually be the 96-h LC50, although in research tests it might be longer, say the seven-day or ten-day LC50.

If an asymptote has been reached in the toxicity curve (namely, acute lethality has ceased), the final value should be called the incipient LC50 or "threshold lethal concentration." Such a threshold has more theoretical significance than an LC50 at an arbitrary time period, and is therefore more useful.

Nomogram Method—The Nomogram method of analysing data for the LC50 is recommended for field work, for situations where one does not have ready access to a computer terminal, or if computer use would cause inconvenience or appreciable delay. The procedure for plotting results is the same as previously described and illustrated in Fig. 2. Additional statistical analysis is done by the simple nomographic methods of Litchfield and Wilcoxon[19] which require 10 to 15 min, after experience. The goodness of fit of the eye-drawn line is estimated by the rapid chi-square test of these authors. In doubtful cases, several lines may be drawn and the best chosen by minimum chi-square value. Confidence limits of the LC50 may then be estimated by the Litchfield-Wilcoxon methods. These limits should be reported along with the LC50 and the "slope function" or *S*.

Computer Methods—Computer methods may now be used for probit analysis, to solve the mathematical procedures which are too formidable for routine use of a hand-operated calculator. The procedures are based on Finney's method for probit analysis[20], which fits the probit line by iteration. There are no doubt many programs available, but one example is program BMDO3S in the well-known BMD package[21]. Programs which might be easier to use are ones in which the data are typed in at a terminal without the need for making punchcards. For example, the students in the author's lab commonly use the relatively simple language, APL, to call up the program PROBITANAL. This is available on request from the Institute of Computer Science at the University of Guelph, and was developed by R. J. Douglas from the basic procedures of Finney[20]. It replaces the Litchfield and Wilcoxon nomographic analysis previously described and, in general, is more accurate, and easier if one has ready access to a computer terminal.

Nevertheless, blind dependence on the numbers generated by any computer program must be avoided. *A graph like Fig. 2 should always be drawn and inspected for reasonableness of the computed LC50.* In some cases of unusual probit lines, the investigator's judgement must take primary place in interpreting and reporting the response of the animals. If desired, the line fitted by the computer may be easily plotted and compared with the eye-drawn line; the computed slope is the number of probits (rise) for one logarithmic cycle of concentration (run).

Alternate Methods—Alternate methods of estimating the LC50 and its confidence limits are available. They have been calculated by means of reciprocal transformations[22], or by using angle transformations instead of probits, and a moving average to estimate the LC50[23,24]. These methods have certain limitations[3].

Any of the above estimates of confidence limits merely indicate the range of results which might be expected if the very same stock of fish were immediately tested against the same sample of material under identical conditions! Tests at different times of year for example, have been known to give results differing by a factor of 2.5, even though the same stock of fish was tested under identical conditions[25].

Each of the methods which provides confidence limits also provides a way of testing for significant differences between LC50's.

Reporting of Results

The final LC50, its confidence limits, and the slope of the probit line (or *S,* the slope function of Litchfield and Wilcoxon) should be reported no matter which method of analysis is used. These are the key data. The slope or *S* is important because it allows future investigators to reconstruct the probit line if desired. Also highly useful is reproduction of the toxicity curve, if this is possible, or else a list of the LC50's for different exposure times.

Beyond this, there should be relatively complete description of the fish, the material, and the test conditions. Some reasonable description should be given of almost all the items mentioned in this section on Basic Method. These are best summarized by the list below. It is taken verbatim from an excellent proposal by Cairns[8] to provide a seven-point rating system for evaluating reliability and usefulness of bioassay data.

1. Test organism clearly identified as to species, size, and weight.
2. Dilution water quality stated.
3. Bioassay organisms preconditioned or acclimated to test environment.
4. Methods and procedures clearly stated.
5. Appropriate controls included.
6. Adequate control of environmental conditions.
7. Statistical evaluation of data.

A system of classifying different grades of toxicity has been given in a report by an international group (Joint IMCO/FAO/UNESCO/WMO Group of Experts. . . , 1969)[44]. The categories seem useful for general description of pollutants. They are given below, with appropriate descriptive phrases taken from human toxicity, also listed in the report.

"Practically non-toxic"	Acute lethal threshold above 10 000 mg/liter or approximately 1 percent
"Slightly toxic"	Threshold 1000–10 000 mg/liter
"Moderately toxic"	Threshold 100–1000 mg/liter
"Toxic"	Threshold 1–100 mg/liter
"Very toxic"	Threshold below 1 mg/liter

Other Types of Tests and Application of Results

Although some of these topics are handled in more detail in other papers in this publication, they are briefly touched upon here because they are similar or relevant to the techniques previously described.

Alternate Method for Research, or for Tests with Short Exposure or Low Mortality

Somewhat more revealing information can be obtained by using a different method of analysis on the same basic observations of mortality, collected at the same observation times suggested. The simple technique is to plot on log-probit paper, the progress of mortality with time, for a single test-concentration (Fig. 5). A line may be fitted by eye. The median lethal time or "median effective time" (ET50) may be read from the graph. If desired, confidence limits of the ET50 may be calculated by simple nomographic procedures[26], or a computer program could be written, using the equations which served as the basis of the nomograms.

For research purposes, plotting the increase in mortality with time, for each concentration, provides somewhat more insight as to what is happening to each group of fish. Any changes in slope will provide clues about the action of the toxicant. A flattening of the line may indicate disappearance or decomposition of the toxicant. A double bend in the line may indicate two modes of action or the presence of two toxic agents.

As the research tests proceed, the ET50's taken from fitted lines, such as those in Fig. 5, should be used to construct a toxicity curve, as was done in Fig. 4. The last step in the research method is to estimate the final LC50 and its confidence limits in exactly the same way as described (similar to Fig. 2). In estimating the LC50, it is imperative to use raw data, that is, the actual percentage mortalities in each concentration at

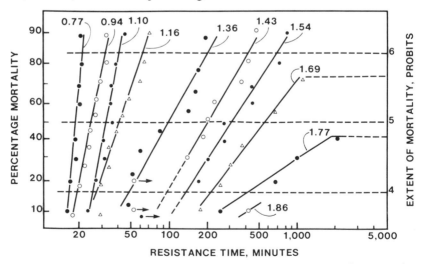

FIG. 5—*An example of plotting data to show progress of mortality in each test tank. These results are for mortality of trout at various low levels of oxygen, but a graph with a toxicant would appear similar. Modified from Shepard [43].*

the selected observation time. It is not legitimate to use derived mortalities picked from fitted lines such as those in Fig. 5!

Mixing zone predictions, and some other practical problems, may make it desirable to know precisely the response of fish swimming through a zone of high concentration for a short time. For example, one might need to know the time-concentration relations which would be lethal to only a small fraction of a population of fish, say 2 percent. Such information could be obtained from graphs such as Fig. 5. Effective times for 2 percent mortality (ET2) could be picked off the fitted lines and used to construct a toxicity curve for 2 percent mortality instead of 50 percent mortality.

On-Line or Field Tests

These may be done following the same procedures as given in the basic method. For on-line tests in a factory, it might be feasible to split and dilute a stream of effluent tapped from a waste pipe to give different percentage compositions. In field tests, such as in a river, the series of concentrations might be replaced by a series of test cages at successive distances from the outfall. The chief difference in these situations is that the character of the waste and its toxicity would usually be fluctuating with time.

Other Methods of Analysing Results

The graph for estimating the LC50 (Fig. 2) is sometimes constructed using an arithmetic scale for percentage mortality instead of a probability scale. Indeed, this is recommended in Ref *1*. However, the probit scale is theoretically more sound, and in actual practice is usually beneficial in linearizing the relationship.

When working with time series, as suggested in the section on alternate method for research, it would be possible to use a simpler technique for estimating the median effective time, if one were satisfied to waste considerable information available from the test. One could dispense with graphs such as Fig. 5, and simply adopt as the ET50, the survival time of the median fish in each tank. This is usually fairly accurate, but wastes information in complex tests. Another apparently simple alternative is neither accurate nor desirable: one should not estimate the ET50 as the arithmetic average of individual survival times, since this may often be strongly affected by extreme response times. It would be possible to calculate the ET50 as the antilog of the average of the logarithms of individual survival times, or by using reciprocal times, but it would probably be easier and more revealing to use a graphic plot.

Toxicity curves are sometimes constructed using different types of axes than the logarithmic ones recommended. A semilog plot is customary and suitable for lethal temperature work[27]. Toxicity curves using the reciprocal of time have sometimes been used with success[28,22] but they do not seem to be suitable for all data.

Highly sophisticated and much improved bioassay approaches using multivariate response surfaces are now available using computer techniques[29,30]. Such high-powered research is vital to progress in understanding the complicated effects of toxic environments on organisms. However, for routine work, the basic method suggested has advantages of simplicity, flexibility, and rapidity.

Bioassays of Sublethal or Chronic Effects

Many such effects have been studied in the search for levels of toxicants which are truly "safe" for aquatic life. Among the responses studied with most success have been growth, swimming performance, behavior (especially avoidance), and, most notably, reproductive success. Other papers in this publication deal with sublethal response and with the "safe"-to-lethal ratios which may be used for practical control problems. However, it should be mentioned here that most of these sublethal and chronic bioassays could be analysed beneficially using the standard techniques described.

An example is shown in Fig. 6, in which the median effective concentration has been estimated for avoidance reactions of fish. The final answer obtained is the concentration which would just cause a significant avoidance response in the typical or "average" fish. Use of this standard technique requires that the data be turned into a quantal (all-or-none) form, that is, each individual either gives the sublethal response or does not give it. So far this has been done for avoidance reactions[31] and for swimming performance[32]. It has not yet been used for determining the median effective concentration for interference with reproduction of fish, but the procedure should be worked out because of the great importance of such experiments.

Joint Toxicity

One of the stumbling blocks in the past has been the impossibility of assessing a pollution situation in which there were two or more effluents, or toxicants, present simultaneously. It is now feasible to make a reasonable evaluation of such situations by expressing the amount of each type of pollutant as a fraction of its LC50.

For the lethal action of a mixture of two or more pollutants, the total toxicity may be estimated by expressing the actual concentration of each toxicant as a proportion of its lethal threshold concentration (equals 96-h

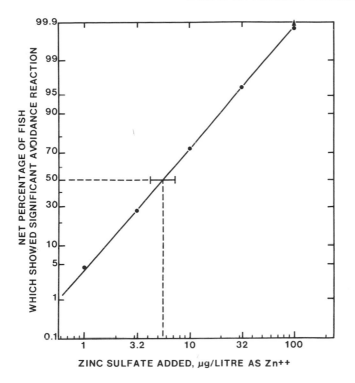

FIG. 6—*Estimating the median effective concentration for a sublethal response. This example is for avoidance reactions of trout to zinc and shows an unusually precise response. The technique for analysis is exactly the same as for the LC50, shown in Fig. 2. Any sublethal response can be treated this way if it can be made quantal, namely, percentage of individuals showing a given effect* [31].

LC50 usually), then adding together the resulting numbers for all the toxicants. If the total is 1.0 or greater, the mixture is predicted to be lethal.

The system of "adding up" different toxicants in this way is based on the premise that their lethal stresses are simply additive, one with the other. Unlikely as it might seem, this simple rule has been found to govern the joint lethal action of many pairs and mixtures of quite dissimilar toxicants. This is true for such diverse toxicants as copper, ammonia, zinc, and phenol in the laboratory[33–35] and also seems to be a reasonably accurate way of assessing most field situations which have a mixture of pollutants[36–39]. The method of addition is only useful for predicting thresholds of lethal effects in mixtures. Although it is not particularly good for predicting survival time of fish in strong mixtures, that is of less interest.

The situation is apparently not so straightforward for the joint sublethal action of pollutants. Sometimes they have appeared to be additive[39] and sometimes not. There also seem to be, for both lethal and sublethal effects, lower thresholds of concentration at which the additive actions cut off. Further research may clarify this situation, but at present it seems most reasonable to assume that all concentrations of different toxicants acting simultaneously will add up.

Other Considerations

Modifying conditions such as water hardness, pH, and temperature may affect the toxicity of a pollutant as has been suggested. Some progress has been made in organizing information on such effects. The best "handbook" so far is a paper from the British Water Pollution Research Laboratory[25], which allows one to predict the lethal concentrations of eight common pollutants, under any given conditions of five natural variables of basic water quality.

Fluctuating concentrations of pollutant are usual in the field, as opposed to constant concentrations used in the laboratory. No definite theoretical base has been worked out for dealing with this situation; but a number of approaches have been made[3] and it does not appear that this will be a difficult problem to resolve.

Invertebrate animals and algae may be profitably assayed using the same basic procedures recommended here, and other papers in this publication tell about working with such organisms.

References

[1] *Standard Methods for the Examination of Water and Sewage,* 13th ed., American Public Health Association, New York, 1971.

[2] Doudoroff, et al, *Sewage and Industrial Wastes,* Vol. 23, 1951, pp. 1380–1397.

[3] Sprague, J. B., *Water Research,* Vol. 3, 1969, pp. 793–821; Vol. 4, 1970, pp. 3–32; Vol. 5, 1971, pp. 245–266.

[4] Quayle, D. B., "Pacific Oyster Culture in British Columbia," Bulletin No. 169, Fisheries Research Board of Canada, 1969, pp. 1–192.

[5] Alderdice, D. F., "The Detection and Measurement of Water Pollution—Biological Assays," Canada Fisheries Report No. 9, Canada Department of Fisheries, 1967, pp. 33–39.

[6] Ball, I. R., *Water Research,* Vol. 1, 1967, pp. 767–775.

[7] Ball, I. R., *Water Research,* Vol. 1, 1967, pp. 777–783.

[8] Cairns, J., Jr., *Revista de Biologia,* Vol. 7, No. 1–2, 1969, pp. 7–12.

[9] Sniesko, S. F., Ed., "A Symposium on Diseases of Fishes and Shellfishes," Special Publication No. 5, Vol. 3, American Fisheries Society, 1970.

[10] Van Duijn, C., Jr., *Diseases of Fishes,* London Iliffe Books, Ltd., Cox and Wyman, Ltd., London Reading and Fakenham, 1967.

[11] Davis, H. S., *Culture and Diseases of Game Fishes,* University of California Press, Berkeley and Los Angeles, 1953.

[12] Alderdice, D. F., Brett, J. R., and Sutherland, D. B., *Journal of the Fisheries Research Board of Canada,* Vol. 23, 1966, pp. 1447–1450.

[13] Brungs, W. A. and Mount, D. I. in *Transactions,* American Fisheries Society, Vol. 96, 1967, pp. 55–57.

[14] Stark, G. T. C., *Laboratory Practice,* Vol. 16, 1967, pp. 594–595.

[15] Mount, D. I. and Brungs, W. A., *Water Research,* Vol. 1, 1967, pp. 21–29.

[16] Mount, D. I. and Warner, R. E., "A Serial-Dilution Apparatus for Continuous Delivery of Various Concentrations of Materials in Water," Publication No. 999–WP–23, U. S. Public Health Service, 1965.

[17] Doudoroff, P. and Shumway, D. L., "Dissolved Oxygen Requirements of Freshwater Fishes," FAO Fisheries Technical Paper No. 86, Food and Agriculture Organization of the United Nations, Rome, 1970.

[18] Warren, C. E., *Biology and Water Pollution Control,* Saunders, Philadelphia and Toronto, 1971.

[19] Litchfield, J. T. and Wilcoxon, F., *Journal of Pharmacology and Experimental Therapeutics,* Vol. 96, 1949, pp. 99–113.

[20] Finney, D. J., *Probit Analysis,* 2nd ed., Cambridge University Press, London, 1952.

[21] Dixon, W. J., Ed., *BMD Biomedical Computer Programs,* in *Automatic Computation Series* No. 2, 2nd ed, University of California Press, Los Angeles, 1970.

[22] Alderdice, D. F. and Brett, J. R., *Journal of the Fisheries Research Board of Canada,* Vol. 14, 1957, pp. 783–795.

[23] Harris, E. K., *Biometrics,* Vol. 15, 1959, pp. 424–432.

[24] Thatcher, T. O. and Santner, J. R. in *Proceedings,* 21st Industrial Waste Conference, Purdue University, Engineering Extension, Series No. 121, 1966, pp. 996–1002.

[25] Brown, V. M., *Water Research,* Vol. 2, 1968, pp. 723–733.

[26] Litchfield, J. T., *Journal of Pharmacology Experimental Therapeutics,* Vol. 97, 1949, pp. 399–408.

[27] Fry, F. E. J., *Publications of the Ontario Fisheries Research Laboratory,* No. 68, University of Toronto Study, Biological Series No. 55, 1947.

[28] Abram, F. S. H., *Proceedings,* 3rd International Conference, Munich, 1966, Pergamon Press, Oxford, Vol. 1, 1967, pp. 75–95.

[29] Alderdice, D. R. in *Transactions,* 3rd Seminar, 1962, U. S. Public Health Service, Publication No. 999-WP–25, 1965, pp. 320–325.

[30] Alderdice, D. F. in *Marine Ecology,* Vol. 1, Part 3, O. Kinne, Ed., Wiley-Interscience, London and New York, 1972, Chapter 12, pp. 1659–1722.

[31] Sprague, J. B., *Water Research,* Vol. 2, 1968, pp. 367–372.

[32] Brett, J. R., *Journal of the Fisheries Research Board of Canada,* Vol. 24, 1967, pp. 1731–1741.

[33] Brown, V. M. and Dalton, R. A., *Journal of Fish Biology,* Vol. 2, 1970, pp. 211–216.

[34] Herbert, D. W. M. and Van Dyke, J. M., *Annals of Applied Biology,* Vol. 53, 1964, pp. 415–421.

[35] Brown, V. M., Jordan, D. H. M., and Tiller, B. A., *Journal of Fish Biology,* Vol. 1, 1969, pp. 1–9.

[36] Brown, V. M., Shurben, D. G., and Shaw, D., *Water Research,* Vol. 4, 1970, pp. 363–382.

[37] Lloyd, R. and Jordan, D. H. M., *Journal and Proceedings of the Institute for Sewage Purification,* Part 2, 1964, pp. 183–186.

[38] Herbert, D. W. M., Jordan, D. H. M., and Lloyd, R., *Journal and Proceedings of the Institute for Sewage Purification,* 1965, pp. 569–582.

[39] Sprague, J. B., Elson, P. F., and Saunders, R. L., *International Journal of Air and Water Pollution,* Vol. 9, 1965, pp. 531–543.

[40] Herbert, D. W. M. and Shurben, D. S., *Water and Waste Treatment Journal,* Vol. 10, 1964, pp. 141–142.

[*41*] Herbert, D. W. M., *Proceedings of the Society for Water Treatment Journal,* Vol. 10, 1961, pp. 135–156.

[*42*] Sprague, J. B., *Journal of the Fisheries Research Board of Canada,* Vol. 21, 1964, pp. 17–26.

[*43*] Shepard, M. P., *Journal of the Fisheries Research Board of Canada,* Vol. 12, 1955, pp. 387–446.

[*44*] Joint IMCO/FAO/UNESCO/WMO Group of Experts on the Scientific Aspects of Marine Pollution, abstract of the report of the first session, *Water Research,* Vol. 3, 1969, pp. 995–1005.

[*45*] McAllister, W. A., Jr., Mauck, W. L., and Mayer, F. L., Jr., *Transactions of the American Fisheries Society,* Vol. 101, 1972, pp. 555–557.

[*46*] Chadwick, G. C., Palensky, J. R., and Shumway, D. L., *Proceedings of the Pacific Northwest Waste Management Conference,* Portland, Oregon, 25–27 Oct. 1972, in press.

[*47*] Courtright, R. C., Breese, W. P., and Krueger, H., *Water Research,* Vol. 5, 1971, pp. 877–888.

C. M. Fetterolf, Jr.[1]

Mixing Zone Concepts

REFERENCE: Fetterolf, C. M., Jr., **"Mixing Zone Concepts,"** *Biological Methods for the Assessment of Water Quality, ASTM STP 528,* American Society for Testing and Materials, 1973, pp. 31 45.

ABSTRACT: There is no uniform approach to the designation of zones to accommodate liquid waste discharges into an aquatic receiving system without interference with other beneficial uses. This leads to confusion and indecision among dischargers and enforcement agencies. Acceptance of universally adaptable guidelines would initiate understanding and progress. Such conceptual guidelines are proposed, including: initial establishment of the waste capacity of the receiving system; control of mass emission rate of critical materials; adoption of aesthetic criteria; establishment of water quality requirements in the mixing zone based on time exposure history; derivation of specialized criteria to permit overlapping mixing zones; limiting the total region of a waterbody devoted to mixing zones; assessment of damage to biota on a population basis; recognition that limited loss of living area may not be significant to populations; early acknowledgment that siting and discharge design can afford protection to uses; and that a case-by-case approach is essential to wise use of natural resources.

KEY WORDS: aquatic biology, assimilation, effluents, mixing zones, time exposure history, thermal discharges, wastes, water quality, water pollution

When a liquid of different quality than the receiving water is discharged to an aquatic system a mixing zone is formed. Attention was drawn to mixing zones and zones of passage as biological considerations of water quality characteristics for protection of aquatic life by inclusion of these concepts of the 1 April 1968 publication "Water Quality Criteria"[1].[2]

---

[1] Scientific coordinator, Water Quality Criteria Project, Environmental Studies Board, National Academy of Sciences, Washington, D. C. 20418, presently, chief environmental scientist, Water Resources Commission, Bureau of Water Management, Michigan Dept. of Natural Resources, Lansing, Mich. 48926.
[2] The italic numbers in brackets refer to the list of references appended to this paper.

This publication, the Report of the National Technical Advisory Committee (NTAC) to the Secretary of the Interior was sponsored by the Federal Water Pollution Control Administration (FWPCA). Better known to water pollution enforcement agencies and those subject to their control as the "Green Book", the report was intended to provide the states with water quality guidelines (p. vii) prior to the states' submission of their interstate water quality standards for acceptance by the Secretary of the Interior. Unavailability of the NTAC report prior to 30 June 1967, the deadline set by the Water Quality Act of 1965 for submission of state standards, resulted in great variations between state-adopted standards and the NTAC recommendations. While some state-adopted standards received Federal approval before the NTAC report was available, other state-adopted standards have still not received Federal approval as of this writing, November 1972.

Apparently the Federal government did not require the states to adopt mixing zone standards, because as of 2 Sept. 1971, 28 states made no reference to mixing zones in their standards[2] and more states than that had received Federal approval by that time. Perhaps it was not the intent of the FWPCA to require the states to submit mixing zone standards, as the format of the zone of passage and mixing zone write-up in the NTAC report (p. 31) differed from much of the text. Recommendations were not set out in special type nor included in the summary and key criteria.

"Water Quality Criteria"[1] has been revised by the National Academy of Sciences (NAS) under contract to the U. S. Environmental Protection Agency (EPA). NAS submitted their report to EPA in late summer 1972. The NAS report includes several recommendations on mixing zones and zones of passage and provides the scientific base necessary for progress towards unification of thought on this subject.

State Standards

To illustrate the lack of uniformity among states in their concepts of mixing zones and zones of passage, I have summarized (Table 1) their approaches to mixing zone standards from an EPA Office of Water Programs report dated 2 Sept. 1971[2]. While 28 governmental units made no reference to mixing zones, 26 did. Among those 26 standards I was able to identify 34 statements which I arbitrarily classified as of a very general nature or having an administrative basis. Dominant in this group were eleven statements that a "reasonable" allowance for mixing would be made. Reasonable is not the type of definitive approach which inspires confidence in the engineer charged with waste treatment or discharge design, or the corporation president or board chairman for that matter. Seven governmental units stated their water pollution control agency was responsible for

TABLE 1—*Concepts included in state, U.S. Territories and District of Columbia mixing zone standards as of 2 September 1971 (54 governmental units), summarized from Ref 2.*

No. of Units	Concept
28	No reference to mixing zones
	General or Administrative Basis
11	"Reasonable" allowance for mixing
8	Allowance made so water sampled for enforcement purposes would be "representative"
7	Designation and/or definition by agency
4	Existence not to affect water use classification
1	Separate water use classification
1	Verbatim adoption of NTAC Water Quality Criteria (Ref 1, p. 31)
2	No unsatisfactory conditions within mixing zones
	Physical or Chemical Basis
6	Case-by-case (fit discharge to receiving system)
5	Recognition of time and distance to allow mixing
1	Size based on flow at time of sampling
1	Allowance for adequate mixing
2	Allowance for necessary mixing
1	Meet receiving water standards outside mixing zone
2	Some allowable decrease in water quality outside mixing zone
	Biological Basis
7	Prevent barriers to passage of fish and/or aquatic life (1-Minimum passage is 50% of X-section or flow) (1-Minimum passage is 75% of X-section or flow) (2-Provide passage between shore and mixing zone)
2	No mortality of the biota
1	No adverse effects on any fishery or other forms of wild or aquatic life

designating and defining mixing zones. Eight statements were included that allowances for mixing zones would be made so that water sampled for enforcement purposes would be "representative". This implies that the enforcement agency will not take samples to determine compliance with standards in an area containing high percentages of effluent, but will take samples after the effluent has had an opportunity to mix with receiving waters and become representative of the "new" adulterated water. This approach suggests ignoring the mixing zone as a region subject to enforcement and is not justified.

There were 18 approaches which I classified as having a physical or chemical basis, including six case-by-case concepts which imply tailoring the discharge to the receiving system and local environment. Five statements recognized time and distance to allow mixing. One state required meeting receiving water standards outside the mixing zone and two states allowed some decrease in water quality outside the mixing zone.

There were ten biologically-based statements, seven of which were aimed at preventing barriers to passage of fish or aquatic life. Of these seven, one provided a minimum of 50 percent of the cross-section or flow as a zone of passage, one a 75 percent zone of passage, and two provided for passage between shore and the mixing zone in non-riverine situations. Two states opted for no mortality of the biota and one for "no adverse effects on any fishery or other forms of wild or aquatic life".

There is no doubt that many states have developed extensive guidelines and, in some cases, standards governing establishment of mixing zones which did not appear in the EPA summary[2]. For example, Michigan's mixing zone standard is stated singly and then interwoven as part of their five page temperature standards[3]. Because their temperature standards had not been approved by EPA at the time of summarization Michigan is listed as making "No reference to mixing zones."

Sizes of Mixing Zones

Blanket Restrictions—The practice of recommending blanket application of a single size limitation on mixing zones for a single waterbody under the guise of designed protection of an aquatic resource is a pretense, a crutch for administrative laziness, and suggests either ignorance of or disregard for intelligent, scientifically-based evaluations as a mutually desirable platform for enforcement programs (see Concept II).

An example of the blanket approach is provided by a recommendation of the Federal-Four State Enforcement Conference on Pollution of Lake Michigan which states in part, "In order to protect Lake Michigan . . . at any time, and at a maximum distance of 1,000 feet from a fixed point adjacent to the discharge, (agreed upon by the State and Federal regulatory agencies), the receiving water temperature shall not be more than 3° F above the existing natural temperature . . ."

A team of scientists from Argonne National Laboratory's Great Lakes Research Program has been studying thermal plume behavior in Lake Michigan for the last few years. Their prediction is that only the smallest of the several heated waste dischargers will be able to meet the recommendation without extensive discharge redesign or backfitting for onshore cooling.[3]

The recommendation was made despite a statement by the Technical Committee on Thermal Discharges to Lake Michigan that, "The committee recognizes the value of receiving water temperature standards but, since there has been no demonstrated significant damage at existing Lake

---

[3] Personal communication with B. M. Hoglund, Great Lakes Research Program, Argonne National Laboratory, U. S. Atomic Energy Commission, Argonne, Ill.

TABLE 2—*Discharge volume—mixing zone relationship from Eq 1.*

Discharge, mgd	Mixing Zone, linear ft	Ratio
1	500	1:500
5	855	1:171
10	1077	1:108
50	1842	1: 37
100	2320	1: 23
500	3968	1: 7.9
1000	5000	1: 5.0
1500	5723	1: 3.8
2000	6300	1: 3.15
3000	7212	1: 2.4

Michigan thermal plume sites from artificial heat inputs, the assignment of numerical effluent values or other engineering design requirements at this time would be arbitrary and not defensible"[4]. Although the technical committee was authorized by the conferees and chaired by an EPA appointee its findings were largely ignored.

Relating Size of Mixing Zone to Discharge Volume—In 1969 two staff members of the Federal Water Pollution Control Administration (now EPA) proposed equations related to discharge volume as guidelines for mixing zone size. Equation 1[4] states the mixing zone should not exceed a linear distance (in any direction from the discharge point) equal in feet to 500 times the cube root of the discharge in million gallons per day (mgd):

$$M \leq 500 \times \sqrt[3]{V} \qquad (1)$$

where M is mixing zone measured in linear feet in any direction from the point of discharge, and V is the volume of discharge in mgd. Equation 1 produces a relationship which to me seems permissive to the small volume discharger and restrictive to the high volume discharger (see Table 2).

Equation 2 states, "As a guideline, the maximum distance of the mixing zone in any direction should not exceed that obtained by multiplying the square root of the discharged number of million gallons per day times 200 feet; and in no case exceed ¾ mile"[5].

$$M \leq 200 \times \sqrt{V} \qquad (2)$$

where M is mixing zone in linear feet in any direction, and V is the volume of discharge in mgd. This guideline was proposed for the Ohio River and

[4] Personal communication with D. I. Mount, Director, National Water Quality Laboratory, U. S. Environmental Protection Agency, Duluth, Minn.

that may clarify inclusion of the ¾ mile limitation. Equation 2 produces a relationship more equitable between small and large dischargers (see Table 3).

In 1971 a modification of the cube root equation (Eq 1) was proposed.[4] Equation 3 states the mixing zone should be defined as a sphere with a specified point as the center (not necessarily the outfall, but limited to one point for each installation) and having a radius equal to the cube root of the volume of the discharge in mgd times a constant whose numerical value is determined for that particular body of water:

$$M = E \times \sqrt[3]{V} \qquad (3)$$

where M is the mixing zone radius of a sphere from a specified point, E is the environmental constant, and V is the volume of discharge in mgd. This approach produces a ratio relationship similar to that of Eq 1, but brings in a three-dimensional concept and relates all mixing zones on a waterbody to environmental factors (see Concepts III and VII).

Michigan has adopted a unique spatial approach to mixing zones in the Great Lakes. They restrict a specific mixing zone to an area not to exceed that equivalent to a circle with a radius of x feet. This accommodates the constantly changing plume configuration while at the same time limiting the area of influence. The radius limitation is assigned on the necessity to protect beneficial uses of the receiving system and is decided on a case-by-case basis.

Concepts to Consider

Concept I. Mixing Zones Apply To All Types Of Wastes

Because attention of the public, water pollution control agencies, scientists, and industrialists has focused recently on mixing zones for the

TABLE 3—Discharge volume—mixing zone relationship from Eq 2.

Discharge, mgd	Mixing Zone, linear ft	Ratio
1	200	1:200
5	447	1: 89
10	632	1: 63
50	1 414	1: 28
100	2 000	1: 20
500	4 472	1: 8.9
1000	6 325	1: 6.3
1500	7 746	1: 5.2
2000	8 944	1: 4.5
3000	10 954	1: 3.65

dispersion of waste heat there is a tendency to overlook the importance of mixing zones for other types of wastes, for example, municipal, metals, acids and bases, and toxic organics. Most concepts discussed below are equally adaptable for all types of wastes.

Concept II. Establishment Of The Waste Capacity Of The Receiving System

Wastes do not simply disappear when they leave the discharge pipe. They enter a physically, chemically, and biologically complex arena called an ecosystem. Unless the waste is exactly similar in all characteristics to the receiving waters, a practical impossibility, changes will occur in the receiving system. The extent of these changes, the accompanying response and the resultant effects on the uses man wishes to make of that ecosystem largely determine their social and economic significance. Because aquatic ecosystems are dynamic and diverse, each has its own ability to assimilate different wastes by a variety of physical, chemical, and biological mechanisms. Understanding the functioning of these mechanisms at each discharge site and the behavior of each type of discharge in the ecosystem is essential. Such knowledge is the first step towards establishment of mass emission limitations on critical constituents and wisely planned discharge design which will permit maximum beneficial use of a natural resource, the receiving system. Such planning must include safety factors and allowances for future discharges.

The concept of waste assimilation capacity is currently in political and Federal enforcement disfavor. Richard Nalesnik, former director (1971) of EPA's Water Quality Standards Office, stated "So-called 'mixing zones' of the past have been to some degree expressions of our technical ignorance. In the future, as we approach closed systems—complete water reuse and effluent controls—the mixing zone panacea will disappear"[6]. I strongly disagree with Mr. Nalesnik's initial statement relative to technical ignorance. I feel that the lack of uniform mixing zone policies has resulted from a lack of leadership by the scientific community; a lack of initiative by state agencies; the reluctance of industry to act because of constantly changing attitudes, regulations, and concepts; the lack of a national forum in which to formulate and enunciate scientifically-based criteria to serve as a platform for standards; and the willingness of the Federal government to impose blanket, arbitrarily-established mixing zones without scientifically-demonstrated need.

It is obvious that the waste assimilation concept has its basis in science, rather than in the areas of politics or social choice. The premise that receiving systems do have a definable assimilative capacity is the basis of this paper. Mathematical models for prediction of discharge behavior and ecosystem effects are available for a variety of situations and can be developed for others. Such models are far from infallible and must be applied with caution to each discharge and the particular local environment.

Concept III. Mass-Emission Rate of Critical Constituents Needs More Control Than Size of Mixing Zone

The mass emission rate of the most critical constituents in the discharge and their relationship to the waste capacity of the receiving waterbody are normally the primary factors determining the pollution potential of an effluent. The same mass emission rate of a critical constituent can be attained with different volume rates of discharge simply by making the effluent more or less concentrated. If two effluents with similar mass emission rates of critical constituents discharge to similar receiving situations they are likely to have similar environmental impact even though their volume is not similar. Thus, the popularly held concept that the size of the mixing zone should be determined by the volume of the discharge may not be a wise basis for protection of the ecosystem and is therefore not universally acceptable (see section on relating size of mixing zone to discharge volume).

Concept IV. Aesthetic Criteria Are Applicable To Mixing Zones

In the past, mixing zones have been generally excepted from receiving system water quality criteria or standards and an arbitrary amount of interference with other beneficial uses of the receiving system has been accepted. This attitude was fostered by the NTAC report[1] which states, "It is recognized, however, that certain areas of mixing are unavoidable. These create harmfully polluted areas and for this reason it is essential that they be limited in width and length and be provided only for mixing." Further, as interpreted by EPA[2], the following very positive statement resulted, "The NTAC report specifies that mixing zones be as small as possible and provided only for mixing in order to preserve the 'welfare of the aquatic life resource.' This is because mixing zones constitute barriers which can harmfully block the spawning migration of anadromous and catadromous species and damage the plankton organisms and aquatic invertebrates in the water flow."

Mixing zones need not "create harmfully polluted areas." I recall speaking with a riparian owner whose property bordered a proposed thermal mixing zone on Lake Michigan. His interpretation and associated mental image of the NTAC words "harmfully polluted", helped along by the environmentalist-conservationist doomsday ideology, bordered on surrealism, that is, a seething, steaming, turbid, watery mass of dead fish, rotting algae, debris, and fecal solids accompanied by a fetid odor, clouds of noxious insects, and an overstory of screaming seagulls gorging on the garbage. That's the public image mixing zones have. I advised him to journey a few miles up the coast where a discharge similar to the one proposed for his vicinity was already in operation. There he could observe the hedonistic sunbathers, fishermen, boaters, and swimmers in action.

Waste treatment technology has made many recent advances, industry has made economic commitments utilizing this technology, and an eco-conscientious image is desirable to industry. Therefore wouldn't it be advantageous to publicize that mixing zones will meet the aesthetic "five freedoms" recommended by the NTAC report and quoted below (Ref *1*, p. 6).

"Surface waters should be free of substances attributable to discharges or waste as follows:

(*a*) Materials that will settle to form objectionable deposits.

(*b*) Floating debris, oil, scum, and other matter.

(*c*) Substances producing objectionable color, odor, taste, or turbidity.

(*d*) Materials, including radionuclides, in concentrations or combinations which are toxic or which produce undesirable physiological responses in human, fish and other animal life, and plants.

(*e*) Substances and conditions or combinations thereof in concentrations which produce undesirable aquatic life."

Some modification of (*d*) may be necessary, such as substitution of "unacceptable" for "undesirable" (see Concept IX). Consider the public confidence that industries and enforcement agencies alike would gain by making such a statement.

Concept V. The Time-Exposure History Concept: Water Quality Characteristics to Protect Aquatic Life in Mixing Zones

Water quality criteria for aquatic life in receiving systems are based on long-term (chronic) exposure to protect all life history stages. However, exposure time to harmful or stress-producing conditions in mixing zones is limited for most organisms to much shorter time-periods (acute) varying from a few moments to a few hours or days. Therefore, knowledge of the time exposure history of organisms traversing or being transported through a mixing zone will permit by bioassay the development of time-effect curves based on acute periods of exposure for important organisms frequenting the mixing zone. Such tests should include retention of the test organisms in water of receiving system quality for several days following exposure for determination of any post-exposure effects. To provide an adequate margin of safety the time-effect curves should be based on a conservative response (sublethal) and maximum predicted residence time in the mixing zone for the organism to be protected. If mortality is the response plotted, a safety factor could be incorporated by doubling the expected residence time.

Concept VI. A Mixing Zone Defines Itself

Acceptance of the time exposure history concept permits the mixing zone to define itself as a region in which water quality characteristics necessary for the protection of aquatic life are determined by the time exposure history of the organisms frequenting the region. Therefore, the boundary of the mixing zone can be defined as the point where water quality characteristics will permit long-term exposure without any interference with any activity or ill effects to any life history stage. Concepts V and VI shift emphasis from spatial concepts to time-dependent concepts.

Mixing zones should not be considered as regions where complete mixing occurs; therefore, the effluent plume may be identifiable outside the time-dependent boundary.

Concept VII. Contiguous or Overlapping Mixing Zones Require Application of Special Criteria

Acceptance of the time-dependency concept allows for contiguous or overlapping mixing zones and requires application of specially developed criteria to protect aquatic life within such regions. Such circumstances extend the exposure time of organisms to stressful situations and bioassay and time of passage prediction procedures must be modified to incorporate additive effects. The possibility of synergistic effects must also be investigated.

Concept VIII. The Total Region of a Waterbody Devoted to Mixing Zones Must Be Limited

The concept of limiting the total region of a waterbody devoted to mixing zones is of crucial importance to the biotic community. The very nature of mixing zones is such that conditions necessary for all life history processes of the subject species are not provided for. When too large a percent of critical habitat in a receiving system is denied a species, the population of that species will decline and an unpredictable chain of events will ensue. Conservatism in delimiting this total region is a necessity since our predictive abilities are limited.

It is in the allocation of individual mixing zones within the constraint of a given percent of the receiving system that the spatial approach of Eqs 1, 2, and 3, and the Michigan approach may be applicable (see section on size of mixing zone to discharge volume). There are two conflicting schools of thought on mixing zones: one advocates keeping them as small as possible; the other advocates rapid mixing with entrainment of as much dilution water as possible, thus creating a much larger area, but insuring rapid dilution.

In determining the percentage of a receiving system to devote to mixing zones the investigation, analysis, definition, decision, allocation, application, and enforcement comprises one of the most difficult procedures facing society. The process demands high priority and the attention of natural, physical, and social scientists, planners, economists, industrialists, lawyers, administrators, and the lay public. Scientists can define the choices, but society at large will have a strong hand in making the final decision.

Concept IX. Damage to Biota Should be Evaluated on Populations, Not Individuals

Natural mortality is accepted as a biological necessity by the most fanatical environmentalist. Man-induced mortality of organisms produces a different response. There is little doubt that large-scale intake and discharge of water will cause some mortality of individual organisms. One objective in the total design of industrial plumbing and mixing zones should be to minimize mortality so damage to receiving system populations is negligible or is not measurable.

Concept X. Mixing Zones May Represent a Loss of Living Area to Benthic Organisms

Relatively immobile benthic and sessile organisms such as clams, oysters, certain insects, plants or the adhesive eggs of fish and invertebrates may be subject to continuous or intermittent exposure to stressful conditions in mixing zones. Having little or no locomotive powers they may be eliminated from the zones, but if this living space is insignificant in comparison to their total suitable habitat in the waterbody the reduction in the organisms' ecosystem population will be negligible (see also Concept XV).

Minimum damage to this group of organisms from the existence of a mixing zone is attained by minimizing the bottom area exposed to concentrations exceeding levels resulting in harm to these organisms from long-term exposure. If the limitation for a given waste component is based on a more sensitive organism than those occurring in the benthic community, damage to these organisms may not occur even within the defined mixing zone.

Concept XI. Discharge Design Can Protect Certain Organisms

As pointed out in Concept X, minimizing habitat exposed to deleterious concentrations of waste can result in lessened impact on populations of certain organisms. Engineering ingenuity can accomplish this if biologists identify the critical regions to be protected or define the behavior of important organisms. Without knowledge of organism behavior a discharge and mixing zone may be designed to protect an organism which will never come in contact with the zone.

Concept XII. Rapid Mixing Is Generally More Favorable Than Slow Mixing

Rapid mixing entrains large volumes of diluent water of receiving system quality. With proper design and controls, concentrations harmful to aquatic life do not exist for as long a time as when slow mixing occurs. However, there will be certain situations when high-volume entrainment is undesirable and the discharge volume should be as small as possible (see Concepts XI and XVII). The advantages and disadvantages may be off-setting with no obvious choice. To illustrate, American Electric Power Service Corporation asked me for biological guidance in 1969 on design of a heated discharge to Lake Michigan. I called in five other scientists and after discussing the ramifications of high-velocity versus low-velocity discharge at this particular site our six opinions were divided three and three.

Concept XIII. Organisms in Mixing Zones Are Vulnerable

Organisms in mixing zones may be under a physiological stress which impairs their compensatory mechanisms, thereby lowering their tolerance to further stress. This vulnerability should be recognized and discharge practices should be regimented and enforced to minimize variable conditions in the mixing zone which could shock the organisms.

Concept XIV. Water Quality Barriers to Passage of Aquatic Organisms Should Not Exist

Water quality barriers may prevent or delay the arrival of fish at spawning areas; prevent or interfere with passage of young fish to areas where they can mature normally; reduce the food supply of down-current feeders by decimating the populations of drifting organisms; or prevent normal hatching of drifting eggs. Any of these phenomena can result in lowering the population of migratory or indigenous species or both. Minimizing the chance that barriers will exist can be designed into mixing zones (see Concepts XV through XVII).

Concept XV. Mixing Zone Location Can Further Protect the Biota

In addition to designing water quality characteristics to protect the organism (Concepts V, XI, and XII) further protection can be provided to critical habitat by knowledgeable location of the mixing zone. Since migrating species select their routes by river bed morphology and currents, and consistently follow the same major route, historic migratory patterns should be known when designing a mixing zone. It is desirable in most cases to have mixing zones on one side of a river to allow free passage on the other. Midstream discharges may be biologically advantageous (as may offshore discharges in lakes, estuaries, and coastal waters) when shore areas are important as migration routes, as spawning or nursery grounds, as producers of fish food organisms, or for other beneficial uses such as municipal water supply or recreational areas.

Concept XVI. Mixing Zones May Either Attract or Repel Organisms

If a waste discharge either strongly attracts or repels organisms it may create a barrier to passage (see Concept XIV). Organisms attracted to discharges containing materials which are bioaccumulatable may remain there long enough to concentrate such materials to levels harmful to themselves or to predators ingesting them, including man. Such phenomena can be identified and designed-out of mixing zones by performing bioassay tests devised to measure such responses.

Concept XVII. The Case-By-Case Concept: Mixing Zones Should Be Designed Individually

There is no substitute for the case-by-case approach. Each mixing zone should be tailored to the physical, chemical, and biological characteristics of each ecosystem and its particular community of organisms. This litany of Concepts culminates, terminates, and is essentially summarized in the preceding sentence.

Evidence that the Federal government recognizes the validity of the case-by-case philosophy is contained in an address John R. Quarles, Jr., EPA Assistant Administrator for Enforcement and General Counsel, presented to the Edison Electric Institute's Financial Conference in May 1972[7]. He stated, "EPA has had thermal policy actively under consideration for many months. We have recently established the policy that each discharge of waste heat to the aquatic environment shall be evaluated on a case-by-case basis."

Despite Mr. Quarles' seemingly explicit policy statement, Mr. Francis Mayo, Regional Director of EPA's Chicago office (Region V) stated in September 1972, he felt there was sufficient latitude in Mr. Quarles' statement to provide for considering a particular body of water, such as Lake Erie or Michigan, as "a case." [5] There is a distinction between what Messrs. Quarles and Mayo stated, the former referring to the individual discharges and the latter to individual bodies of water. The statements are compatible and each fits within the framework of the Concepts enumerated in this

---

[5] Personal communication.

text. Each discharge is a case to be considered separately and so is each body of water.

Concluding Remarks

The individualized case-by-case approach is not the enforceably easy way to control mixing zones; it is the difficult way. However, the right way is often the difficult way and the degree of difficulty should not be a deterrent to proceeding in the right way to accomplish an avowed purpose.

Edmund Burke, a British statesman, parliamentary orator and political thinker who influenced political theory from 1765 to 1795, stated, "The public interest requires doing today those things that men of intelligence and good will would wish, five or ten years hence, had been done." To initiate the right accomplishments today requires systematic acquisition of data which permit evaluation of risks versus benefits in all instances where man's intervention threatens the environment. This takes great thought, careful planning, proper allocation of resources, and a public attuned to reality, not emotional panic.

The public reaction has lessened to the doomsayers' cries of "wolf" that the mass media like to quote because it gives them controversial material for headlines and TV specials. In the future, emotional appeals are even less likely to be effective, but I hope the public does not become so inured and insensitive that they will no longer respond to environmental facts couched in the unemotional text of the practical scientist-investigator.

There is no technological reason (if we work with nature, not against her), nor should there be a socio-economic one, that man today cannot leave the next generation their rightful heritage of a clean, very livable environment. The solutions lie with the working professionals. There are no magic potions; but there are new ways of doing things, and new attitudes and concepts to embrace. We will not solve our problems with a few years of effort. We will be working on them until eternity.

Acknowledgments

As an aquatic biologist working with an enforcement agency, and also as a private citizen with a concern for social and economic interests, I have been involved in the equitable tailoring of waste discharges to receiving systems, the establishment of mixing zones, since 1957. The concepts expressed in this paper are the distillate of many experiences and personal convictions, and, above all, discussions with the general public, riparian owners, and with hundreds of biologists, chemists, engineers, planners, and administrators from industry, academia, and state and Federal enforcement and natural resources agencies. Many of the concepts originated with my peers, and as the author of this paper, I am only serving as a gatherer and disseminator of their viewpoints.

References

[1] "Water Quality Criteria, Report of the National Technical Advisory Committee to the Secretary of the Interior," National Technical Advisory Committee, Federal Water Pollution Control Administration (now EPA), Washington, D.C., 1968, pp. x–234.

[2] "Summary of Mixing Zone Standards," Water Quality Standards Division, EPA, Washington, D.C., Sept. 1971.

[3] "Interstate and Intrastate Water Temperature Standards for Protection of Fish and Aquatic Life," Michigan Water Resources Commission, Bureau of Water Management, Michigan Dept. of Natural Resources, Lansing, Aug. 1971, p. 6.

[4] Hartley, R. P., Barber, Y., Blomgren, C. T., Fetterolf, C. M., Hert, O. H., and McKersie, J., "Recommendations of the Lake Michigan Enforcement Conference Technical Committee on Thermal Discharges to Lake Michigan," EPA, Region V, Chicago, Jan. 1971, p. 10.

[5] Mackenthun, K. M. in "FWPCA Presentations to ORSANCO Engineering Committee," Ohio Basin Region, Federal Water Pollution Control Administration, USDI, Cincinnati, 10 Sept. 1969, pp. A1–A2.

[6] Lewicke, C. K., Environmental Science and Technology, Vol. 5, No. 12, 1971, pp. 1170–1172.

[7] Quarles, J. R., "The Electric Power Industry and the Environment," EPA, Washington, D.C., GPO No. 0–470–732, 1972, p. 12.

C. I. Weber [1]

Biological Monitoring of the Aquatic Environment

REFERENCE: Weber, C. I., "**Biological Monitoring of the Aquatic Environment by the Environmental Protection Agency,**" *Biological Methods for the Assessment of Water Quality, ASTM STP 528,* American Society for Testing and Materials, 1973, pp. 46–60.

ABSTRACT: A nation-wide water quality monitoring network was operated from 1957 to 1968 by a central Federal laboratory in Cincinnati. The network was decentralized in 1968, and the responsibility for its operation was transferred to the regional offices of the Federal Water Quality Administration. Following the creation of the Environmental Protection Agency, an Office of Monitoring was established to provide overall technical coordination of the monitoring program and to standardize methodology and maintain quality control of the data. The responsibility for water quality monitoring in the EPA will be shared by the Office of Monitoring, Office of Air and Water Programs, Office of Enforcement and General Counsel, and Office of Research. Four types of monitoring have been identified— ambient trend monitoring, source monitoring, case preparation monitoring, and research monitoring. The water quality monitoring network of the EPA will consist of 5000 to 10 000 EPA-funded stations and 40 000 to 50 000 stations operated by state and local agencies. The data will be stored in a central EPA computerized system called STORET. The responsibility for quality control and the development, validation and standardization of chemical, microbiological, and biological methodology for water and waste water has been assigned to the Analytical Quality Control Laboratory (AQCL) in Cincinnati.

Water quality is reflected in the species composition and diversity, population density and physiological condition of indigenous communities of aquatic organisms. Biological methodology employed in water quality monitoring in the EPA deals primarily with sample collection, sample processing, counting and identification of aquatic organisms, biomass measurements, measurement of bioaccumulation and biomagnification of pollutants, and biological data processing and interpretation. The AQCL conducts research in all areas of biological methodology for water quality

[1] Chief, Biological Methods, Analytical Quality Control Laboratory, National Environmental Research Center, Environmental Protection Agency, Cincinnati, Ohio 45202.

monitoring, develops reference samples for quality control, and conducts agency-wide interlaboratory methods studies. An Agency biological methods manual is in preparation and will be available in 1973.

KEY WORDS: water pollution, environmental surveys, biomass, marine microorganisms, biological methods, plankton, periphyton, macrophyton, macroinvertebrates, fishes, bioassay, water quality monitoring

The first national water quality monitoring program employing biological parameters was begun by the Division of Water Supply and Pollution Control, U.S. Public Health Service, in 1957. By 1962, grab water samples were collected routinely at approximately 145 stations operated by Federal, state, and local agencies, and located at municipal water treatment plants, locks and dams, industrial water supply intakes, and at interstate and international boundaries (Fig. 1). The samples were shipped to the central laboratory in Cincinnati, Ohio, for analysis. During the first few years, the biological analyses were limited to phyto- and zooplankton counts and identifications. In 1962, the biological program was broadened to include the macroinvertebrates and fish. Periphyton sampling was added in 1965. Initially called the National Water Quality Network, the monitoring program was later renamed the Water Pollution Surveillance System. Chemical and microbiological analyses were also carried out, and with the biological analyses yielded a total of approximately 100 data items per sample (Table 1). A computerized data storage and retrieval system (STORET) was

TABLE 1—*Water quality and biological parameters measured by the Water Pollution Surveillance System.*

Water Quality Parameters, WPSS	
Physical and Chemical	*Biological*
Temperature, DO, pH	Total live algae
Color, turbidity	Blue greens (Cocc, Fil)
BOD, COD, TDS	Greens (Cocc, Fil)
Cl⁻Alk, HARD	Green flagellates
NH_3, PO_4, SO_4	Other flagellates
	Centric diatoms
Microbiological	Pennate diatoms
Total Coliforms	Dominant diatom species
	Zooplankton
	Rotifers
	Microcrustacea

developed to handle the large amount of data generated by the network[1].[2] A compilation of data was prepared annually[2] until 1963, when it was

[2] The italic numbers in brackets refer to the list of references appended to this paper.

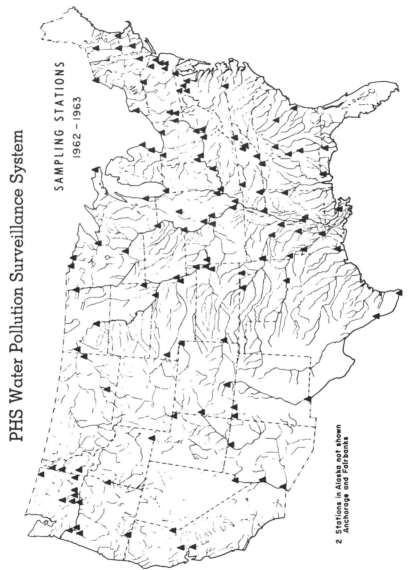

PHS Water Pollution Surveillance System

SAMPLING STATIONS
1962 – 1963

2 Stations in Alaska not shown
Anchorage and Fairbanks

FIG. 1—*Sampling stations operated by the Water Pollution Surveillance System.*

decided to cease publication of the data because of spiralling printing costs. Since then, requests for data have been filled on an individual basis by computer retrieval.

The responsibility for operating the national water quality monitoring program was transferred from the central laboratory in Cincinnati to the regional offices of the Federal Water Quality Administration in 1968. Many of the regions were not adequately staffed to maintain their segment of the monitor program, however, and the biological phases of the monitoring activity declined rapidly during subsequent years.

The importance of monitoring was recognized within the Environmental Protection Agency (EPA) by the creation of an Office of Monitoring, under the Assistant Administrator for Research and Monitoring (Figs. 2 and 3).

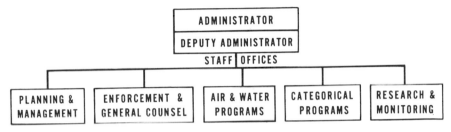

FIG. 2—*Organizational structure of the Environmental Protection Agency.*

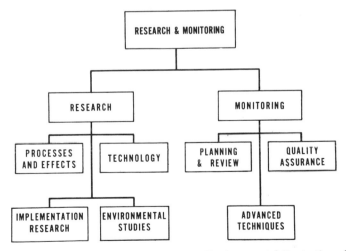

FIG. 3—*Office of Research and Monitoring, Environmental Protection Agency.*

The Office of Monitoring has the following responsibilities: (1) provide overall technical coordination, assure technical feasibility of proposed monitoring, and review and concur on all budgetary and planning actions; (2) provide technical guidance on quality control and standardization, and methods of sampling and analysis; (3) develop and implement a total quality control program; (4) design and implement a program for improving and auditing the quality of monitoring data, equipment, and laboratory techniques; and (5) develop and demonstrate improved monitoring equipment and methods, and recommend them to the responsible program offices. The responsibility for the water quality monitoring program will be shared by the Office of Monitoring, Office of Air and Water Programs (OAWP), Office of Enforcement and General Counsel (OEGC), and Office of Research (OR).

Types of Monitoring

Current Agency strategy calls for four types of monitoring[3]:

1. Ambient Trend Monitoring—measure conditions and trends in relation to standards and guidelines (OAWP),

2. Source Monitoring—locate and measure toxicity of effluents (OAWP) and assess compliance of pollution sources (OEGC),

3. Case Preparation Monitoring—gather evidence for enforcement actions (OEGC), and

4. Research Monitoring—support research activities (OR).

Ambient Trend Monitoring will be conducted to (a) understand ambient conditions in setting or revising standards, (b) estimate ambient pollution loads in setting regulatory criteria and policies, (c) review adequacy of abatement plans for achieving objectives, and (d) measure abatement progress and report environmental trends.

Source Monitoring will be conducted to (a) complete pollution source inventories, (b) help establish effluent guidelines and pollution control plans, and (c) assess source compliance with enforcement programs and Refuse Act permits. Case Preparation Monitoring and Research Monitoring are special purpose activities. Except for Research Monitoring, data will be collected by regional personnel within the Divisions of Surveillance and Analysis.

Current Agency monitoring plans envision a basic network of 5000 to 10 000 EPA funded stations, most of which will be sampled intermittently, and an additional 40 000 to 50 000 stations operated by state and local agencies. Approximately 60 priority geographic areas have been identified (such as Cleveland, Washington, Houston, etc.), which involve multiple waste discharges into receiving waters that are under great stress. These areas will be monitored at a high level of intensity every two or three years on a rotating basis. Four or five stations will be maintained in each area for monitoring throughout the year, and will be part of a key-station network maintained to keep abreast of water quality in problem areas, at interstate and international boundaries, and at the mouths of minor basins[4].

Data Storage and Retrieval System

The central data storage and retrieval system (STORET) has continued to grow over the years and is now accessed by approximately 145 remote terminals located at EPA regional offices and at state and other Federal agencies. At present, STORET accrues effluent and surface water quality data at rates ranging from 50 000 to 200 000 items per week. Each regional office will prepare periodic region-wide pollution index and water quality trend reports based on the monitoring data it has collected. EPA headquarters will prepare similar reports which are national in scope.

Within the Agency, the responsibility for quality control and the development, validation and standardization of chemical, microbiological, and biological methodology for water and waste water has been assigned to the Analytical Quality Control Laboratory (AQCL), National Environmental Research Center (Fig. 4), Cincinnati, Ohio, which contains segments of the Quality Assurance and Advanced Techniques programs, Office of Monitoring, and the National Analytical Methods Research Program, Office of Research. The quality control program conducted by the AQCL is designed to assure the validity, and where necessary, the legal defensibility of all water quality information collected by the EPA. The laboratory is responsible for conducting chemical, microbiological, and biological methods research, carrying out Agency-wide interlaboratory methods evaluations, supplying reference samples, advising laboratories in the development of internal quality control programs, and preparing Agency methods manuals. Methods manuals have been published for general chemical analyses, organic pesticides, and the identification of petroleum products in water and waste water[5,6,7].

A national advisory committee of senior Agency biologists was organized in 1970 to assist the Biological Methods Research Program in selecting and describing field and laboratory methods for Agency use (Table 2). The manual is nearing completion and will contain techniques for the collection and analysis of plankton, periphyton, macrophyton, macroinvertebrate, and fish samples, and include sections on bioassay, algal assay, and biometrics. The methods are intended for use in ambient trend, source and case preparation monitoring, and for routine field and laboratory work in the EPA national research programs.

In addition to the biological methods manual, biological reference samples are employed in Agency-wide methods studies. A simulated plankton sample was distributed to participating laboratories for microscope calibration,

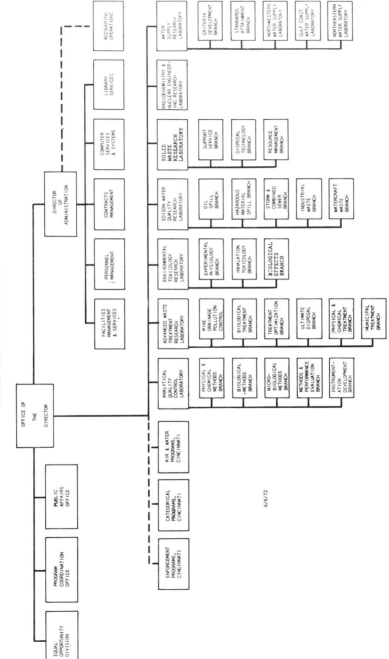

FIG. 4—*Interim structure of the National Environmental Research Center, Cincinnati.*

TABLE 2—*EPA programs represented on the National Biological Advisory Committee.*

National Biological Advisory Committee
Regional Surveillance and Analysis Divisions (ten regions)
National Research Programs
Coastal pollution
Thermal pollution
Oil spill research
Eutrophication
Large lakes research
Fate of pollutants
Water quality control
National Water Quality Laboratory (Duluth)
National Marine Water Quality Laboratory (Narragansett)
National Field Investigation Centers
Cincinnati
Denver

particle sizing, and Sedgwick-Rafter counts in 1970. A chlorophyll reference sample will be distributed in 1973.

Biological Methodology

For the purposes of this discussion, biological methods employed in monitoring the aquatic environment are divided into three general categories:

1. methods for studying the effects of pollutants on indigenous (natural) communities of aquatic organisms in receiving waters;

2. methods employing captive organisms or controlled conditions to determine the toxicity or other biological effects of substances or conditions in effluents or receiving waters, and

3. methods employing bioaccumulation or biomagnification to detect or monitor trends in the concentration of pollutants in surface waters.

Water quality is reflected in the species composition and diversity, population density, and physiological condition of indigenous communities of aquatic organisms[8]. Thus, the methodology commonly employed by Agency biologists in field studies of ambient trends in water quality, and for source monitoring and case preparation monitoring, deals primarily with sample collection, sample processing and counting, identification of aquatic organisms, biomass determinations, measurement of metabolic rates, and data processing and evaluation. Historically, responsibility within the EPA for the development and evaluation of methods for field studies of natural communities of aquatic organisms has been centered at AQCL, whereas acute and chronic bioassay techniques have been developed and employed principally at the two National Water Quality Laboratories (Duluth, Minn., and Narragansett, R. I.). Techniques employing bioaccumulation and bio-magnification of pollutants have not been studied intensively or used widely within the Agency.

Biological methodology under development or evaluation at AQCL in-cludes the following:

1. Sample Collection
   (a) Station selection
   (b) Optimum sampling frequency
   (c) Replication and precision
   (d) Sampling devices
       (1) Grabs—comparison of performance of Ekman, Petersen and Ponar grabs
       (2) Artificial substrates—effect of substrate texture, configuration, exposure time, and depth on performance of macroinvertebrate and periphyton samplers
       (3) Macroinvertebrate drift
2. Sample Processing
   (a) Sample preservation and stability
   (b) Staining
   (c) Sample splitting
   (d) Sorting (macroinvertebrates)
       (1) Effect of sieve mesh size
       (2) Mechanical (automatic) sorting devices
   (e) Counting techniques
       (1) Sedgwick-Rafter counting
       (2) Automatic counting devices (optical and electrical)
3. Organism Identification
   (a) Photo- and electron microscopy
   (b) Taxonomic keys and descriptions
       (1) Diatoms
       (2) Midges
       (3) Mayflies
   (c) Karyosystematics and biochemical techniques
4. Biomass Measurements
   (a) Wet, dry and ash-free weights; freeze drying
   (b) Caloric content
   (c) Pigment content
       (1) *In-vivo* and *in-vitro* fluorometric methods
       (2) Spectrophotometric methods
       (3) Corrections for pheophytin and other interferences

(*d*) Biomass/chlorophyll *a* relationship in plankton and periphyton
(*e*) ATP as a total viable plankton biomass parameter
(*f*) DNA as a plankton biomass parameter
5. Metabolic Rate Measurements
    (*a*) Photosynthesis (Carbon-14 uptake and oxygen evolution)
    (*b*) Respiration
    (*c*) Electron Transport
    (*d*) Nitrogen fixation
6. Data Processing and Evaluation
    (*a*) Indicator organism profiles
    (*b*) Environmental requirements of common species
    (*c*) Toxicity data
    (*d*) Computer programs
        (1) Community diversity indices
        (2) Chlorophyll and biomass computations
        (3) Rank correlations
        (4) Storage and retrieval of taxonomic data

Ambient Trend Monitoring is frequently conducted in waters having a higher quality than encountered in Source Monitoring and Case Preparation Monitoring. Changes in population parameters in relatively unpolluted waters are more subtle and require more sensitive and precise methodology, and more care must be taken in the preparation of the sampling design, selection of sampling devices and substrates, and organism identification. Consistency in the use of techniques of sample collection and analysis is especially important.

Parameters which have proven useful in long-term water quality monitoring include phytoplankton and zooplankton counts and species composition —especially the diatoms[9–12], chlorophyll[13], seston and primary production[14], and the abundance and taxonomic composition of the macroinvertebrates[15,16]. The development of techniques to measure chlorophyll in surface waters was assigned top priority in recommendations prepared by the International Biological Program Committee on Global Monitoring[17]. Fish populations are more difficult and expensive to sample, but a fish monitoring program has been conducted in the Ohio River Basin[18,19]. Catch records of commercial fisheries are also very useful in determining changes in fish populations which might reflect changes in water quality[20].

Source Monitoring and Case Preparation Monitoring usually involve comparisons of indigenous communities in the immediate vicinity of the outfall(s) and at reference stations. The most widely used biological parameters include (as for ambient trend monitoring) the abundance, species composition and diversity of the plankton and periphyton (especially the diatoms

[21–23]), and macroinvertebrates[24–27]. Information on the age class distribution, species composition, general condition, and disease and parasitism of fish is also very useful. In streams, the periphyton are often more useful than the plankton in evaluating the effects of pollution, because they more accurately reflect conditions at a given sampling location.

Developing Techniques

Techniques now under development for the measurement of chlorophyll in marine and inland surface waters from air- and spacecraft will soon permit frequent and simultaneous determinations of this parameter over large geographic regions[28]. Other new and promising plankton techniques include the determination of pheophytin in algal pigments as a measure of phytoplankton condition, the use of ATP as a measure of total viable plankton biomass[29], and the chemical analysis of phytoplankton to identify limiting nutrients[30]. The recent development of standardized artificial substrates for the collection of macroinvertebrates and periphyton has resulted in the collection of more precise data than can be obtained from natural substrates and has provided more control over the sampling process. Also, new indices of community structure, such as mathematical expressions of species diversity[26] and periphyton heterotroph-autotroph relationships [31], have improved our ability to quantitate taxonomic data. However, because of the continued lack of widely accepted quantitative norms by which to evaluate biological field data and the complexity of ecological processes, biologists must rely heavily on the interpretation of the presence or absence of indicator organisms, and use other subjective approaches.

The use of captive organisms or controlled conditions or both in determining the acute toxicity or other biological effects of pollutants includes measurements made in-plant, in-stream (or stream-side), or in remote laboratories. Short-term static and flow-through tests of acute toxicity of a single pollutant, physical condition or effluent, or combinations of test conditions have been employed primarily with fish and macroinvertebrates[32–34]. Short-term effects of pollutants on algae are usually measured in terms of the reduction in growth rate[35,36], photosynthesis rates[37], and increased susceptibility to normal environmental stresses[38]. The Algal Assay Procedure Bottle Test[39], developed by the National Eutrophication Research Program, EPA, is a biostimulatory test that measures algal growth response to nutrients in surface waters or effluents in terms of cell count, dry weight, or chlorophyll content. It would also be suitable for toxicity tests, but it has not been used for that purpose.

Long-term (chronic) flow-through bioassays extending over the entire life cycle of the test organisms are used to determine the highest (safe) concentration of a pollutant at which no adverse biological effects are observed. Information from these studies has been used to derive "application factors" that permit the calculation of "safe" concentrations of pollutants from short-term acute toxicity data[40–43].

Continuous monitoring of physiological and behavioral responses of fish, such as opercular movement, locomotion, and feeding activity, permits rapid detection of responses to pollutants at stressing levels as low as those found by chronic tests to be biologically safe[44–46]. These techniques may prove useful for in-plant and stream-side monitoring of the toxicity of industrial effluents and receiving waters, and may protect aquatic organisms in receiving waters from sudden exposure to adverse conditions[47]. However, the ultimate proof that receiving waters are adequately protected can be obtained only by periodically examining the natural communities of aquatic organisms. Ambient trend and source monitoring programs, therefore, must include field studies of indigenous aquatic organisms in receiving waters (Fig. 5).

The bioaccumulation and biomagnification of trace amounts of pollutants in water have been extensively documented and are useful in monitoring

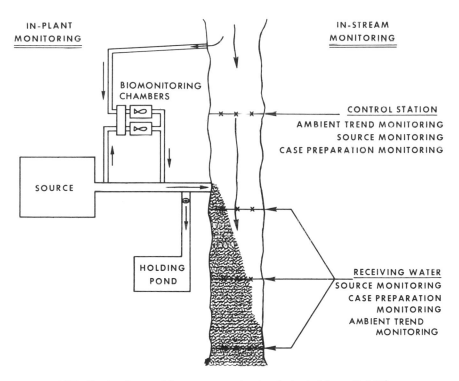

FIG. 5—*In-plant and in-stream monitoring (adapted from Ref 47).*

trends in the levels of pollutants in the biosphere. Examples of this technique include the use of caged fish to determine the presence of fish flesh tainting substances in effluents and receiving waters[48,49], the use of caged clams to monitor trends in DDT concentrations[50], and the analysis of periphyton, fish, and water fowl to monitor radionuclide levels "downstream" from nuclear reactors[51]. These techniques have been used only on a limited scale in the Federal water pollution control program.

Conclusion

In this discussion of biological monitoring of the aquatic environment, I have attempted to provide an overview of the EPA monitoring program and available methodology. The monitoring policy of the Agency is still in the developmental stage, however, and it is not possible at this time to predict the role that will be played by the various techniques in the monitoring program.

References

[1] Green, R. S., "The Storage and Retrieval of Data for Water Quality Control, PHS, Division of Water Supply & Pollution Control, USDHEW, Washington, D.C., 1964.

[2] "Annual Compilation of Data," National Water Quality Network, PHS, USDHEW, Washington, D.C., 1957–63.

[3] Fri, R. W., "EPA Management of Monitoring," Intra-Agency Memorandum, EPA, Washington, D.C., 18 April 1972.

[4] Personal communication with C. R. Horn, Office of Water Programs, EPA, Washington, D.C.

[5] "Methods for Chemical Analysis of Water and Wastes," 2nd ed., Analytical Quality Control Laboratory, EPA, Office of Research & Monitoring, National Environmental Research Center, Cincinnati, 1971.

[6] Kawahara, F. K., "Laboratory Guide for the Identification of Petroleum Products," USDI, FWPCA, Analytical Quality Control Laboratory, Cincinnati, 1969.

[7] "Methods for Organic Pesticides in Water and Wastewater," J. J. Lichtenberg, Ed., EPA, National Environmental Research Center, Analytical Quality Control Laboratory, Cincinnati, 1971.

[8] "Standard Methods for the Examination of Water and Wastewater," 13th ed., American Public Health Association, New York, 1971.

[9] Hasler, A. D., Ecology, Vol. 28, No. 4, 1947, pp. 383–395.

[10] Rawson, D. S., Limnology and Oceanography, Vol. 1, No. 1, 1956, pp. 18–25.

[11] Hohn, M. H., "Quantitative and Qualitative Analyses of Plankton Diatoms," Bulletin of the Ohio Biological Survey, Vol. 3, No. 1. 1969, pp. 1–211.

[12] Stoermer, E. F. and Yang, J. J., "Distribution and Relative Abundance of Dominant Plankton Diatoms in Lake Michigan," Publication 16, Great Lakes Research Division, University of Michigan, Ann Arbor, 1970.

[13] Edmundson, W. T. and Anderson, G. C., Limnology and Oceanography, Vol. 1, No. 1, 1956, pp. 47–53.

[14] Lee, G. F., "Eutrophication," Occasional Paper 2, Water Resources Center, University of Wisconsin, Madison, 1970.

[15] Beeton, A. M., Limnology and Oceanography, Vol. 10, No. 2, 1965, pp. 240–254.

[16] Carr, J. F. and Hiltunen, J. K., *Limnology and Oceanography*, Vol. 10, No. 4, 1965, pp. 551–569.

[17] "Global Environmental Monitoring System," technical report from Sweden to the IBP *ad hoc* Committee on Global Monitoring, Swedish Natural Science Research Council, Stockholm, 1970.

[18] Tebo, L. B., "Fish Population Sampling Studies at Water Pollution Surveillance System Stations on the Ohio, Tennessee, Clinch, and Cumberland Rivers," Application & Development Report 15, Water Quality Section, Basic Data Branch, Division of the Water Supply & Pollution Control, PHS, USDHEW, Washington, D.C., 1965.

[19] Preston, H. R., "Fishery Composition Studies, Ohio River, 1967–68," presented at the 70th Meeting of the Ohio River Valley Sanitation Commission Engineering Committee, Cincinnati, Sept. 1969.

[20] Fruh, E. G., Stewart, K. M., Lee, G. F., and Rolich, G. A., *Journal of the Water Pollution Control Federation*, Vol. 38, No. 8, 1966, pp. 1237–1258.

[21] Patrick, R., Hohn, M. H., and Wallace, J. H., *Notulae Naturae*, Vol. 259, 1954, pp. 1–12.

[22] Fjerdingstad, E., *Hydrobiologia*, Vol. 50, No. 4, 1965, pp. 475–604.

[23] Hohn, M. H., *Institute of Marine Science*, University of Texas, Vol. 5, 1969, pp. 206–212.

[24] Patrick, R., *Proceedings*, Academy of Natural Sciences, Philadelphia, Vol. 101, 1949, pp. 277–341.

[25] Gaufin, A. R. and Tarzwell, C. M., *Sewage and Industrial Wastes*, Vol. 28, No. 7, 1956, pp. 906–924.

[26] Wilhm, J. L., *Journal of the Water Pollution Control Federation*, Vol. 42, No. 5, 1970, pp. R211–R224.

[27] Mason, W. T., Jr., Lewis, P. A., and Anderson, J. B., "Macro-invertebrate Collections and Water Quality Monitoring in the Ohio River Basin, 1963–1967," cooperative report by the Office of Technical Programs, Ohio Basin Region and the Analytical Quality Control Laboratory, EPA, Cincinnati, 1971.

[28] Clarke, G. L., Ewing, G. C., and Lorenzen, C. J., *Science*, Vol. 157, No. 3921, 1970, pp. 1119–1121.

[29] Weber, C. I., "Recent Developments in the Measurement of the Response of Plankton and Periphyton to Changes in Their Environment," presented at the Symposium on Bioassay Techniques in Environmental Chemistry held at the 162nd Annual Meeting of the American Chemical Society, Washington, D.C., Sept. 1971, (in press).

[30] Fitzgerald, G. P., and Nelson, T. C., *Journal of Phycology*, Vol. 2, No. 1, 1966, pp. 32–37.

[31] Weber, C. I. and McFarland, B. H., "Periphyton Biomass-Chlorophyll Ratio as an Index of Water Quality," presented at the 17th Annual Meeting of the Midwest Benthological Society, Gilbertsville, Ky., April 1969.

[32] Jackson, H. W. and Brungs, W. A., *Industrial Water Engineering*, Vol. 45, 1966, pp. 14–18.

[33] Basch, R. E., "*In Situ* Investigations of the Toxicity of Chlorinated Municipal Wastewater Treatment Plant Effluent to Rainbow Trout (Salmo gairdneri)," presented at the Symposium on Bioassay Techniques in Environmental Chemistry, at the 162nd National Meeting, American Chemical Society, Washington, D.C., Sept. 1971.

[34] Warnick, S. L. and Bell, H. L., *Journal of the Water Pollution Control Federation*, Vol. 41, No. 2, 1969, pp. 280–284.

[35] *ASTM Annual Book of Standards*, Part 23, American Society for Testing and Materials, 1964, pp. 517–525.

[36] Patrick, R., Cairns, J., Jr., and Scheier, A., *Progressive Fish Culturist*, Vol. 39, No. 3, 1968, pp. 137–140.

[37] Menzel, D. W., Anderson, J., and Randtke, A., *Science*, Vol. 167, 1970, pp. 1724–1726.
[38] Batterton, J. C., Boush, G. M., and Matsumura, F., *Science*, Vol. 176, 1972, pp. 1141–1143.
[39] "Algal Assay Procedure Bottle Test," EPA, Office of Research and Monitoring, National Eutrophication Research Program, Corvallis, Ore., 1971.
[40] Brungs, W. A., *Transactions*, American Fisheries Society, Vol. 98, No. 2, 1969, pp. 272–279.
[41] Mount, D. I. and Stephan, C. E., *Journal of the Fisheries Research Board of Canada*, Vol. 26, No. 9, 1969, pp. 2449–2457.
[42] Pickering, Q. H. and Thatcher, T. O., *Journal of the Water Pollution Control Federation*, Vol. 42, No. 2, 1970, pp. 243–254.
[43] Brungs, W. A., *Transactions*, American Fisheries Society, Vol. 100, No. 4, 1971, pp. 659–664.
[44] Spoor, W. A., Niehielsen, T. W., and Drummond, R. A., *Transactions*, American Fisheries Society, Vol. 100, No. 1, 1971, pp. 22–28.
[45] Waller, W. T. and Cairns, J., Jr., *Water Research*, Vol. 6, 1972, pp. 257–269.
[46] Heath, A. G., *Water Research*, Vol. 6, 1972, pp. 1–7.
[47] Cairns, J., Jr., Sparks, R. E., and Waller, W. T., "The Design of a Continuous-flow Biological Early Warning System for Industrial Use," presented at the 27th Purdue Industrial Waste Conference, 2–4 May 1972, Purdue University, Lafayette, Ind.
[48] "Affects of Pollution on Aquatic Life: Fish Tainting," in "A Report on Pollution of the Ohio River and Its Tributaries in the Pittsburgh, Pennsylvania Area," EPA, Region III, Wheeling Field Office, W. Va., 1971, pp. 88–89.
[49] "Affects of Pollution on Aquatic Life: Fish Tainting," in "A Report on Pollution of the Ohio River and Its Tributaries in the Pittsburgh, Pennsylvania Area," EPA, Region III, Wheeling Field Office, W. Va., 1971, pp. 44–47.
[50] *1970 Annual Report*, Ontario Water Resources Commission, Toronto, Canada, 1971.
[51] Cushing, C. E., *Hydrobiologia*, Vol. 29, No. 1 and 2, 1967, pp. 125–139.

T. L. Bott [1]

Bacteria and the Assessment of Water Quality

REFERENCE: Bott, T. L., "**Bacteria and the Assessment of Water Quality,**" *Biological Methods for the Assessment of Water Quality, ASTM STP 528,* American Society for Testing and Materials, 1973, pp. 61–75.

ABSTRACT: Bacteria are important in the assessment of water quality because certain organisms may be used as indicators of pollution of various types, and because bacteria possess diverse metabolic capabilities that bring about the mineralization of substances, many of which other organisms are unable to use. The limitations of the widely used coliform procedures are discussed and some new approaches to the detection of organisms of fecal origin are presented.

Methods for determining bacterial biomass are presented. However, measures of bacterial activity are more desirable because it is activity that will affect water quality. Some recent approaches to the measurement of bacterial growth and metabolism directly in natural habitats are presented.

KEY WORDS: water pollution, water quality, bacteria, diseases, sanitation, water treatment, waste disposal

Bacteria possess tremendous variability in metabolic abilities and in environmental tolerances and, therefore, are ubiquitous in the environment. They are found over broad ranges of pH, temperature, and oxygen concentration, and many will utilize substrates other organisms are unable to metabolize. The large and variable group of heterotrophic microorganisms consumes organic materials (many of which may be pollutants), bringing about the production of mineralized end products. Therefore, what bacteria do in the aquatic habitat is important to water quality. In addition, some bacteria are pathogenic, either by producing diseases directly through infection or by producing toxins which bring on illness, paralysis, or death.

[1] Assistant curator, Department of Limnology, Academy of Natural Sciences, Philadelphia, Pa. 19103.

Therefore, the bacteria that are present in water are important in an assessment of its quality.

Health Aspects

The organisms most often associated with outbreaks of waterborne disease are: bacteria of the genera *Salmonella* (which produce typhoid fever and gastrointestinal disorders), *Shigella* (which produce diarrheal diseases), certain *Escherichia coli* serotypes (which produce nausea, dehydration, and diarrhea, particularly in infants), *Leptospira* (which produce kidney, liver, and central nervous system infections), *Pasteurella* (which produce tularemia), and *Vibrio* (which produce cholera); the protozoan *Entamoeba histolytica* (which produces dysentery); and the enteric viruses (polio, Coxsackie, E.C.H.O., infectious hepatitis, reovirus, and adenovirus which produce paralytic poliomyelitis, asceptic meningitis, respiratory diseases, flu, and eye infections). A recent review[1][2] summarizes much of the available information. These pathogenic organisms will find their way into the aquatic habitat in the urine or feces of man, domestic, and wild animals. Contamination occurs through domestic sewage effluents, storm sewer run-off, and run-off from natural areas as well as feed lots.

Indicator Organisms for Fecal Pollution

Over the years the coliform count has become the accepted measure of the sanitary quality of water. The coliform organisms are those facultatively anaerobic, gram negative, nonspore forming rod-shaped bacteria that ferment lactose with gas production within 48 h at 35° C. Members of the coliform group are normally present in large numbers in the fecal flora of warm-blooded animals, whereas only a small percentage of the population will carry pathogens at a given time. In addition, techniques for the isolation and identification of pathogens are less amenable to routinization than those used for coliforms. Therefore, coliform detection is used to indicate fecal pollution and potential exposure to pathogens.

There has been and is considerable effort to develop techniques so that results may be obtained with greater sensitivity, with greater accuracy with respect to the identification of organisms, and more rapidly. For example, the membrane filter technique adopted in 1957 provides increased sensitivity by allowing large volumes of water to be tested.

Because there are sources of coliforms other than animal feces, if tests for sanitary quality are to have meaning, differentiation according to source should be made. Originally the IMViC (indole production, methyl red reaction, Voges-Prokauer test, citrate utilization) test series proposed by

---

[2] The italic numbers in brackets refer to the list of references appended to this paper.

Parr[2] was used for this purpose. The elevated temperature incubation test (gas production in lactose broth at 44.5° C, the Eijkman reaction) is also used to detect fecal coliforms[3], and the studies of Geldreich[4] have confirmed the reliability of this approach. More recently, however, Hendricks [5] reported that certain *Enterobacter* isolates were capable of gas production at the elevated temperature and would therefore give a false positive result for fecal coliforms. He postulated that the possession of the enzyme formic hydrogenlyase, active at 44.5° C could be used with greater accuracy to differentiate those coliforms of fecal origin. Organisms of fecal origin did not possess the enzyme at 44.5° C, whereas those originating in soil or vegetation did.

In attempts to obtain results more rapidly and accurately, Guthrie and Reeder[6] used fluorescent antibody procedures for identification following preliminary incubation of organisms collected on membrane filters. They detected *E. coli* in 12 h as opposed to the 18 to 24 h conventionally required. Mitruka and Alexander[7] were able to identify organisms in 4 h by incubating pure cultures of *E. coli*, *S. typhimurium* and *S. aureus* in media containing cometabolized substrates (that is, halogenated organic acids not used as a major energy or carbon source) and detecting by gas chromotography end products characteristic for a given species. Mixtures of organisms were not tested, but the potential of the technique is evident. Others[8] incubated populations filtered onto membrane filters with ^{14}C lactose for 4 h at 42° C and collected $^{14}CO_2$ liberated from lactose fermentation.

The need for more rapid detection procedures is evident from the results of a study of almost 1000 water supply systems done in 1969[9]. Ninety percent of the systems did not collect a sufficient number of samples for bacteriological testing or the samples that they did collect showed poor quality or both. Even allowing for a 50 percent sampling intensity, 69 percent of the systems would have not collected a sufficient number of samples. One reason for this failure was undoubtedly the inability of personnel to routinely test the recommended number of samples using acceptable procedures on the budgets provided. It was suggested that a test for chlorine residual in the system might be a more practical way to monitor for deficiencies, because coliforms were invariably absent where a chlorine residual was maintained.

Indicator organisms should be present only when pathogens are, and their presence must be related to the chance of encountering pathogens. Reliable methodology for the isolation of the pathogen *Salmonella* now exists, and the relationship of coliform indicators to pathogens has been studied using this organism. In 1968, Gallagher and Spino[10] reported that a summary of available data showed little correlation between the levels of total or fecal coliform organisms and *Salmonella*. Geldreich[11], however, pointed out that the inability to detect *Salmonella* in samples containing coliforms may be due to the variable occurrence of *Salmonella* in the environment in the absence of an epidemic rather than to the absence of a correlation. In addition, pathogens other than *Salmonella* might be present. He analyzed data from numerous studies and showed that when the number of fecal coliforms was 200 per 100 ml or more, there was a significantly greater chance of isolating *Salmonella*. The organism was isolated from fewer than 27.6 percent of water samples when the fecal coliform concentration was less than 200 organisms per 100 ml, but isolates were obtained from 85.2 percent of the samples when the range of fecal coliforms was 201 to 2000 per 100 ml and 98.1 percent when the fecal coliform count was more than 2000 per 100 ml. Smith and Twedt[*12*] in a study of organisms in two Michigan rivers found additional evidence to support this claim.

Van Donsel and Geldreich[*13*] also pointed out that although bottom samples are usually examined for fauna in pollution studies, the sediment also reflects the microbial (or sanitary) quality of the overlying water and that bacteria were concentrated in the upper 2 in. The percent *Salmonella* isolates from mud for ranges of fecal coliforms in the overlying water used above were 19.1, 50.0, and 80.0, respectively. No correlation between total coliforms and *Salmonella* or fecal streptococci and *Salmonella* were found.

It has been suggested[*14*] that the ratio of fecal coliforms to fecal streptococci could be used to identify the source of fecal pollution. The quotient was greater than 4 in human feces and domestic wastes, whereas the quotient was less than 0.7 in the feces of farm animals, cats and dogs, or waste waters polluted with the same. On this basis, Smith and Twedt[*12*] suggested that *Salmonella* may more often be associated with human wastes than those of domesticated or wild animals. However, because human pathogens may be harbored in nonhuman hosts, suggestions to limit concern to fecal pollution from human sources are unwise[*11*].

Bacterial self-purification refers to the decline in numbers of enteric organisms downstream from a sewage outfall. The die-away of indicator organisms in the environment ought also to be related to the disappearance of pathogens. Gallagher et al[*15*] reported that although total and fecal coliform numbers at a point 62 miles downstream from their introduction were approximately 1 percent of their initial concentration, *Salmonella* isolates were still obtained. The water temperature was 8° C. At another time when samples were taken from under an ice cover, *Salmonella* organisms were isolated 73 miles downstream although total and fecal coliform numbers had been reduced 96 and 95 percent, respectively. In a laboratory study, Van Donsel and Geldreich[*13*] found that the disappearance of fecal coliforms and five serotypes of *Salmonella* exhibited similar patterns when the organisms were inoculated into mud and held at 20° C for seven days. This relationship did not hold for fecal streptococci or total coliforms and *Salmonella*.

E. coli has been reported to multiply in sewage effluents and highly polluted waters. In addition, nutrients sufficient to support the growth of several *Enterobacteriaceae* species including pathogens (*Esch. coli, Enter. aerogenes, Proteus rettgeri, Salmonella senftenberg, Arizona arizonae, Shigella flexneri*) were demonstrated in the water and sediment of a clean mountain stream[16,17]. Therefore, it has been proposed by several workers that other organisms be used to indicate fecal pollution. Some fecal streptococci (*Streptococcus faecalis, S. equinis, S. bovis*) that do not multiply outside the intestinal tract have been studied[14,18]. However, because there are atypical varieties which do reproduce outside the body, it is not likely that they will replace, but will rather supplement, the use of fecal coliforms in sanitary surveys. Abshire and Guthrie[19] have recently developed fluorescent antibody techniques for the detection of *S. faecalis* strains of fecal origin as opposed to those of nonfecal origin. Bonde[20] found that incidence of *Clostridium perfringens* and the ratio of vegetative cells to spores of the organism was proportional to degree of pollution.

Bacterial Standards and the Evaluation of Drinking Water

The first Public Health Service drinking water standard was introduced in 1914 and required that water on interstate carriers be examined for the presence of coliform organisms. In 1925 the bacteriological criterion was developed to permit evaluation of the supply on the basis of a certain percent positive results. In 1942 requirements were introduced that samples be taken not only at the treatment facility, but also throughout the distribution system and that a minimum number of samples be taken according to the population served. Although the standards still apply strictly to interstate carriers, most states use them either as guidelines or requirements. The total coliform count (not the fecal coliform count) is used for evaluation of drinking water because finished water should contain no coliform organisms. Depending on methodology used, the permissible number of positive results varies, but the upper limit for the samples taken within a given month is approximately 1 per 100 ml.

There is no doubt that the coliform determination provides a reliable measure of the safety of drinking water with respect to the potential presence of bacterial pathogens. Outbreaks of dysentery, cholera, and typhoid are a thing of the past in this country and most people take for granted the high quality of our drinking water. However, sporadic outbreaks of waterborne disease do still occur; for example, an outbreak in Riverside, Calif. in

1965 affected some 16,000 people[21]. In addition, it was stated in the 1962 Drinking Water Standards[22] that it was not certain whether a water that met bacterial requirements would be free of viral or rickettsial organisms.

Although drinking water treatment procedures such as chlorination, flocculation, adsorption, precipitation, or filtration will eliminate bacteria, viruses may be present. Their numbers will be greatly reduced, but some feel that a great many subclinical cases of viral diseases may go unrecognized and that isolated cases may serve as foci for more widespread transmission by other routes[23]. The only viral disease for which the waterborne route has been epidemiologically established is infectious hepatitis[24,25]. However, the Environmental Protection Agency recently reported three enteric viruses (E.C.H.O., reo, and polio) in finished water from two Massachusetts cities. James McDermott, Director of Water Supply Programs Division, Environmental Protection Agency, remarked that the cities involved had treatment systems that were of higher quality than those in most waters in the United States. It would be advantageous to have a viral monitoring system similar to the coliform determination, but for this considerable development of methodology is needed.

Standards for Water Used in Food Production and Processing

It is expected that water used in food processing will meet drinking water standards. However, as pointed out by Wolf[26], it is in food processing that water quality meets its severest test. This is because the foodstuffs contain nutrients for bacterial multiplication which will encourage the growth of pathogens introduced in the water. Irrigation water is expected to meet guidelines put forward in the Report of the Technical Advisory Committee on Water Quality Criteria[27]. Wolf also mentions the need for establishing standards for water offered to livestock.

Standards for Shellfish-Growing Waters

The bivalve molluscs, owing to their feeding habits, are capable of concentrating bacteria, viruses, and other microbial pathogens, toxic chemicals, and radionuclides when these are present in the surrounding waters. Cabelli and Heffernan[28], among others, have shown that shellfish (northern quahaug) take up microorganisms to an equilibrium level which is dependent upon the concentration of the microbe of interest and the amount of particulate material in the water. The microbes were accumulated in the digestive gland and in the siphon. Elimination of organisms took place when the quahaugs were transferred to clean seawater[29].

Infectious hepatitis may be contracted by eating raw shellfish, although the number of cases contracted is small compared with the number of infections contracted in other ways. It is possible typhoid and other bacterial infections may also be contracted by the shellfish route, although there is no established numerical relationship between the bacterial quality of the water and the hazard to the consumers at this point. Thus far, it appears there have been no outbreaks from shellfish taken from waters meeting established standards. The standards describe four categories of shellfish waters: approved, conditionally approved, restricted, and prohibited, according to an evaluation based on coliform count and sanitary survey[30].

Standards for Recreational Waters

It has been pointed out by Krishnaswami[31] and Foster, Hanes, and Lord[32], among others, that the coliform standard used to analyze drinking water quality is not necessarily that which ought to be used to evaluate recreational waters. Gastrointestinal illnesses occurred more frequently among swimmers than nonswimmers in one study[33]. However, epidemiological studies show that swimmers are more often affected by eye, ear, nose, throat, and skin ailments than gastrointestinal disturbances. Most swimming related illnesses result from contact with pathogens rather than ingestion of them. Thus, many feel that the coliform index cannot be used reliably to estimate this type of risk, although others support its validity[11].

It has been suggested that *Pseudomonas aeruginosa* be adopted as an indicator organism for recreational waters because of its known association with ear infections[34]. Streptococci have also been proposed for this purpose because one study[35] indicated a closer relationship between their numbers in swimming intensity than coliforms and bathing use. On the other hand, Foster, Hanes, and Lord[32] found that coliform densities, streptococcal numbers, and the incidence of *P. aeruginosa* varied independently of swimming activity. They point out, however, that ear infections during the study period were more often associated with swimmers using pools meeting strict requirements than with people using bathing beaches that failed to meet coliform standards. The authors also point out the wide variation in regulations (ranging from an upper limit of 70 to 50 000 organisms per 100 ml) used by individual states and countries to monitor the safety of recreational waters. The most common values used by 29 of the 54 states and territories that have a monthly mean value for coliforms are 200 per 100 ml and 1000 per 100 ml.

It has been shown by Smith[36] that large numbers of *E. coli* with antibiotic resistance factors (R factors) transferrable to pathogenic organisms have been found in British rivers and in the Hudson River of New York. It was pointed out that bathers might be exposed to an increased number of pathogens possessing antibiotic resistance.

Bacterial Activity and Water Quality

The large group of heterotrophic microorganisms plays an active role in the self-purification of water. This has been generally defined as the restoration of the condition of a water body from a polluted state back to its normal original state. As pointed out by Wuhrmann[37], the rate at which this process takes place is affected by the geometry of the biotope, type and concentration of material to be removed, contact time, temperature, dissolved oxygen, pH, the inorganic composition of the water, flow velocity, and incident light.

Bacteria as Indicators of Non-Fecal Pollution

In a manner similar to that used by sanitary bacteriologists, some investigators have attempted to use specific bacteria or groups of bacteria as indicators of pollution. For example, Luchterowa[38] and Luchterowa and Grela[39] found higher numbers of sulfate and nitrate reducers, phenol decomposers, and hydrocarbon oxidizers in rivers below cities with their industrial discharges than above. Brock and Yoder[40] studied the bacterial flora in a thermally polluted stream and several cold water springs and found *Thermus aquaticus,* an extreme thermophile, only where heated effluents were introduced and suggested that the organism might be useful as an indicator of thermal pollution.

Some workers[41] have reported higher populations of yeasts near wastewater discharges although others have found no such relationship[42]. Meyers, Ahearn, and Cook[43] found a distinct yeast population dominated by species of *Candida, Trichosporon,* and *Saccharomyces* near a paper mill that discharged heated waste waters into Lake Champlain, a deep, relatively unpolluted lake. Approximately 400 organisms per 100 ml were found near the outfall compared with 5 per 100 ml at points distant. It was suggested that *Trichosporon* strains, owing to their tolerance to sulfate and sulfite liquors and their ability to grow at temperatures above 40° C, could be used as indicators of pulp wastes.

Considerable attention has been focused on nuisance growths of *Sphaerotilus sp.* in streams. Large populations of this bacterium and associated organisms characteristically develop under conditions of high organic loading, such as the introduction of raw sewage or improperly stabilized pulp mill effluents. The presence of this "sewage fungus" leads to increased oxygen consumption and the destruction of habitats, as well as eggs and larval organisms by coating them. In addition to bringing about unsightly conditions, growths may foul lines and clog nets, thus interfering with fishing activities. Much information has been reviewed in recent papers[44, 45].

Estimates of Biomass

An accurate estimate of the population size is essential to measures of bacterial growth and are a valuable supplement to other investigations of bacterial activity. A technique that has been commonly used to assess the size of the bacterial population has been the total plate count. This, however, provides little reliable information about the true size of the mixed bacterial population in natural or polluted waters, because no one medium or incubation condition will support the growth of all types of organisms including the fastidious heterotrophs, strict autotrophs, or strict anaerobes. Therefore, it has become generally accepted that plate counts should be reserved for use with defined media for the enumeration of a specific organism or closely related groups of organisms. Such viable counts are useful in establishing the presence or absence of a particular organism or in studying the dispersal of bacteria throughout a system. This approach may also be used to qualitatively assess the ability of a bacterial population to carry out a specific metabolic activity (for example, glucose fermentation, hydrocarbon utilization). Such techniques may be adapted to studies of how various environmental conditions (temperature shifts) or waste materials might affect the activity of an isolate or groups of organisms. The results of such tests cannot be taken to mean activity in the environment, however, for the response in pure batch culture under high nutrient is probably altogether different from the response in an open system at low nutrient levels. Furthermore, a considerable number of organisms in natural habitats may be present in a dormant state.

The accuracy of enumeration by cultural procedures, whether by plate counts or most probable number (MPN) estimates, is affected by organisms that are clumped together or attached to particulate matter. Therefore, direct microscopic counts are also used. Although they are tedious, they do permit differentiation of morphological types and are useful if an organism possesses a distinct morphology. They suffer from the fact that both viable and nonviable cells are counted and that specific identification of most organisms is impossible without the use of special fluorescent antibody procedures[6,46,47]. However, various techniques involving the use of fluorescent stains[48,49,50] are used in addition to classical procedures and when coupled with epifluorescent illumination permit visualization of organisms attached to silt and sand grains or other opaque materials. Casida photographed soil populations with infrared film to reveal the presence of living cells[51] and has recently described some other approaches to the visualization of soil organisms[52,53].

Other approaches to the estimation of bacterial biomass have been to assay the amount of certain cellular constituents, for example, protein. The major disadvantages to the use of this as assay in natural habitats is that it is not specific for bacteria and that detrital particles may also contain significant amounts of protein. Even so, Bott and Brock[54] found that increasing protein content on coverslips immersed in water compared well with developing bacterial biomass determined by direct microscopic counting. The measurement of adenosine triphosphate (ATP) has been used to assay the number of viable organisms in a sample[55]. A pulse of light proportional to the ATP content of the sample is generated when the firefly reactants luciferin and luciferase are mixed with the sample containing viable organisms. The assay is not specific for bacterial biomass, however, and it is not certain that the ATP content of a cell is constant.

Measurement of diaminopimelic acid[56] and muramic acid[57] has been used to assay the size of the bacterial populations in rumen and soil habitats. These materials are found in the cell wall of both bacteria and blue-green algae, but such assays may be valuable in estimating bacterial biomass if blue-green algae are absent or constitute negligible biomass. It should be pointed out that all biomass determinations are the net result of opposing dynamic processes; generation of new cells and loss of organisms through death and predation.

Measures of Activity

Biomass estimates, however, are frequently used to infer something about microbial activity. The microbial ecologist, therefore, attempts to measure the activity directly and *in situ*. As Brock[58] has pointed out, studies with pure cultures in the laboratory merely indicate the potential activity of an organism in nature. Therefore, microbial ecologists are interested in developing techniques whereby bacterial activity can be assayed in the natural habitat or at least under laboratory conditions that closely approximate the natural and in which processes of competition and cooperation are operative.

Respirometric techniques in which oxygen uptake is measured in Warburg or Gilson flasks have been used to measure microbial activity[59]. However, what one is really interested in is the utilization of specific nutrients. By studying the uptake of radioactively labeled compounds, bacterial activity in natural habitat can be measured with relative ease. This approach also provides a tool whereby the effects of environmental changes or toxic wastes on the metabolism of organisms may be measured.

Inorganic carbon-14 has been used to study activity of autotrophic bacteria in a manner similar to studies of algal primary productivity[60,61]. Sorokin[62] and Romenenko[63] have also shown that heterotrophic microorganisms may derive as much as 6 percent of their carbon needs from inorganic carbon sources.

Utilizing techniques used initially by Parsons and Strickland[64], Wright and Hobbie[65,66], among others, have measured bacterial activity by analyzing uptake data for radioactive organic substrates according to Michaelis-Menton enzyme kinetics. The maximum heterotrophic potential procedure permits an estimate of the turnover time for the substrate being tested, the natural substrate concentration, and the maximum uptake velocity for the substrate. Utilization of glucose, acetate, amino acids[67], and certain disaccharides[68] has been measured in several habitats.

It has been demonstrated that, depending on the compound, between 8 to 60 percent of incorporated substrate may be respired by the organisms, and this must be included in calculation of activity[69]. The technique works well in relatively enriched waters, but in oligotrophic situations the normal uptake pattern has not been obtained unless samples were pre-enriched[70]. This suggests either the selective enrichment of one species in the mixed population or the induction of an enzyme system in many species took place during preenrichment. This technique may be best used to demonstrate the presence or absence of organisms adapted to metabolizing a given substrate. It may be possible to use the approach with certain waste materials. Munro and Brock[71] supplemented uptake studies with microscopic autoradiography to identify the organisms involved in uptake.

In recent years, there has been considerable emphasis on the measurement of bacterial growth rates directly in the natural aquatic habitat. Brock [72] used tritiated thymidine (which is incorporated specifically into replicating DNA) and autoradiographic techniques to estimate the growth rate of the filamentous bacterium *Leucothrix mucor* in the marine environment. From laboratory experiments in which the organisms were grown at two different temperatures, it was calculated that 1 percent of the cells became radioactive in 0.002 generations. This constant was then used to analyze data from field experiments. The generation time could be estimated from the percentage of cells labeled in a given incubation time. The bacterium must be morphologically distinct if this technique is to work in mixed populations.

Bott and Brock[54] measured the growth rates of unicellular bacteria attached to microscope slides in a small pond using photomicrography with a water immersion lens. Generation times were obtained by following the development of microcolonies from a sequence of photographs of identifiable microscopic fields. Slides were placed in a sterile dialysis sac with membrane filtered water to exclude the attachment of new organisms from the environment during the experiment. In another approach, the authors used ultraviolet radiation[54,73] to differentiate between organisms attaching to or growing on glass slides. By irradiating slides at intervals of approximately one generation, newly-attached cells were killed before they could divide. Direct microscopic quantification was used to measure the increase in cell numbers on untreated and irradiated slides removed from the habitat at predetermined intervals. This technique provides a measure of immigration rate and a generation time for the population. Generation times of from 2 to 7 h were obtained in several habitats.

The growth rate of filamentous organism *Sphaerotilus* was also measured in a small stream and a generation time of 2.3 h was obtained at a time when the water temperature was 18 to 22° C[74]. In studies of bacteria in the headwater region of the White Clay Creek (Chester County, Pa.), generation times have been determined at different seasons of the year (Bott, unpublished data). When the stream was between 0 to 5° C, unicellular organisms had a doubling time of approximately 40 h; when the temperature was between 7 to 15° C, the generation time was 11 h; when the stream was 15 to 22° C, the generation time was 4 h. Similar generation times were obtained for filamentous organisms.

Summary and Conclusions

Bacteria have been used in the assessment of water quality largely to indicate the presence of fecal pollution, and the reliability of coliform detection has been of great benefit to public health. Nevertheless, there is still effort to refine the methods with which we demonstrate their presence, to validate the significance of the test, and to determine whether other organisms may be even more reliable indicators. The possibility that viruses may be present in water free of bacterial pathogens has prompted much current interest in their detection and removal. In addition, there is increasing concern that water used for recreational purposes should be evaluated using organisms other than coliforms. The possibility also exists that other microorganisms may be useful in revealing the presence of other types of pollutants, for example, thermal additions or a specific chemical in a process waste.

The ability of bacteria to metabolize most chemical compounds has made them important in the treatment of wastes. Similarly, they are also important agents in the self-purification of water. In most instances, a population of organisms will arise in response to the introduction of a given substance, whether it be a nutrient or one with toxic properties. New organisms with the appropriate physiological capability invade, or selection of mutants from the pre-existing flora occurs. However, it is possible for the metabolic capabilities of bacteria to be overwhelmed, and the persistence of certain recalcitrant molecules in the natural systems is widely discussed.

Measurement of the activity of bacteria directly in natural habitats is essential to a full understanding of their importance. I have tried to briefly review some of the methods that the microbial ecologist has at his disposal, many of which have only recently been developed. Bacteria respond more quickly than most other organisms to changes in their environment and, therefore, should be sensitive indicators of perturbation. However, because they are sensitive, it is imperative that populations be studied over short time intervals so that oscillations or changes will not be missed.

References

[1] Geldreich, E. E. in *Water Pollution Microbiology*, R. Mitchell, Ed., Wiley, New York, 1972, pp. 207–241.

[2] Parr, L. W., *Bacteriological Reviews*, Vol. 3, 1939, pp. 1–48.

[3] "Standard Methods for the Examination of Water and Waste Water," American Public Health Association, Inc., New York, 1965.

[4] Geldreich, E. E., "Sanitary Significance of Fecal Coliforms in the Environment," Federal Water Pollution Control Administration Series, Publication WP–20–3, 1966.

[5] Hendricks, C. W., *Applied Microbiology*, Vol. 19, 1970, pp. 441–445.

[6] Guthrie, R. K. and Reeder, D. J., *Applied Microbiology*, Vol. 17, 1969, pp. 399–401.

[7] Mitruka, B. M. and Alexander, M., *Applied Microbiology*, Vol. 17, 1969, pp. 551–555.

[8] Korsch, L. E., Zhevverzheeva, V. F., and Nikiforova, E. P., *Hygiene and Sanitation* (USSR), Vol. 35, No. 46, 1970, p. 99, cited in E. E. Geldreich, *Journal of the Water Pollution Control Federation*, Vol. 44, 1971, pp. 1159–1172.

[9] McCabe, L. J., Symons, J. M., Lee, R. D., and Robeck, G. G., *Journal of the American Water Works Association*, Vol. 62, 1970, pp. 670 687.

[10] Gallagher, T. P. and Spino, D. F., *Water Research*, Vol. 2, 1968, pp. 169–175.

[11] Geldreich, E. E., *Journal of the American Water Works Association*, Vol. 62, 1970, pp. 113–120.

[12] Smith, T. J. and Twedt, R. M., *Journal of the Water Pollution Control Federation*, Vol. 43, 1971, pp. 2200–2209.

[13] Van Donsel, D. J. and Geldreich, E. E., *Water Research*, Vol. 5, 1971, pp. 1079–1087.

[14] Geldreich, E. E. and Kenner, B. A., *Journal of the Water Pollution Control Federation*, Vol. 41, 1969, pp. R336–R352.

[15] Gallagher, T. P., Thomas, N. A., Hogan, J. E., and Spino, D. F., "Pollution of Interstate Waters of the Red River of the North (Minnesota, North Dakota)," HEW, Robert A. Taft Sanitary Engineering Center Publications, Cincinnati, 1965, pp. 35 48.

[16] Hendricks, C. W. and Morrison, S. M., *Water Research*, Vol. 1, 1967, pp. 567–576.

[17] Hendricks, C. W., *Canadian Journal of Microbiology*, Vol. 17, 1917, pp. 551–556.

[18] Morris, W. and Weaver, R., *Applied Microbiology*, Vol. 2, 1954, pp. 282–284.

[19] Abshire, R. and Guthrie, R. F., *Water Research*, Vol. 5, 1971, pp. 1089–1097.

[20] Bonde, G., *Health Laboratory Science*, Vol. 3, 1966, pp. 124–128.

[21] Boring, J. R., III, Martin, W. T., and Elliott, Lora M., *American Journal of Epidemiology*, Vol. 93, 1971, p. 49.

[22] "Public Health Service Drinking Water Standards," HEW, Washington, D.C., 1962.

[23] Okun, D. A., *Journal of the American Water Works Association*, Vol. 61, 1969, pp. 215–221.

[24] Grabow, W. O. K., *Water Research*, Vol. 2, 1968, pp. 675–701.

[25] Garibaldi, R. A., Murphey, G. D., III, and Wood, B. T., "Infectious Hepatitus Outbreak Associated with Cafe Water," Health Services and *Mental Health Administration Health Reports,* Vol. 87, 1972, pp. 164–171.
[26] Wolf, H. W. in *Water Pollution Microbiology,* R. Mitchell, Ed., Wiley, New York, 1972, pp. 333–345.
[27] "Report of the Committee on Water Quality Criteria," Federal Water Pollution Control Administration, U.S. Government Printing Office, Washington, D.C. 1968.
[28] Cabelli, V. J. and Heffernan, W. P., *Applied Microbiology,* Vol. 19, 1970, pp. 239–244.
[29] Heffernan, W. P. and Cabelli, V. J., *Journal of the Fisheries Research Board of Canada,* Vol. 27, 1970, pp. 1569–1577.
[30] Houser, L. S., Ed., "Sanitation of Shellfish Growing Areas," National Shellfish Sanitation Program Manual of Operations, *Public Health and Sanitation,* Publication No. 33, HEW, Washington, D.C. 1965.
[31] Krishnaswami, S. K., *American Journal of Public Health,* Vol. 61, 1971, pp. 2259–2268.
[32] Foster, D. H., Hanes, N. B., and Lord, S. M., Jr., *Journal of the Water Pollution Control Federation,* Vol. 43, 1971, pp. 2229–2241.
[33] Stevenson, A. H., *American Journal of Public Health,* Vol. 43, 1953, pp. 529–538.
[34] Hoadley, A. W., *Journal of the New England Water Works Association,* Vol. 83, 1968, p. 99.
[35] Mallmann, W. L. and Sypien, A., *American Journal of Public Health,* Vol. 24, 1934, pp. 681–688.
[36] Smith, H. W., *Nature,* Vol. 228, 1970, pp. 1286–1288.
[37] Wuhrmann, K. in *Water Pollution Microbiology,* R. Mitchell, Ed., Wiley, New York, 1972, pp. 119–151.
[38] Luchterowa, A., *Verhandlungen der internationale Verein theoretischen angewissen Limnologie,* Vol. 16, 1966, pp. 1535–1540.
[39] Luchertowa, A. and Grela, J., *Acta Hydrobiologica,* Vol. 11, 1969, p. 273, and *Water Pollution Abstracts,* Vol. 43, 1970, p. 3.
[40] Brock, T. D. and Yoder, I. in *Proceedings,* Indiana Academy of Science, Vol. 80, 1971, pp. 183–188.
[41] Spencer, J. S. P., Gorin, P. A. J., and Gardner, N. R., *Canadian Journal of Microbiology,* Vol. 16, No. 11, 1970, pp. 1051–1057.
[42] Simard, R. E. and Blackwood, A. C., *Canadian Journal of Microbiology,* Vol. 17, 1971, pp. 252–257.
[43] Meyers, S. P., Ahearn, D. G., and Cook, W. L., *Mycologia,* Vol. 62, 1970, pp. 504–515.
[44] Phaup, J. D., *Water Research,* Vol. 2, 1968, pp. 597–614.
[45] Curtis, E. J. C., *Water Research,* Vol. 3, 1969, pp. 289–311.
[46] Schmidt, E. L., Bankole, R. O., and Bohlool, B. B., *Journal of Bacteriology,* Vol. 95, 1968, pp. 1987–1992.
[47] Bohlool, B. B. and Schmidt, E. L., *Science,* Vol. 162, 1968, pp. 1012–1014.
[48] Strugger, S., *Canadian Journal of Research,* Vol. 26, 1948, pp. 188–193.
[49] Pital, A., Janowitz, S. L., Hudak, C. E., and Lewis, E. E., *Applied Microbiology,* Vol. 14, 1966, pp. 119–123.
[50] Babiuk, L. A. and Paul, E. A., *Canadian Journal of Microbiology,* Vol. 16, 1970, pp. 57–62.
[51] Casida, L. E., *Science,* Vol. 159, 1968, pp. 199–200.
[52] Casida, L. E., *Applied Microbiology,* Vol. 18, 1969, pp. 1065–1071.
[53] Casida, L. E., *Applied Microbiology,* Vol. 21, 1971, pp. 1040–1045.
[54] Bott, T. L. and Brock, T. D., *Limnology and Oceanography,* Vol. 15, 1970, pp. 333–342.

[55] Hamilton, R. D. and Holm-Hansen, O., *Limnology and Oceanography*, Vol. 12, 1967, pp. 319–324.

[56] el-Shazley, K. and Hungate, R. E., *Applied Microbiology*, Vol. 14, 1966, pp. 27–30.

[57] Millar, W. N. and Casida, L. E., *Canadian Journal of Microbiology*, Vol. 16, 1970, pp. 299–304.

[58] Brock, T. D., *Principles of Microbial Ecology*, Prentice Hall, Englewood Cliffs, N.J., 1966.

[59] Pomeroy, L. R. and Johannes, R. E., *Deep Sea Research*, Vol. 15, 1968, pp. 381–391.

[60] Sorokin, U. I. in *Primary Productivity in Aquatic Environments*, C. R. Goldman, Ed., University of California Press, Berkeley, 1965, pp. 187–205.

[61] Smith, D. W., Fliermans, C. B., and Brock, T. D., *Applied Microbiology*, Vol. 23, 1972, pp. 595–600.

[62] Sorokin, U. I., *Journal of General Microbiology*, Vol. 22, 1961, pp. 265–272.

[63] Romanenko, V. I., *Microbiology*, Vol. 32, 1964, pp. 679–683.

[64] Parsons, T. R. and Strickland, J. D. H., *Deep Sea Research*, Vol. 8, 1962, pp. 211–222.

[65] Wright, R. T. and Hobbie, J. E., *Limnology and Oceanography*, Vol. 10, 1965, pp. 22–28.

[66] Wright, R. T. and Hobbie, J. E., *Ecology*, Vol. 47, 1966, pp. 447–464.

[67] Hobbie, J. E., Crawford, C. C., and Webb, K. L., *Science*, Vol. 159, 1968, pp. 1463–1464.

[68] Wood, L. W. in *Estuarine Microbial Ecology*, L. H. Stevenson and R. R. Colwell, Eds., Belle W. Baruch Library in Marine Science, Vol. 1, University of Southern California Press, Columbia. In press.

[69] Hobbie, J. E. and Crawford, C. C., *Limnology and Oceanography*, Vol. 14, 1969, pp. 528–532.

[70] Vacarro, R. F., *Limnology and Oceanography*, Vol. 14, 1969, pp. 726–735.

[71] Munro, A. L. S. and Brock, T. D., *Journal of General Microbiology*, Vol. 51, 1968, pp. 35–42.

[72] Brock, T. D., *Science*, Vol. 155, 1967, pp. 81–83.

[73] Bott, T. L. and Brock, T. D., *Science*, Vol. 164, 1969, pp. 1411–1412.

[74] Bott, T. L. and Brock, T. D., *Applied Microbiology*, Vol. 19, 1970, pp. 100–102.

Ruth Patrick [1]

Use of Algae, Especially Diatoms, in the Assessment of Water Quality

REFERENCE: Patrick, Ruth, "Use of Algae, Especially Diatoms, in the Assessment of Water Quality," *Biological Methods for the Assessment of Water Quality, ASTM STP 528,* American Society for Testing and Materials, 1973, pp. 76–95.

ABSTRACT: Two main systems of approach used to determine if algae can reliably indicate water quality are discussed in this paper. One approach is to observe and analyze natural communities. The effect of a pollutant can be estimated by shifts in species composition and structure of the community in this type of study. The second approach studies a single or a few species in cultures in the laboratory under known and carefully regulated conditions. These studies are valuable in determining the physiological and morphological changes in function rates and polymorphism due to concentration of a given chemical or physical factor.

KEY WORDS: water pollution, diatoms, algae, bioassay, artificial substrates, environmental surveys

The title of this paper might be turned into a question, "Are algae reliable indicators of water quality?" It is a well established fact that most of the nutrition of algae is derived from dissolved chemicals in water and, therefore, they should indicate the chemical environment. However, there are many other physical factors such as current speed, light, and temperature that influence the ability of a given species to compete with other species. Its desirability as a food source greatly influences its susceptibility to predator pressure. Thus, there are many gradients of factors that determine the multidimension niche of an algal species and the breadth of its realized niches. The degree of success of a species in an algal community is the result of the interaction of favorable and unfavorable stresses. For these reasons it

[1] Curator and chairman, Department of Limnology, Academy of Natural Sciences, Philadelphia, Pa. 19103.

is difficult to predict in the natural environment that a given concentration of a chemical will cause a given amount of stress or that a given abundance or lack of abundance of a species is a direct result of a specific concentration of a chemical. However, associations of algae are very useful toward indicating water quality.

To answer the above question, two main systems of approach have been used in determining if algae can reliably indicate water quality. The first is to observe and analyze natural communities; by shifts in species composition and structure of the community, the effect of a pollutant can be estimated. The data for this type of study of algal communities are accumulated from autoecology and synecology studies.

A second approach is to study a single or a few species in cultures in the laboratory under known and carefully regulated conditions. These studies are valuable in determining the physiological and morphological changes in function rates and polymorphism due to concentration of a given chemical or physical factor. The results may be misleading in precisely estimating how a species will behave in streams, lakes, or estuaries, because the species under laboratory conditions may not be subjected to the various combinations of stresses or stimulating factors which occur in nature.

Field Evaluations of Algae as Indicators

Although several publications had indicated that algae were characteristic of various degrees of degradation of water quality, it was Kolkwitz and Marsson in 1908[1] [2] who published the first paper that classified species of algae as to their tolerance to various kinds of pollution and stated that by the presence of certain species of algae one could define various zones of degradation in the river. They described these zones as the polysaprobic zone which was characterized by a wealth of high molecular decomposable organic matter. Chemicals were usually present in a reduced state, and little, if any, dissolved oxygen was present. The gamma mesosaprobic zone represented the stage in the recovery of the river from heavy pollution in which complex matter was present, but oxidation was proceeding. The beta mesosaprobic zone was that area in which most of the organic matter had been mineralized. The oligosaprobic zone was the zone in which cleaner water mineralization had been completed. The katharobic zone was characterized as the clean, unpolluted water often found in mountain streams.

Each of these zones or conditions contained species belonging to a given condition (for example, gamma mesosaprobic) indicated that this condition existed.

Many workers such as Hentschel[2], Naumann[3,4], Butcher[5], and

[2] The italic numbers in brackets refer to the list of references appended to this paper.

Liebmann[6] used these systems and became aware of the fact that some species classified as characteristic of a zone of pollution often did not occur when such a condition was present or might be found under very different river conditions[7,8]. This lack of applicability was due to several things. One was the realization, as Butcher[5] stated, that species of algae are often resistant to other types of pollution than organic and grow rather well in these substances. Thus, these species may be found in many other river conditions besides those to which they are assigned by Kolkwitz and Marsson.

Another important reason why this system failed was that the types of pollution had changed greatly since the early part of the century. In the first part of the 20th century pollution was mainly organic in nature. Today pollution is a collective noun referring to conditions resulting from the inflow of (1) many kinds of chemicals, some of which are very toxic; (2) various physical conditions such as warm water; and (3) various kinds of organic materials coming from industrial sources, farms, and homes. Thus, owing to the complexity of pollution, it has become increasingly difficult to state that any one species characteristically might be found in all kinds of pollution or be generally indicative of pollution. Wuhrmann[9], Sramek-Husek[10], and Fjerdingstad[11] increased the number of zones characteristic of stages of pollution from five recognized by Kolkwitz and Marsson to a total of 15 recognized by Wuhrmann. Pantle and Buck[12] tried to improve the system by developing an index of pollution based upon saprobic zones. Oligosaprobic was rated as one, beta mesosaprobic was two, gamma mesosaprobic was three, and polysaprobic noted as follows; (1) occurring incidentally, (2) occurring frequently, and (3) occurring abundantly.

For this purpose, a mean saprobic index S is calculated for each locality.

$$S = \frac{\Sigma\, rh}{\Sigma\, h}$$

where

S = saprobic index,
r = saprobic zone rating, and
h = the occurrence rating.

They concluded that a saprobic index equal to 1.0 to 1.5 denoted oligosaprobic; 1.5 to 2.5 denoted beta mesosaprobic, 2.5 to 3.5 denoted gamma mesosaprobic, and 3.5 to 4.0 denoted polysaprobic. Wantanabe[13] developed an index of relative degree of water pollution based upon types of diatoms.

$$\frac{2A + B - 2C}{A + B + C} \times 100$$

where

A = number of intolerant species,
B = the number of indifferent species, and
C = that of exclusively pollution species.

Fjerdingstad[14,15], realizing the importance of recognizing that species may or may not occur only in a given kind of pollution, revised the system. He recognized as saprobiontic species those that occurred only in heavily polluted waters in large numbers; saprophilous, organisms that occur generally in polluted waters may occur also in other communities, namely, organisms that to a certain extent are indifferent; saproxenous, organisms that occur generally in biotopes other than polluted ones but may survive even in the presence of pollution; and saprophobous, organisms that will not survive in polluted waters. He then put forth the following table of saprobic zones (see Table 1).

The author in various studies of diatoms has realized that the kinds of species change greatly over time with no change in the quality of water, and that such changes are due to other environmental conditions. It seemed important, therefore, that another means, other than the species indicator system, should be developed. In 1949[16] she set forth the principle that in natural or healthy streams the algal flora was represented by a high number of species, most of them with relatively small populations. Furthermore, the species were largely diatoms with a few greens, and blue-greens present. The effect of pollution was to reduce species numbers; to cause a greater unevenness in sizes of populations of species, with some becoming extremely common; and to cause a shift of kinds of species composing the algal community from one being dominated by diatoms to one being dominated by various kinds of filamentous greens or, in a few cases, unicellular greens or by blue-green algae. Smaller shifts were noted by the kinds of diatoms changing from narrowly tolerant to broadly tolerant species. The types of shifts were dependent upon the effects of various kinds of pollution.

Nygaard[17] following Thunmark[18] recognized the following phytoplankton quotients: Myxophyceae/Desmidieae, Chlorococcales/Desmidieae, Centrales/Pennales, Euglenineae/(Myxophyceae + Chlorococcales).

The compound quotient was: (Myxophyceae + Chlorococcales + Centrales + Euglenineae)/Desmidieae.

If the compound quotient was below 1, the water is probably oligotrophic. If the compound quotient is above 1, the water is probably eutrophic. The true saprotrophy is revealed only by the Euglenineae quotient. The border between eutrophy and saprotrophy being 2 to 3 as saprotrophy is above 3. Stockner and Benson[19] used the Centrales/Pennales index to follow the enrichment of Lake Washington over time.

TABLE 1—*Survey of the saprobic zones and the corresponding communities.*

Zone I.   Coprozoic zone
a. the bacterium community
b. the *Bodo* community
c. both communities

Zone II.   α-polysaprobic zone
1. *Euglena* community
2. Rhodo-Thio bacterium community
3. pure Chlorobacterium community

Zone III.   β-polysaprobic zone
1. *Beggiatoa* community
2. *Thiothrix nivea* community
3. *Euglena* community

Zone IV.   γ-polysaprobic zone
1. *Oscillatoria chlorina* community
2. *Sphaerotilus natans* communities

Zone V.   δ-mesosaprobic zone
a. *Ulothrix zonata* community
b. *Oscillatoria benthonicum* community
(*Oscillatoria brevis, O. limnosa, O. splendida* with *O. subtilissima, O. princeps,* and *O. tenuis* present as associate species)
c. *Stigeoclonium tenue* community

Zone VI.   β-mesosaprobic zone
a. *Cladophora fracta* community
b. *Phormidium* community

Zone VII.   γ-mesosaprobic zone
a. Rhodophyce community (*Batrachospermum moniliforme* or *Lemanae fluviatilis*)
b. Chlorophyce community (*Cladophora glomerata* or *Ulothrix zonata* (clean-water type)

Zone VIII.   Oligosaprobic zone
a. Chlorophyce community (*Draparnaldia glomerata*)
b. pure *Meridion circulare* community
c. Rhodophyce community (*Lemanea annulata, Batrachospermum vagum* or *Hildenbrandia rivularis*)
d. *Vaucheria sessilis* community
e. *Phormidium inundatum* community

Zone IX.   Katharobic zone
a. Chlorophyce community (*Chlorotylium cataractum* and *Draparnaldia plumosa*)
b. Rhodophyce community (*Hildenbrandia rivularis*)
c. lime-incrusting algal communities (*Chamaesiphon polonius* and various *Calothrix* species)

NOTE—a, b, c = as alternatives.
1, 2, 3 = as differences in degree.

Cholnoky, according to Patrick[20], developed a method for measuring changes in amount of pollution by changes in the dominant species of diatoms (Fig. 1). This system is only applicable if ecological changes do not produce shifts in kinds of species.

The use of artificial substrate to indicate the condition of a stream was first developed by Butcher[5]. His interpretations were based on the indicator species present or the dominance of certain species. The question

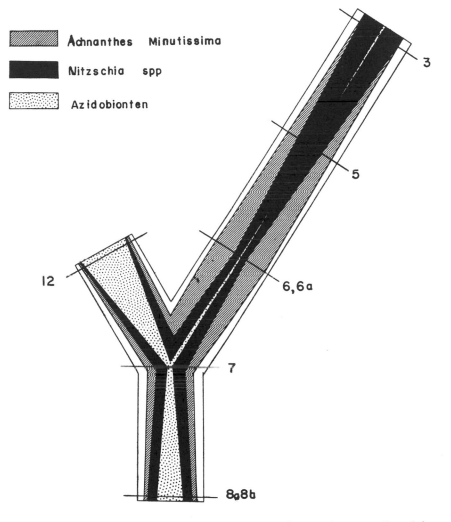

FIG. 1—*Relative abundance of various species of diatoms in areas affected by pollution.*

arose whether these substrates produced communities similar to those naturally occurring in a river. A series of studies carried out at the Academy of Natural Sciences[21] showed that if the slides were mounted in an instrument known as a diatometer (Fig. 2), the communities developed on the slides were very similar to the benthic communities. The communities on slides also included the more common species in the "plankton" or floating communities. It was found that if one thoroughly collected the stream area in which the diatometer was placed, 75–85 percent of the species found in the collections were found on the slides. Furthermore that 95 percent of the species represented by eight or more specimens when 8000 specimens were counted on the slides were found also in the benthic communities. This showed that it was only the rare species which were different. These studies have been repeated many times.

More recent studies have shown that the relative amount of biomass on the slides is an excellent way to compare the nutrient levels of various bodies of water. These algal growths on slides are also useful in determining if radioactive chemicals are present in a body of water, because diatoms are very effective in concentrating radioactivity[22].

Patrick et al[21] were the first to develop a mathematical model which simulated the structure of a diatom community and to demonstrate how shifts in this structure occurred under the effect of various kinds of pollution. In 1954 they set forth the principle that in a natural freshwater stream a sample of a diatom community was represented by a truncated normal

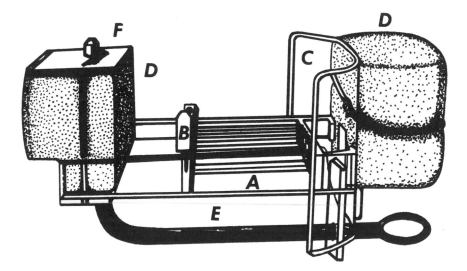

FIG. 2—*Catherwood diatometer:* (A) *slide holder,* (B) *retaining bar,* (C) *deflector,* (D) *styrofoam float,* (E) *brass rod, and* (F) *identification tag.*

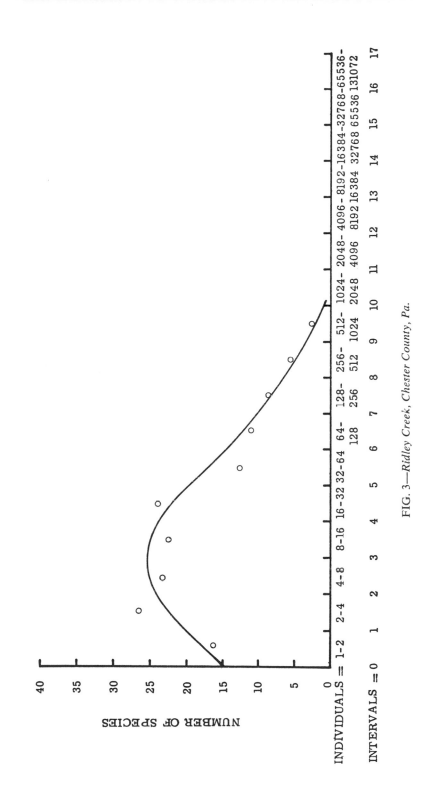

FIG. 3.—*Ridley Creek, Chester County, Pa.*

curve. If 5000 to 8000 specimens were counted, which are usually sufficient to put the mode of the curve in the second to third interval, the structure of the curve has great reliability in maintaining its shape[23]. It was found under these conditions that typically the height of the mode was greater than 18 species, and the curve covered up to 10 to 12 intervals (Fig. 3). The effect of organic pollution was to cause certain species to become excessively common, and thus, the curve with the height of the mode in the second to third interval covered many more intervals, usually 13 to 15 (Fig. 4). More severe organic pollution would bring about a reduction in the height of the mode. Sigma squared would increase and the curve would cover 15 to 16 intervals.

The effect of toxic pollution, however, was to greatly decrease the height of the mode and usually the curve did not increase very much as to the numbers of intervals covered (Fig. 5). However, under some types of pollution where one or two species were able to tolerate the pollutant and grow successfully, the curve would become much longer. Under these conditions σ^2 greatly increased. In 1968 Patrick et al[24] showed that toxic pollutants such as low pH (5.15 in the spring of the year when conditions were favorable) limited diatom reproduction but did not kill the diatoms. As a result, the height of the mode was high, σ^2 was very small, and the truncated curve covered only a relatively few intervals (Fig. 6). This type of pollution might be confused with natural conditions, but if one considers the amount of biomass, it is very evident that it is much less when the pH is low than under any natural condition. These studies clearly show that one should consider not only the structure of the diatom community but also the kinds of species and the total biomass. Furthermore, one is able to predict what kinds of pollution are occurring by the types of shifts in the structure of the curve.

Patrick and Hohn[25] applied this method of studying the structure of diatom communities to brackish waters in Maryland and Texas. They found that typically in brackish water the height of the mode was somewhat less as were the numbers of observed species. The curve typically covers a few more intervals. Based upon studies in brackish and fresh waters, Patrick and Strawbridge[26] developed a method whereby one could determine from a single analysis whether a community fell within a 95 or 99 percent confidence interval for a natural stream (see Fig. 7).

Margalef in 1957[27] was the first to use diversity indices to indicate variation in structure of phytoplankton communities. He has compared various indices, and sets forth the use of the information theory of Shannon-Weiner in studying communities of algae. This index has been used by many researchers.

Patten[28] in his study of Chesapeake Bay used the Shannon-Weiner index to measure H or community diversity:

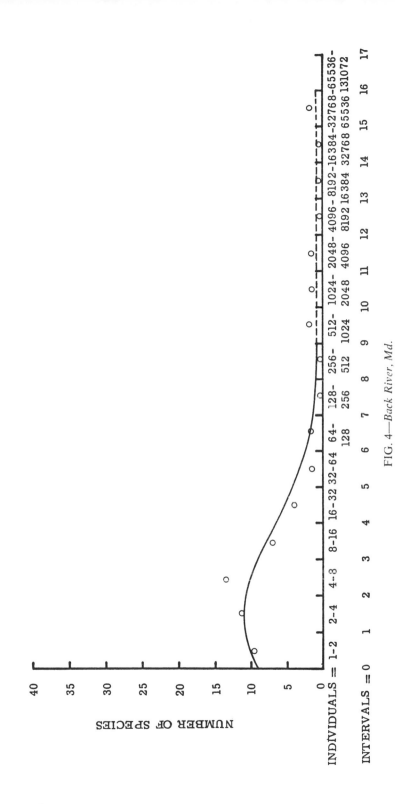

FIG. 4—*Back River, Md.*

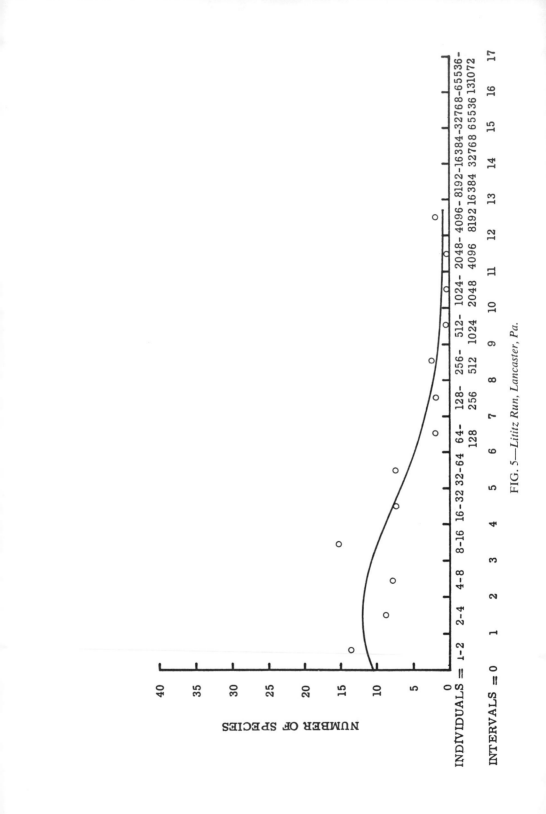

FIG. 5—*Lititz Run, Lancaster, Pa.*

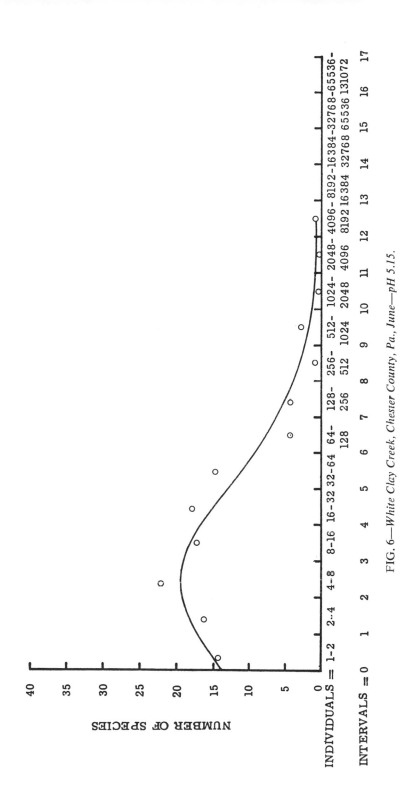

FIG. 6—*White Clay Creek, Chester County, Pa., June—pH 5.15.*

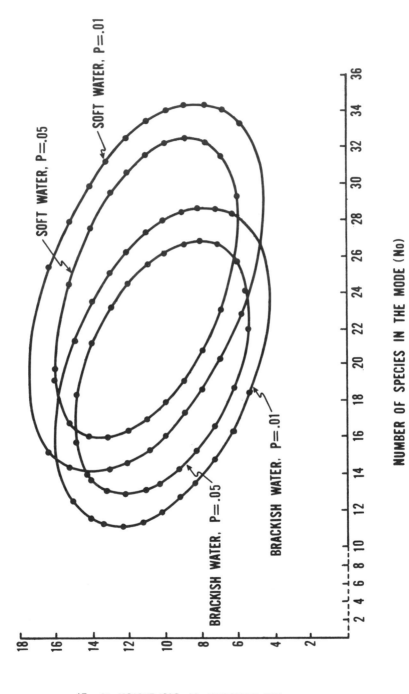

FIG. 7—*Confidence intervals as shown by elliptical curves.*

$$H = -\sum_{i=1}^{s} \frac{n_i}{N} \log_e \frac{n_i}{N}$$

where

H = community diversity,
N = total number of organisms,
n = number of individuals per taxon, and
s = total number of species in a unit area.

He measured redundancy for comparing the diversity of a given community with the maximum and minimum possible diversity as follows:

$$H_{\max} = k[\log N! - m \log(N/m)!]$$

$$H_{\min} = k\{\log N! - \log[N - (m-1)]!\}$$

$$R = \frac{H_{\max} - H}{H_{\max} - H_{\min}}$$

McIntire[29] has used a distance index to compare the structure of two diatom communities:

$$Djh = \sqrt{\sum_{i=1}^{s} (Xij - Xih)^2}$$

where

Xij = the proportion of the i species in the j community,
Xih = the proportion of the i species in the h community, and
D = the degree of difference between the j and h community.

Patrick following MacArthur[30] has used another method for measuring the differences between two communities of diatoms.

$$\text{Difference} = \sum_{i=1}^{s} \frac{p_i 1 + p_i 2}{2} \log_e \frac{p_i 1 + p_i 2}{2} - \frac{\sum_{i=1}^{s} p_i 1 \log_e p_i 1 + \sum_{i=1}^{s} p_i 2 \log_e p_i 2}{2}$$

where $p_i = \dfrac{ni}{N}$.

More recently the Jaccard coefficient has been applied to measuring the similarity of diatom communities[31].

Margalef[32] has tried to measure the diversity of a community by the diversity of pigments present. Other workers have studied the relation of the amount of chlorophyll "a" to the amount of primary production. Others have used primary production as a measure of the amount of algae present. These measures are based on protoplasmic activity which, of course, is variably correlated with the amount of living algae present.

Laboratory Use of Algae as Indicators

Laboratory bioassay tests to study the effects of various ranges of chemical and physical characteristics of the aquatic environment on algae have been studied by many workers. Usually the effect on reproductive rate is measured. Other measurements are photosynthetic rates and the amount of chlorophyll present. More recent studies have been initiated which measure the effects of chemical and physical changes upon the adenosine triphosphate (ATP) present in an algal cell.

The first detailed procedure on using algae, particularly diatoms as bioassay organisms, was developed at the Academy of Natural Sciences in Philadelphia under the direction of the author[33]. In these studies it was found that an inoculum must be in the log phase of growth in order to produce reliable and repeatable results. It is necessary that fairly large counts of the inoculum be made in order to determine the mean and standard error of the mean and to make sure that the standard error of the mean is small enough to give reliable estimates of amounts of cells present in each of the flasks under test.

Batch cultures are typically run for a period of five to seven days. At various intervals during the experiment flasks are withdrawn, cell counts are made, and comparisons developed between the control and various concentrations of the test chemicals. It is usually best to terminate these experiments in five to seven days. It has been found that concentrations which produce 50 percent reduction in reproduction rate in diatoms are quite similar to those concentrations producing the TL_m or LD_{50} in fish and invertebrates. This is particularly true in the case of mixed industrial wastes[34]. When single chemicals are tested this correlation is not so evident. It would appear that most industrial wastes contain substances of varying toxicity to different kinds of organisms and that a species reacts to the chemical to which it is most sensitive, and as a result, these mixtures of chemicals produce similar results. Often it appears that the diatoms are slightly more sensitive than the fish or the invertebrates.

Watts and Harvey[35] developed a method to use a continuous flow technique in bioassaying diatoms. The inoculum, as in batch cultures, is always in the log phase of growth. A relatively large inoculum is used and great care is taken to make sure it is homogenized in order that a given volume of inoculum will contain a similar number of cells. The diatoms in the inoculum are deposited on a Millipore filter by suction. Aqueous medium is continuously introduced through a small tube placed a short distance above the inoculum in order to give an even flow of the new solution over the growing diatoms. In this manner diatoms in test may be maintained in the log phase of growth for two months or longer. This type of test is particularly useful when volatile substances or substances that rapidly deteriorate are being studied. In the case of radioactive materials, the waste solutions can be collected and disposed of properly.

More recently, the author[36] has developed a method for studying communities of diatoms under semi-laboratory conditions. This is accomplished by diverting part of a stream into a large container from which samples of the water containing diatoms are pumped through each of a series of boxes containing four slides each. She has shown that at any given point in time a sample consisting of 5000 to 7000 specimens will have 95 percent of specimens in the same species in all of the boxes. Thus, one is able to compare the effects of various concentrations of a given test chemical on similar communities of diatoms and other algae. By this method one is able to isolate the effect of a single chemical and study it under almost natural conditions, such as exist in the stream, and to evaluate the ability of species of diatoms to survive under competition with other types of algae and in the presence of predators. The results of many of these studies have shown that varying concentrations of chemicals—namely, chromium, vanadium and manganese—will favor the development of one group of algae such as blue-greens over another group such as diatoms.

Another type of bioassay test has been developed by Dr. Bartsch and is known as the PAAP test[37]. This involves the introduction into lake water of varying amounts or concentrations of a medium which is known to promote the growth of certain blue-green algae. By adding a known amount of this solution to various lake waters and then introducing blue-green algae, one can compare the stimulating effects of different lake waters. This type of test[37] has been used extensively to measure the extent to which a lake or a body of water can support algal growths and is often referred to as a method to measure the degree of eutrophication that exists in a body of water. Matulova[38] developed a method of using *Chlamydomonas gelatinosa* to bioassay the effects of sewage and industrial wastes. He was able to differentiate various degrees of harmfulness as well as stimulating effects.

Stewart et al[39] have developed a method for using starved cells of *Anabaena flos-aquae* to detect available phosphorus in aquatic ecosystems. They find the sensitivity of this measure compares favorably to conventional methods of measuring dissolved orthophosphates.

Discussion

From this review it is evident that certain species of algae have wide ranges of tolerance, whereas other species have very narrow ranges of tolerance. Many of a more tolerant algae, such as *Nitzschia palea, Cyclotella meneghiniana, Gomphonema parvulum, Anacystis cyanae,* and *Stigeoclonium lubricum,* have their best development in the presence of certain kinds of pollution, and therefore, if they are abundant they truly indicate the presence of a given type of pollution. However, it may be difficult to predict the amount of pollution present by the size of the population of a so-called indicator species. The reason for this is that the growth of an algal population is dependent upon many variables in the aquatic environment. The lack or excess of any one of these may cause a stress and thus enhance the effect of some other deleterious condition, or if great enough they may eliminate a species regardless of the concentration of the pollutant chemical. For example, turbidity in a stream which prevents light from penetrating the water will eliminate the algal population regardless of whether a pollutant is present. In a similar manner, too low temperatures will greatly restrict the reproduction of diatoms and thus obscure the effect of a pollutant that might tend to increase growth. It has been found often that toxic substances will limit cell division in algae and thus obscure the presence of nutrients which would inevitably enhance algal growth. For these reasons it is important to use a variety of parameters in diagnosing the quality of water by the use of algae. One should consider the structure of a community—that is, the numbers of species, the relative abundance of the species, the kinds of species, and the total biomass present. Using various combinations of these parameters, one can define the effects of various types of pollution such as organic load, toxic materials, suspended solids, and temperature effects.

In measuring the effect of a pollutant upon an algae community, one often is tempted to use a single diversity index. However, since many indices are biased in their evaluation of various characteristics of a community, it is best, as Levins[40] has pointed out, to use a variety of indices to determine whether they all indicate similar conditions or, at least, whether a majority indicate similar conditions. The use of a model to indicate conditions, such as a truncated normal curve, is more descriptive, because one can see at a glance more characteristics of a community than is true with an index. However, a model can only be developed if a great many specimens are present. Time also may be a factor, for the developing of a truncated normal curve takes a longer time than the calculating of a diversity index.

One should take great care to count sufficient diatoms to indicate the true structure of the community under study. Too often workers limit counts to 200 or 500 specimens without mathematically testing to see whether or not such counts are large enough to truly reflect the structure of the diatom community. Counting is a laborious task and various people have used other approaches to estimate numbers of specimens present. Most common is the measurement of the amount of chlorophyll "a" or other pigments or the amount of turbidity produced by the algal suspension. More recently

Cairns et al[41] have used the laser beam to estimate the number and kinds of diatoms present.

If one wishes to continually monitor a body of water to determine if anything is inimical to aquatic life, the best way is to use algal community assays. The reason is that algal cells integrate all stresses that might deleteriously affect growth and reproduction or, in a similar way, they integrate all stimulants that may be present. Chemical analyses only define amounts and kinds of chemicals present if specific tests are run to determine such chemicals. Furthermore, they only provide information concerning a sample taken at a given time. For these reasons artificial substrates as described by Patrick et al[21] are extremely useful for continually determining the condition of the aquatic environment. If deleterious conditions result, chemical analyses can be made and bioassay tests run to more specifically determine what is the cause of a shift in the structure of the community.

Many new procedures for denoting physiological changes have recently developed and should be reliable sensitive indicators. However, such changes as the amount of ATP in a cell, need further study to interpret what they mean.

Today we have very few species that only occur in the presence of a given pollution. The reasons are several, but probably the most important are the facts that pollution is new and highly variable. Not enough time has elapsed for species to evolve to only survive when a given pollution is present. It is interesting to note that most of the forms which have evolved to require a given pollutant to live (namely, cyanide) belong to the bacteria or fungi which have rapid reproduction rates and often mutate. Whether specific diverse pollution floras will ever evolve is highly speculative.

References

[1] Kolkwitz, R. and Marsson, M., *Berichte Der Deutschen Botanischen Gesellschaft,* Vol. 26, 1908, pp. 505–519.
[2] Hentschel, E., *Abderhalden's Handbuch der biologischen Arbeitsmethod,* Abteil 9, Teil 2, 1 Häfte, 1925, pp. 233–280.
[3] Naumann, E., "Die Arbeitsmethoden der regionalen Limnologie," *Abderhalden's Handbuch der biologischen Arbeitsmethod,* 1925.
[4] Naumann, E., *Binnengewässer,* Band 11, 1932.
[5] Butcher, R. W., *Journal of Ecology,* Vol. 35, Nos. 1 and 2, Dec. 1947, pp. 186–191.
[6] Liebmann, H., *Handbuch der Fritschwasser- und Abwasser-biologie,* Vol. 1, Verlag R. Oldenbourg, München, 1951.
[7] Liebmann, H., *Vom Wasser,* Vol. 15, 1942, pp. 92–102.
[8] Thomas, E. A., *Untersuchungen und Hyg.,* Vol. 35, 1944, pp. 119–228.
[9] Wuhrmann, K., "Uber die Biologische Prüfung von Abwasserreinigungsanlagen," *Gesundheits-Ingenieur,* Vol. 72, 1951.
[10] Sramek-Husek, R., *Archiv Feur Hydrobiologie,* Vol. 51, 1956, pp. 376–390.

[11] Fjerdingstad, E., *Nordisk Hygienish Tidskrift,* Vol. 41, Nos. 7 and 8, 1960, pp. 149–196.

[12] Pantle, R. and Buck, H., *Gas- und Wasserfach,* Vol. 96, Sept. 1955, p. 604.

[13] Watanabe, T., *Japanese Journal of Ecology,* Vol. 12, No. 6, December 1962, pp. 216–222.

[14] Fjerdingstad, E., *Internationale Revue Der Gesamten Hydrobiologie,* Vol. 49, No. 1, 1964, pp. 63–131.

[15] Fjerdingstad, E. in *Biological Problems in Water Pollution,* 3rd Seminar, 1962, Public Health Service Publication 999–WP–25, 1965, pp. 232–235.

[16] Patrick, R., *Proceedings,* Academy of Natural Sciences of Philadelphia, Vol. 101, 1949, pp. 277–341.

[17] Nygaard, G., *Kongelige Danske Videnskabernes Selskab, Biologiske Skrifter,* Vol. 7, No. 1, 1949, pp. 1–293.

[18] Thunmark, S., *Folia Limnologica Scandinavica,* Vol. 3, 1945.

[19] Stockner, J. G. and Benson, W. W., *Limnology and Oceanography,* Vol. 12, No. 3, July, 1967, pp. 513–532.

[20] Patrick, R. in *Biological Problems in Water Pollution,* PHS Publication 999–WP–25, U.S. Department of Health, Education and Welfare, Cincinnati, 1965, pp. 225–231.

[21] Patrick, R., Hohn, M. H., and Wallace, J. H., *Notulae Naturae,* Academy of Natural Sciences of Philadelphia, No. 259, 1954.

[22] Harvey, R. S. and Patrick, R., *Biotechnology and Bioengineering,* Vol. 9, 1967, pp. 449–456.

[23] Preston, F. W., *Ecology,* Vol. 29, 1948, pp. 254–283.

[24] Patrick, R., Roberts, N. A., and Davis, B., *Notulae Naturae,* Academy of Natural Sciences of Philadelphia, No. 416, 1968.

[25] Patrick, R. and Hohn, M. H., *Proceedings,* American Petroleum Institute, Section III, Refining, Vol. 36, No. 3, 1956, pp. 332–339.

[26] Patrick, R. and Strawbridge, D., *American Naturalist,* Vol. 97, No. 892, Feb. 1963, pp. 51–57.

[27] Margalef, R., *Memorias, Real Academia des Ciencias y Artes de Barcelona,* Vol. 32, 1957, pp. 373–449.

[28] Patten, B. C., *Journal of Marine Research,* Vol. 20, March 1962, p. 57.

[29] McIntire, C. D., "Ecological-physiological Investigations of Littoral Diatom Communities of the Yaquina River Estuary, Oregon," Progress Report, National Science Foundation Research Grant GB–7203, 1969.

[30] MacArthur, R. H., *Biological Reviews of the Cambridge Philosophical Society,* Vol. 40, No. 4, Nov. 1965, pp. 510–533.

[31] Cairns, J. C., Jr., Kaesler, R. L., and Patrick, R., *Notulae Naturae,* Academy of Natural Sciences of Philadelphia, No. 436, 1970.

[32] Margalef, R., "Valeur Indicatrice de la Composition des Pigments du Phytoplancton sur la Productivite, Composition Taxonomique et Proprietes Dynamiques des Populations," Comité Internationale pour la Exploration de la Mer Méditeranée, Monaco, Vol. 15, No. 2, 1960, pp. 277–281.

[33] *ASTM Annual Book of Standards, Part 23,* American Society for Testing and Materials, 1964, p. 517.

[34] Patrick, R. in *Biological Problems in Water Pollution,* C. M. Tarzwell, Ed., Robert A. Taft Sanitary Engineering Center, Cincinnati, 1956, pp. 71–83.

[35] Watts, J. R. and Harvey, R. S., *Limnology and Oceanography,* Vol. 8, No. 1, Jan. 1963, pp. 45–49.

[36] Patrick, R., *American Naturalist,* Vol. 102, No. 924, March-April 1968, pp. 173–183.

[37] Joint Industry-Government Task Force on Eutrophication, *Provisional Algal Assay Procedure*, A. F. Bartsch, Ed., 1969, pp. 1–62.

[38] Matulova, D., *Hydrobiologia*, Vol. 30, Nos. 3 and 4, 1967, pp. 494–502.

[39] Stewart, W. D. G., Fitzgerald, G. P., and Burris, R. H., *Proceedings,* National Academy of Sciences, Vol. 66, No. 4, 1970, pp. 1104–1111.

[40] Levins, R., *American Scientist,* Vol. 54, No. 4, Dec. 1966, pp. 421–431.

[41] Cairns, J. C., Jr., Dickson, K. L., Lanza, G. R., Almeida, S. P., and DelBalzo, D., *Archiv Feur Mikrobiologie,* Vol. 83, 1972, pp. 141–146.

A. R. Gaufin [1]

Use of Aquatic Invertebrates in the Assessment of Water Quality

REFERENCE: Gaufin, A. R., **"Use of Aquatic Invertebrates in the Assessment of Water Quality,"** *Biological Methods for the Assessment of Water Quality, ASTM STP 528*, American Society for Testing and Materials, 1973, pp. 96–116.

ABSTRACT: Pollution is essentially a biological phenomenon in that its primary effect is on living organisms. A biological investigation of a polluted lake or stream has several advantages over chemical analyses. It is less time-consuming because a single series of samples can reveal the status of the animal and plant communities which themselves represent the results of the summation of the prevailing conditions. The animals and plants provide a record of the prevailing conditions and are not affected by a temporary alleviation of a polluting effluent.

Intensive studies were carried out by Gaufin and Tarzwell in 1952 and 1956 to determine the effects of organic pollution on the aquatic communities of Lytle Creek and the value of these populations as indicators of pollutional conditions. The studies revealed that little reliance could be placed upon the mere occurrence of a single species in a given locality as an indicator of pollution. In the creek the nine species of macroinvertebrates which were most numerous in the septic zone also occurred in the recovery and clean water zones, but in much smaller numbers. The septic zone had less than one fifth as many species as the clean water zone, but the total number of organisms per unit area was many times greater. The septic zone was characterized by species adapted to live in low dissolved oxygen concentrations or those able to secure their oxygen directly from the air.

In the clean water zone there was a great variety of invertebrate communities, each consisting of many different species. Most of the species which occurred in the septic and recovery zones were also found in very limited numbers in the clean water zones. In addition, there was also present a wide variety of forms which were intolerant of conditions in the polluted zones. Most of these were the gill-breathing, immature stages of such insects as the mayflies, stoneflies, caddis flies, and alder flies.

In evaluating the reliability of aquatic organisms as indicators of pollutional conditions and water quality, one must consider the different indicator organisms not separately but as biological associations or communities.

[1] Professor of Zoology, University of Utah, Salt Lake City, Utah 84112.

The organisms should be considered as groups according to their morphological adaptations and physiological requirements.

Several formal systems for the biological assessment of pollution based on community composition have been suggested. A reduction in community diversity has been noted in a number of rivers polluted by organic wastes. Diversity indices, based on information theory, are very useful for comparing changes in community composition in streams altered by pollution.

KEY WORDS: water pollution, invertebrates, aquatic biology, water quality, indicator species, macroinvertebrates

The assessment of water pollution is principally a biological problem in that its primary effect is on living organisms. Nevertheless, despite this biological relationship, most studies of water pollution have been directed toward obtaining primarily chemical and physical measurements such as dissolved oxygen, BOD, suspended solids, and other such parameters. Since chemical studies give information on physical-chemical conditions only at the time of sampling, and pollution surveys frequently cannot be made during the period of the most critical conditions, there is need for additional methods that can be used throughout the year for determining the extent and severity of brief critical or limiting environmental factors. The qualitative and quantitative composition of an aquatic population is determined by recurring critical conditions, even though of short duration, as well as the more stable or long-term environmental factors. Therefore, the complex of organisms which develops in a given area is, in turn, indicative of environmental conditions which have occurred during its development. Organisms having life histories of a year or more will thus serve to indicate unfavorable or limiting conditions that have occurred several months previously. Because aquatic populations are a result of past environmental conditions, they serve as a means for determining such conditions in a stream. They are especially valuable because they can be used during fall, winter, or spring months, when flows may be large, dilution is at a maximum, dissolved oxygen is near saturation, and visual evidence of pollution at a minimum, to delineate former septic areas or to indicate critical conditions of short duration.

Changes in Aquatic Ecosystems Caused by Organic Pollution

Pollutants may alter stream environments and thereby affect aquatic life in a number of ways. These changes may include an increase in dissolved nutrients, a decrease or increase in dissolved oxygen or both, increase in turbidity, changes in the character of the stream bottom, production of undesirable growths, an increase in stream temperatures, and the addition of toxic wastes. The degree or extent of the effect of these changes on aquatic life varies with the type and amount of the pollutant and the character of the receiving water.

Kolkwitz and Marsson[1,2][2] first described the various ecological conditions associated with the different stages of recovery during the self-purification of rivers which had been grossly polluted with putrescible organic matter as sewage. In their Saprobiensystem they recognized three major zones based on physical and chemical characteristics and the number and kinds of organisms that inhabited them. The zones were designated as polysaprobic, mesosaprobic, and oligosaprobic. These workers classified a great number of both microscopic and macroscopic plants and animals and grouped them according to the zones under which they were found. They then used the presence and absence of different organisms to indicate the degree of organic pollution. From the work of these and other men there developed the concept of biological indicators of pollution.

Kolkwitz and Marsson published long lists of plants and animals they believed to be associated with each of these zones. Their system and lists of organisms have been widely used in Europe for the assessment of organic pollution. This system, while having some validity, has been subject to much criticism primarily directed against the placing of certain organisms in certain zones. Many of the organisms listed in particularly the mesosaprobic zone may be found in a wide range of conditions and not restricted to any one area. Another weakness of the system is that simple lists of species present are insufficient for the assessment of the condition of the water. The mere presence of certain species gives very little indication of the condition of the habitat, rather the whole community must be considered.

Macroinvertebrates as Indicators of Organic Pollution

Numerous stream surveys conducted during the last 50 years illustrate the effects of organic pollution on the physical and chemical characteristics and the biota of receiving waters. Time and space will permit consideration of only one of these, a study with which the author was personally involved[3,4].

Year-round field studies of the composition and ecology of stream communities associated with the purification of organic wastes in streams were conducted on Lytle Creek, Ohio, from October 1949 until 1955 (Fig. 1). This creek, located about 45 miles northeast of Cincinnati, Ohio, is a tributary of the Little Miami River. The principal natural source of water in the stream was surface drainage augmented at a point about 7.3 miles above the mouth by the effluent from the Wilmington sewage treatment plant. Primary treatment including chemical precipitation was provided at

---

[2] The italic numbers in brackets refer to the list of references appended to this paper.

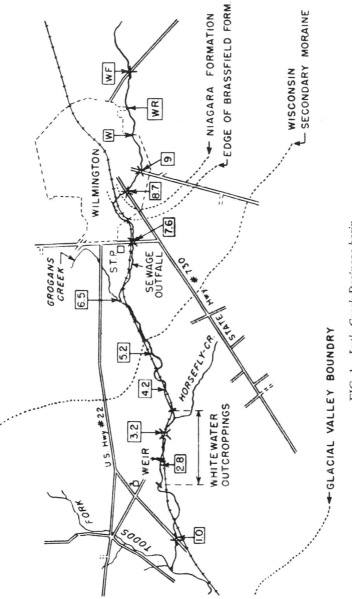

FIG. 1—*Lytle Creek Drainage basin.*

this plant until 1954 when secondary treatment of the activated sludge type was installed. During low flow stage in summer and autumn, the sewage effluent comprised from 80 to 90 percent of the total stream flow.

The Lytle Creek studies revealed that during the summer months when flows were low, septic, recovery, and clean water zones were distinct. Further, the major satisfaction of the biochemical oxygen demand, most of which was contributed by the effluent from the primary sewage treatment plant, took place in a relatively short section below the sewage outfall (Figs. 2 and 3). From May to November of each year, variations in dissolved oxygen and pH were at a maximum, and the most severe conditions of oxygen depletion occurred. During the winter months higher flows and lower temperatures resulted in the pollutional zones changing their location and extent. During the period from December to April, natural purification proceeded at a slower rate, sewage fungus grew farther downstream, and dissolved oxygen was abundant throughout the stream (Figs. 4 and 5).

In the Lytle Creek studies emphasis was placed on determining the role and value of the macroinvertebrates as indicators of pollution. The decision to do this was based on their size and more distinctive morphological characteristics, which facilitate their identification under field conditions. In addition, most representatives of this group have longer life histories

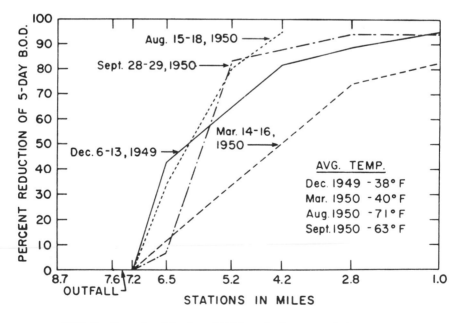

FIG. 2—*Rate of satisfaction of BOD in Lytle Creek, 1949 to 1950.*

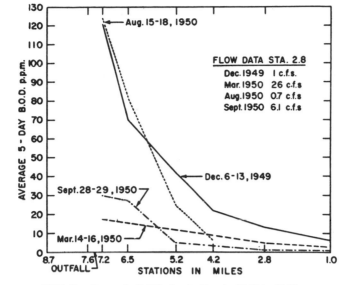

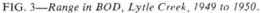

FIG. 3—*Range in BOD, Lytle Creek, 1949 to 1950.*

than the microbenthic fauna and are thus better fitted for indicating past ecological conditions in any given area.

Bacteriological studies and studies of the relationship of blue-green algae, flagellates, and protozoa to nutrients in the stream were also conducted

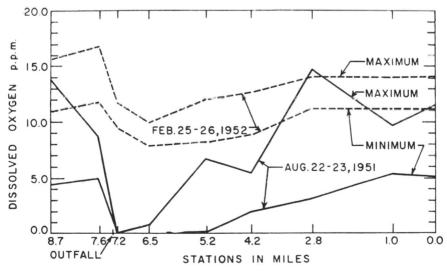

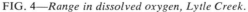

FIG. 4—*Range in dissolved oxygen, Lytle Creek.*

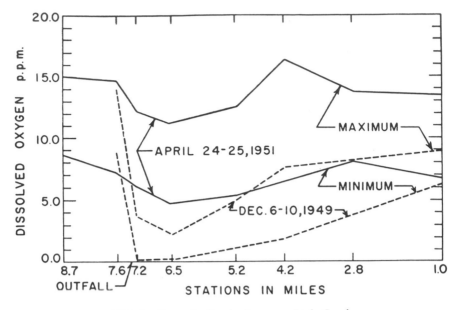

FIG. 5—*Range in dissolved oxygen, Ltyle Creek.*

during 1949. The distribution of these organisms in the stream during December 1949 is given in Figs. 6, 7, and 8 as a basis for the interpretation of macroinvertebrate distribution in the stream.

Intensive qualitative and quantitative studies of the macroinvertebrate inhabitants of the stream were carried out during all seasons of the year. During the qualitative surveys conducted in connection with the sampling runs, 144 species representing 110 genera of animals were collected and identified. The studies revealed striking seasonal differences in the numbers of species and faunal associations occurring in the various sections of the stream. The number of species of macroinvertebrates found in different sections of the stream during each of the seasons is shown in Fig. 9.

One third to one sixth as many species, depending on the season, were found in the septic zone as in the stream above the outfall. This reduction is believed to have been due largely to oxygen depletion during periods of high temperature and low flow and to changes in the nature of the stream bottom. The largest number of species (70) was taken in the lower clean water zone at Station 1.0 during October 1951. The variety and abundance of life present in that section reflect the favorable effects of organic enrichment and relatively constant stream flow during the late summer months.

Analyses of the species composition and abundance of individual orga-

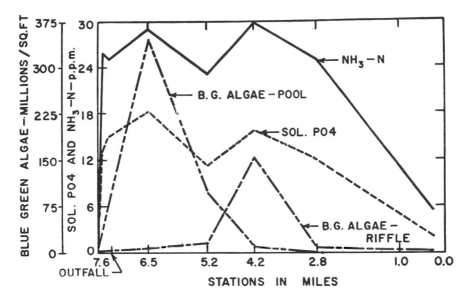

FIG. 6—*Relation of blue-green algae to nutrients, Lytle Creek, December 1949.*

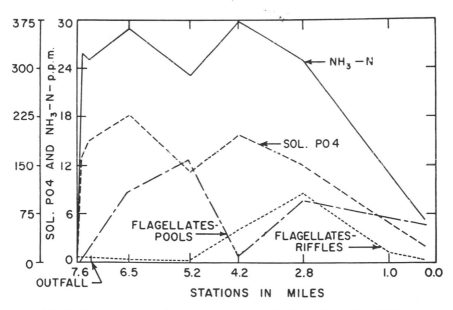

FIG. 7—*Relation of flagellates to nutrients, Lytle Creek, December 1949.*

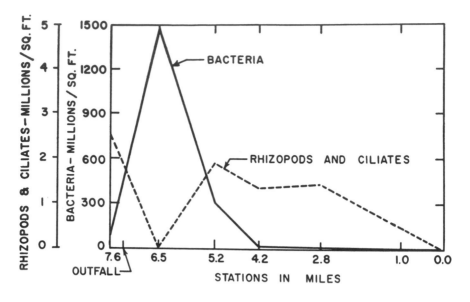

FIG. 8—*Distribution of bacteria and protozoa, Lytle Creek, December 1949.*

nisms in the various zones point to biological phenomena which constitute valuable criteria for evaluating the role and value of such associations as indicators of pollutional conditions in a stream. Because the entire stream below the sewage treatment plant was affected to some extent by the effluent which it received, only the two-mile section above the outfall displayed what may be considered as clean water conditions at all times. The number and variety of macroinvertebrates occurring in that upper section were typical of the fauna which existed in nonpolluted streams in the area.

The fauna at all times in the upper clean water section consisted of a variety of species representing many different genera, families, and orders of invertebrates. The smallest number of species collected at one sampling was 29, taken in August 1951; the largest number (63) was encountered in April 1952. The latter number, collected at Station 8.7, very well illustrates the diversity of life present. The following species of invertebrates were taken; water fleas (Collembola), 1; true flies (Diptera), 18; beetles (Coleoptera), 13; mayflies (Ephemeroptera), 4; caddis flies (Trichoptera), 6; stoneflies (Plecoptera), 3; dragon flies (Odonata), 4; water bugs (Hemiptera), 3; crayfish and shrimps (Crustacea), 3; snails (Mollusca), 4; segmented worms (Annelida), 1; flatworms (Platyhelminthes), 1; and roundworms (Nematoda), 2. Among this variety of organisms, no one species was found in numbers exceeding 50 per square yard; whereas, 45

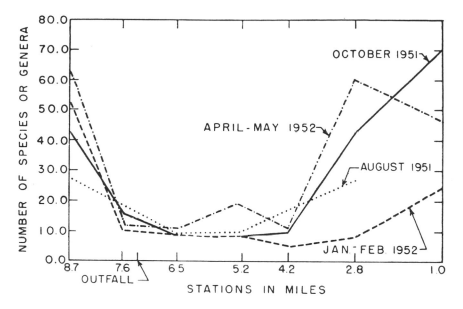

FIG. 9 *Macroinvertebrate distribution, Lytle Creek.*

species were represented by less than five individuals per square yard of bottom area.

The distribution and numbers of species and individuals occurring in the septic and recovery zones contrasted sharply with those of the clean water zone. Only eight to ten species of macroinvertebrates were collected at any one time from the septic zone under low water conditions. This number included such forms as the mosquito larva, *Culex pipiens;* rattail maggot, *Eristalis bastardi;* horsefly larva, *Tabanus atratus;* water scavenger beetle, *Tropisternis natator;* water boatman, *Hesperocorixa* sp.; pulmonate snail, *Physa integra;* and sludgeworms, *Limnodrilus* sp. and *Tubifex* sp. As many as 18 species were taken from that section in the spring when the flow was high. However, eight of that number were drift forms traceable to a nearby tributary.

Of the eight to ten species of macroinvertebrates occurring in the septic zone during the late summer and autumn, not one species was restricted to that section of stream. All occurred, but in far smaller numbers, in both the recovery and clean water zones. In these latter areas, however, they were very restricted in their distribution, being largely confined to quiet water microhabitats having dissolved oxygen, food supplies, and bottom conditions similar to those which existed in the septic zone.

Analysis of the macroinvertebrate population characteristic of the septic zone in August 1951 revealed that 40 percent were Diptera, 20 percent Coleoptera, 20 percent Annelida, 10 percent Hemiptera, and 10 percent Mollusca. All of the insects generally found in this zone were characterized by the possession of special adaptations for obtaining oxygen, such as the caudal respiratory tubes of the mosquito larva and rattail maggot, or the air space under the elytra of the beetles.

During summer and early autumn, an abundant food supply and other favorable conditions for reproduction and growth enabled several species occurring in the septic and recovery zones to attain great abundance. As many as 3000 mosquitoes, *Culex pipiens,* and 20 000 Tubificids were collected in a square foot sample from the septic zone during these months. Rattail maggots, *Eristalis bastardi,* were so numerous at times that their respiratory tubes had the appearance of closely crowded blades of grass.

The variety and number of organisms in the recovery zone were much less constant than they were in either the clean water or septic zones. Environmental conditions ranged from near septicity in the upper end of the recovery zone to practically clean water in the lower portion. The limits of the zone also shifted frequently with the seasons and change in flow. The least number of species encountered in the middle section of the recovery zone was nine, found in October 1951; the greatest number was 32, collected in April 1952. During the former month the fauna consisted of species typically found farther upstream, while during the latter month the fauna was more typical of clean water conditions. The community of organisms encountered in April included seven species of relatively sensitive mayflies, stoneflies, and caddis flies which apparently had drifted into the main stream from tributaries. Each of these species had been able to survive in numbers up to five per square yard. Such seeding of additional fauna did not occur in the autumn of 1951 when all the tributaries were dry.

Aquatic Macroinvertebrate Communities as Indicators of Organic Pollution

Analysis of the distribution of the major groups of aquatic macroinvertebrates in Lytle Creek reveals that no community was made up entirely of clean water representatives. The mayflies (Ephemeroptera), stoneflies (Plecoptera), and caddis flies (Trichoptera), all gilled forms, were more nearly restricted to and comprised a larger portion of the clean water association than any of the other groups. Members of these orders and other gill-breathing immature insects scattered through several orders were most affected and restricted in their distribution by the very low dissolved oxygen concentrations often present in the polluted zones.

These are, however, exceptions. Two species of mayflies, *Stenonema femoratum* and *Callibaetis* sp., were taken on several occasions in sections of the recovery zone where the dissolved oxygen content was reduced to as low as 1 ppm at night. It is possible that the oxygen concentrations in the niches occupied by the two species, of which the former occurred in the fastest riffles and the latter in marginal or shoal areas, where the water was less than 6 in. deep, were higher than the value recorded for the stream section. However, both species displayed much greater tolerance to low oxygen levels than had heretofore been thought possible.

Further, representatives of one family of Trichoptera, the net building *Hydropsychidae,* also were found commonly in areas where the oxygen supply at night was often reduced to less than 3.0 ppm. In all such cases, however, the larvae or pupae were located in the most rapid portions of riffles where they could obtain the maximum available supply of oxygen, as well as food.

With only two exceptions the stoneflies were entirely restricted to clean water areas. *Allocapnia viviparia* and *Perlesta placida* were taken both as nymphs and adults in limited numbers from the upper recovery zone of the stream during the winter and early spring months when conditions were temporarily favorable for their existence. The minimal dissolved oxygen value recorded during the period when they were collected was 7.8 ppm. All evidence indicated that they were contributed to the main stream from nearby tributaries where they occurred in large numbers. Since both species pass through the summer and early fall in either the egg stage or as very small inactive nymphs, it is debatable whether or not they could have lived and completed their earlier development in the stream proper when much lower dissolved oxygen levels existed.

While there are exceptions, such as those just considered, in general an association of mayflies, stoneflies, and caddis flies in a stream is indicative of clean water conditions, and their absence denotes the presence of pollution or a low oxygen supply or both, if the physical nature of the habitat is otherwise suitable. Usually the presence or absence of representatives of other orders of aquatic insects which breathe by gills, and which are, therefore, dependent upon oxygen dissolved in the water for their respiratory needs, has similar indicator significance. For example, while most aquatic beetles can renew their oxygen supply directly from the atmosphere and are thus unaffected by oxygen-depleting wastes, the larvae, pupae, and adults of those species which are entirely aquatic are dependent upon dissolved oxygen and are restricted to clean water streams which are well aerated. In Lytle Creek several species of riffle beetles, such as *Stenelmis crenata* and *Stenelmis sexlineata,* were found only in the upper and lower clean water zones. Their distribution in the stream indicates that the family, Elmidae, to which they belong, is a member of the clean water association.

While most gill-bearing aquatic insects are limited in their distribution by low dissolved oxygen supplies, some forms which have more than one means of respiration, such as the dragonflies and damselflies, display considerable tolerance to low levels of dissolved oxygen. Their greater adaptability to environments low in dissolved oxygen is made possible by the possession of respiratory structures which are the most highly developed of the various gill systems. These insects can carry on respiration by means of four different structures, namely, (1) caudal tracheal gills, (2) rectal folds, (3) the integument, and (4) spiracles. Since all four organs may function at the same time and many of the stream forms occur in either riffles or shallow marginal areas, the group is remarkably well adapted to withstand the oxygen depleting effects of organic pollution. As a result of this adaptability, the nymphs of both dragonflies and damselflies were often taken in Lytle Creek in sections of the recovery zone where the dissolved oxygen supply during the summer was as low as 1.0 ppm for a short time during the night or in the early morning hours.

In Lytle Creek, insects of the orders Hemiptera, Coleoptera, and Diptera had the most varied representation, were the most widespread in their distribution, and were least affected by dissolved oxygen concentration. Representatives of these orders were found in all stream habitats representing all degrees of pollution and stream recovery. Some species from each group were found fairly widely distributed through the stream; others, while not restricted to either a clean water or polluted area, showed by their abundance a strong preference for one or the other type of habitat. Still other species, particularly among the Diptera, were restricted to clean water or to water rich in organic materials.

Of the three orders, the Hemiptera and Coleoptera were the poorest indicators of organic pollution and oxygen depletion in the stream. With the exception of the Elmidae, or riffle beetles, other species of beetles and all of the species of water bugs collected were found throughout the stream, usually occurring most abundantly in the polluted areas where they found an abundant food supply. The ability of members of these two orders to withstand the oxygen-depleting effects of organic pollution is due to special modifications of their tracheal system. These modifications serve to increase the internal air capacity of the tracheal system, supplement tracheal diffusion by ventilation movements when the insects come to the surface for air, and provide supplementary external air stores. Common to all of these forms are the modification of the body surface for breaking the water surface film, and changes in the wings and body surface for capturing and holding stores of air, and in the tracheal system for surface ventilation and connection with the external air stores. In oxygen-deficient waters members of these two groups have only to increase the frequency of their visits to the surface to cope with decreasing oxygen supplies.

Aquatic Diptera were found in the stream in many different ecological niches in both the clean water and polluted zones. However, with the exception of only a few species, representatives of this order were highly selective in their choice of habitat. A number of species such as *Diamesa nivoriunda, Cricotopus absurdus,* and *Calopsectra neoflavella* were found only in the cleanest, most highly aerated sections of the stream, while others such as the mosquito, *Culex pipiens,* and rattail maggot, *Eristalis bastardi,* while found in limited numbers in clean water areas, showed a decided preference for the polluted sections. The variability in choice of habitat and in the range of distribution of the species taken was determined largely by the food-getting and respiratory requirements and adaptations of the different individual species. The larvae and pupae of the mosquito and rattail maggot, with their special respiratory tubes, were unaffected by low oxygen supplies as evidenced by the extremely large numbers of each taken in the most septic areas. Certain red-blooded Chironomids, such as *Chironomus riparius,* also demonstrated a remarkable ability to thrive in the septic and recovery zones. The hemoglobin possessed by midge larvae such as *Chironomus riparius, Chironomus plumosus,* and closely related species apparently acts in both the transportation and storage of oxygen. Its greatest transport role is during anaerobiosis when it permits the larva to continue filter feeding in low oxygen tensions and thereby increases the rate of recovery from exposure to such conditions.

Indicators of Other Types of Pollution

Although indicators of organic pollution in streams have received greatest attention, toxic substances and physical changes in the environment can often be detected by changes in the community of organisms.

Jones[5,6] in his studies of metallic pollution of the river Rheidol in western Wales clearly demonstrated biological succession. As the river recovered, both in time as the exposed ore became leached out, or in space as ore proceeded downstream to regions of greater dilution, many algae reappeared, together with worms, and a few fishes at intervals. The number of species of animals found in the affected sections of the river was 14 in 1922, 29 in 1923, 57 in 1927, and 104 in 1937, when lead was no longer detectable.

In the earlier stages of the work no distinction was made between the effects of lead and zinc[6], but it was apparent that some forms, particularly stoneflies, mayflies, and some midges, were very resistant to both and they were found living in water containing nearly 60 ppm of zinc[7]. Worms, leeches, crustaceans, molluscs, and fishes were very susceptible, as were the rooted plants and algae. Jones[6,8] suggested that the normal attached algae and rooted plants were absent because of an unstable shifting bed due to mine wastes and not because of metal toxicity. Absence of some caddis fly larvae appeared to be a direct result of the shortage of algae on which they feed. Jones[5,7] found that the caddis fly larvae could tolerate high concentrations of zinc, but those species which eat algae were scarce where the river bed was covered with loose mine grit. Carnivorous Trichoptera, such as *Rhyacophila* and *Polycentropus,* were common in the area, and detritus feeders such as the stonefly, *Leuctra,* were particularly abundant, because of lack of competitors[5].

The effects of pollution by copper were studied in the river Churnet, a tributary of the river Dove in Western Wales by Pentelow and Butcher[9] and Butcher[10,11]. The river, when the research was conducted, was polluted by organic matter but was showing signs of recovery a few miles farther downstream. It then received a copper works effluent which raised the copper content of the water to 1 ppm and above. The copper effluent had a very striking effect on the biota. All the animals, which above the copper works consisted of Tubificidae, *Chironomus, Asellus,* leeches and molluscs, disappeared. None was found in the next 11 miles to the confluence with the Dove, where the copper content had fallen to 0.6 ppm. The algae were also seriously affected. Above the works they consisted of species associated with organically enriched water, such as *Stigeoclonium, Nitzschia palea,* and *Gomphonema parvulum* in concentrations of 1000 per mm^2 of suspended test slides. Below the outfall this number fell to 15 to 200 per mm^2. Thirty miles below the outfall numbers of over 50 000 per mm^2 were recorded. The enormous numbers of algae that developed were probably due to the absence of animals to graze them.

Most aquatic organisms can withstand changes in temperature only within very narrow limits. The discharge of heated water into a stream can create a hot water barrier which effectively blocks the spawning migrations of many species of fish. Heat pollution can effect aquatic organisms in a number of different ways including death through direct effects; death through indirect effects of reduced oxygen, disruption of food supply, and decreased resistance to toxic substances; interference with spawning; and competitive replacement by more tolerant species[12]. Coutant[13] found substantial reductions in the volume and numbers of macroinvertebrates in the Delaware River in sections receiving heated water. Nebeker and Lemke[14] tested the relative sensitivity of twelve species of aquatic insects to heated water in the laboratory. The lethal temperature at which 50 percent of the test specimens died after 96 h exposure (TLm^{96}) ranged from 21° C for winter stoneflies to 33° C for dragonflies. Gaufin and Hern[15] found that an artificial increase in stream temperatures during the winter will cause stoneflies to develop more rapidly, emerge earlier, and be subject to exposure and death from cold air temperatures.

Discussion

Indicator Species

Since Kolkwitz and Marsson, Richardson[16,17], and Liebmann[18] published their classification of organisms associated with various zones of pollution in rivers receiving putrescible organic wastes, numerous studies have been conducted utilizing the Kolkwitz-Marsson concept of indicator organisms. Comparison of the lists of species collected during many of these pollutional surveys will show considerable lack of agreement as to the indicator significance of many of the organisms listed. A species which one worker may consider as being characteristic of polluted water may be reported by others as being found only under clean water conditions. There are several reasons for the lack of agreement in the different lists. Perhaps foremost is the fact that, in making use of such environmental classifications for the setting up of lists, little reliance can be placed upon the mere occurrence of a single species in a given locality. Many organisms which occur in large numbers in extremely polluted water also are found in limited numbers in clean situations. For example, all of the species of invertebrates which occurred in the septic or recovery zones of Lytle Creek were also found in limited numbers in similar microhabitats in the clean water zones. Conversely, many aquatic organisms that are intolerant of persistent organic pollution can live for a short period of time in a polluted area when pollutional effects are at a minimum. Such occurrences were particularly evident in Lytle Creek during periods of high flow in the winter and spring months when temperatures were low and dissolved oxygen concentrations were high. Under such conditions several species of mayflies, stoneflies, and caddis flies, which drifted into the septic and recovery zones of the stream from nearby tributaries, were able to remain alive for periods sufficient to allow them to emerge as adults. In all such instances, however, the numbers of such clean water forms were distinctly limited when compared with the populations of organisms usually found in the stream.

Another reason for the lack of agreement as to the indicator value of specific aquatic organisms is that several environmental factors, other than the presence of a pollutant, may affect or limit the distribution of certain species. Chief among these are geographical location, erosion, floods, and size of the stream, the type of bottom, and the flight range of the insect. Specific lists compiled for one section of the country or world may be of little value in another region, because of the fact that many aquatic organisms are very restricted in their distribution. In order for any comprehensive list or grouping of indicator organisms to be applicable to all sections of the country, the pollutional status of typical aquatic organisms throughout the country must be studied and such information incorporated into the list.

Type of bottom, speed of current, depth of water, and many other factors affect the distribution of the stream fauna in any given section. Due to the differing physiological requirements and morphological adaptations of aquatic organisms, the populations found in soft muck, sand, or gravel bottoms, and in riffles, pools, and marginal areas are quite distinct.

Aquatic Communities as Biological Indices

A knowledge of the relative abundance of species, either common or rare is much more useful in evaluating environmental conditions in a stream than is knowledge only of their presence or absence. Community composition is now recognized as being much more reliable than particular indicator organisms for evaluating environmental conditions.

In clean water streams there may be a great variety of aquatic communities, each consisting of many different species. With ecological conditions less restrictive, and greater competition for food and space existing between the different organisms that make up the population, no one species is able to increase in numbers and become represented by the large numbers of individuals characteristic of a polluted stream. Each community is a dynamic unit, consisting of herbivores, carnivores, and omnivores; prey and predators; lung, tracheal tube, and gill breathers. Each organism is adapted to its own ecological niche and offers check reins against too rapid growth or reproduction of the others. Most of the species which occur in the septic and recovery zones of polluted streams may also be found in very limited numbers in the clean water zones. In addition, there may also be present a wide variety of forms which are intolerant of conditions in the polluted zones.

Several formal systems for the biological assessment of pollution based on community composition have been suggested. On the basis of extensive studies of streams in the Conestoga Basin in Pennsylvania, Dr. Ruth Patrick[19] proposed a "biological measure of stream conditions." This method involved the examination of a number of stations in a healthy section of the river and the identification and counting of the number of species in each of seven groups. The assumption is made that each group is a unit and that "those species which are grouped together seem to behave in the same way under the effect of pollution." Histograms were prepared in which the height of the bar for each group represented the number of species in that group at a particular station expressed as a percentage of the number of species in that group found at nine typical healthy stations. If any species occurred in exceptionally large numbers at a station, the bar for the group was doubled in width. Stations were classified as healthy, semihealthy, polluted, or very polluted.

This system has been criticized as not specifying the stream conditions, pollutional or otherwise, to which the organisms in each group are supposed to respond similarly[20]. This criticism is not valid, however, since in conducting a stream survey Dr. Patrick's organization determines the chemical characteristics of the water, total bacterial and coliform counts are made, and BODs are determined. Dr. Patrick's method is to be commended for the completeness of its scope, but it requires the services of a considerable number of well trained scientists to conduct a "complete" stream survey and is costly as a result.

Wurtz[21] reanalyzed data from the Conestoga Basin and developed a somewhat less complicated system for conducting stream surveys. He classified organisms into four groups: burrowing, sessile, foraging, and pelagic. He further classified these organisms into tolerant and nontolerant groups. According to his system, the data are presented in histograms in which each bar represents the number of species at a location classified into one of the four ways of life. Each histogram represents a percentage of the total number of species at a location. The absolute numbers of tolerant and nontolerant species in each group are shown by numerals above or below its bar. A community in which 50 percent of the species were in the nontolerant category was considered to be typical of clean water. This system requires information as to the tolerance of the species involved and often such data is not available.

Another system which utilizes simple numerical indices that can easily be included along with other water quality data was developed by Beck[22]. He proposed the use of a "biotic index."

Biotic index $= 2(n$ Class $I) + (n$ Class II), where n represents the number of macroscopic invertebrate species either in Class I (organisms tolerant of little organic pollution) or Class II (tolerant of moderate organic pollution but not of anaerobic conditions). More weight in the composition of the index was given to Class I organisms, because they are the least tolerant of pollutional conditions. A stream nearing septic conditions will have a biotic index value of zero; whereas, streams receiving moderate amounts of organic wastes will have values from 1 to 6 and streams receiving little or no waste will have values usually over 10. This system has been of considerable value to Beck in his role as a biologist with the Florida State Board of Health.

Community Diversity

The introduction of putrescible organic wastes into a river may lead to a reduction in the number of species present but a considerable increase in numbers of those species tolerant of the changed conditions produced by the pollution. This reduction in community diversity has been noted in a number of studies of rivers polluted by organic wastes[3,17,19,23].

Wilhm and Dorris[24] computed diversity indices, based on information theory, for comparing changes in the diversity of communities above and below the points of introduction of different kinds of wastes into fresh and marine waters.

Species diversity has two components which have been used singly or in combination. The first involves the actual number of species from a given community. There is a corresponding increase in diversity as the number of species increases. The second component deals with the numerical distribution of individuals among species. Both components are an integral part of the species diversity concept; however, different indices of diversity may measure only one of these.

Wilhm[25] made a comparison of five diversity indices applied to populations of benthic macroinvertebrates. The simplest index is $d = S/N$, where S is the number of species, and N is the total number of individuals. A diversity index based on information theory was described by Margalef[26] and later modified and applied to stream communities by Wilhm and Dorris[24]. This diversity index is independent of sample size (dimensionless) and takes into account the relative importance of each species. Community diversity (D), diversity per individual $(\bar{D})$, maximum diversity (D_{max}), minimum diversity (D_{min}), redundancy (R), the number of species (S), the total number of individuals (N), and the number of individuals in the ith species (ni) are used in the following equations based on information theory:

$$D = \sum_{i=1}^{s} n_i \log \frac{n_i}{N}$$

$$\bar{D} = \sum_{i=1}^{s} \frac{n_i}{N} \log \frac{n_i}{N}$$

$$D_{max} = \log N! - s \log(N/s)!$$

$$D_{min} = \log N! - \log N - (s-1)!$$

$$R = \frac{D_{max} - D}{D_{max} - D_{min}}$$

Redundancy (R) was described by Wilhm and Dorris[24] as an expression of the dominance of one or more species and is inversely proportional to the wealth of species. It also corresponds to a measure of the evenness of species numbers.

Any unit of measure can be used in those indices derived from information theory. Most of the studies using these equations have let ni equal the number of individuals in the ith species (Species 1, 2, 3 . . . i). Biomass or energy units can be used in place of numbers of individuals[24]. Both of these substitutions may give a more accurate description of community structure and information concerning energy flow through the community. The expression for average diversity per individual has been correlated with levels of pollution. Wilhm and Dorris[24] showed that values of less than one have been obtained in zones of heavy pollution, values between one and three in zones of moderate pollution, and values above three in clean water zones.

Summary

The waste products of civilization when discharged into a lake or stream bring about changes in the environment that lead to changes in the distribution and abundance of individual species and, hence, to alterations in the community. Changes in the number of species, number of individual organisms, and the species and community composition have been found to be most useful in evaluating the effects and degree of organic pollution in a body of water and in delineating zones of pollution in a stream.

In evaluating aquatic organisms as indicators of pollutional conditions in a lake or stream, little reliance can be placed upon the mere occurrence of a single species in a given locality. Many organisms which occur in large numbers in extremely polluted water can be found in limited numbers in cleaner situations. Conversely, many aquatic organisms that are intolerant of persistent organic pollution can live for a short period of time in a polluted area when pollutional effects are at a minimum. In evaluating the reliability of aquatic organisms as indices of environmental changes due to pollution, one must consider the different indicator organisms not separately but as biological associations or populations. The organisms should be considered in groups or communities according to their morphological adaptations and physiological requirements.

Community composition and diversity of an aquatic community can be extremely sensitive biological indices of environmental change. Even slight changes in environmental conditions, if persistent, can lead to changes in community composition and diversity.

A number of complex formal methods have been developed for the biological assessment of pollution utilizing indicator species and communities. These methods have been particularly useful for reporting complex biological changes in forms readily usable by engineers and other non-biologists. However, such complex formal methods often are not only unnecessary but also undesirable since, as Hynes[27] points out, "in nature little is simple and straightforward, and a rigid system can often lead only to rigidity of thought and approach." Experienced biologists, with very limited sampling and simple means of analysis and representation, can often detect even slight environmental changes in aquatic habitats by means of biological indices.

References

[1] Kolkwitz, R. and Marsson, M., *Berichte Der Deutschen Botanischen Gesellschaft*, Vol. 26, 1908, pp. 505–519.

[2] Kolkwitz, R. and Marsson, M., *Internationale Revue Der Gesamten Hydrobiologie*, Vol. 2, 1909, pp. 126–152.

[3] Gaufin, A. R. and Tarzwell, C. M., *Public Health Reports*, Vol. 67, No. 1, 1952, pp. 57–64.

[4] Gaufin, A. R. and Tarzwell, C. M., *Sewage and Industrial Wastes*, Vol. 28, No. 7, 1956, pp. 906–924.

[5] Jones, J. R. E., *Journal of Animal Ecology*, Vol. 9, 1940, pp. 188–201.

[6] Jones, J. R. E., *Journal of Animal Ecology*, Vol. 27, 1958, pp. 1–14.

[7] Jones, J. R. E., *Annals of Applied Biology*, Vol. 27, 1940, pp. 368–378.

[8] Jones, J. R. E., *Journal of Animal Ecology*, Vol. 18, 1949, pp. 67–88.

[9] Pentelow, F. T. K. and Butcher, R. W., "Observations on the Condition of Rivers Churnet and Dove in 1938," Report of the Trent Fisheries District Appl. 1, 1938.

[10] Butcher, R. W., *Journal of the Institute for Sewage Purification*, Vol. 2, 1946, pp. 92–97.

[11] Butcher, R. W., *Verhandlungen Internationale Vereinigung Limnology*, Vol. 12, 1955, pp. 823–827.

[12] Cairns, J., *Journal of the Water Pollution Control Federation*, Vol. 43, No. 3, 1971, pp. 55–66.

[13] Coutant, C. C., *Proceedings*, Pennsylvania Academy of Sciences, Vol. 36, 1962, pp. 58–71.

[14] Nebeker, A. V. and Lemke, A. E., *Journal of the Kansas Entomological Society*, Vol. 41, No. 3, 1968, pp. 413–418.

[15] Gaufin, A. R. and Hern, S., *Journal of the Kansas Entomological Society*, Vol. 44, No. 2, 1971, pp. 240–245.

[16] Richardson, R. E., "Changes in the Bottom and Shore Fauna of the Middle Illinois River and Its Connecting Lakes since 1913–1915 as a Result of Increase Southward of Sewage Pollution," *Bulletin*, Illinois Natural History Survey, Vol. 14, 1921, pp. 33–75.

[17] Richardson, R. E., "The Bottom Fauna of the Middle Illinois River 1913–1925; Its Distribution, Abundance, Valuation, and Index Value in the Study of Stream Pollution," *Bulletin*, Illinois Natural History Survey, Vol. 17, 1929, pp. 387–475.

[18] Liebmann, H., *Vom Wasser*, Vol. 15, 1942, pp. 181–188.

[19] Patrick, R., *Proceedings*, Academy of Natural Sciences of Philadelphia, Vol. 101, 1949, pp. 277–341.

[20] Warren, C. E., *Biology and Water Pollution Control*, W. B. Saunders Co., 1971, pp. 322–348.

[21] Wurtz, C. B., *Sewage and Industrial Wastes*, Vol. 27, 1955, pp. 1270–1278.

[22] Beck, W. M., *Sewage and Industrial Wastes*, Vol. 27, 1955, pp. 1193–1197.

[23] Bartsch, A. F., *Sewage Works Journal*, Vol. 20, 1948, pp. 292–302.

[24] Wilhm, J. L. and Dorris, T. C., *Biological Science*, Vol. 18, No. 6, 1968, pp. 477–480.

[25] Wilhm, J. L., *Journal of the Water Pollution Control Federation*, Vol. 39, No. 10, pp. 1673–1683.

[26] Margalef, R., *Memorias de la Real Academia de Ciencias y Artes de Barcelona*, Vol. 32, 1957, pp. 373–449.

[27] Hynes, H. B. N., *The Biology of Polluted Waters*, Liverpool University Press, Liverpool, 1960.

W. A. Brungs [1]

Continuous-Flow Bioassays with Aquatic Organisms: Procedures and Applications

REFERENCE: Brungs, W. A., **"Continuous-Flow Bioassays with Aquatic Organisms: Procedures and Applications,"** *Biological Methods for the Assessment of Water Quality, ASTM STP 528,* American Society for Testing and Materials, 1973, pp. 117–126.

ABSTRACT: The current concern for protection of important water uses has greatly increased the use of aquatic bioassays. Their use in quality control of products and effluents and the development of water-quality criteria have led to a proliferation of techniques and approaches. The results of bioassays with aquatic organisms are subject to a great degree of variability depending on the quality of the dilution water, the test species, and the quality of the organisms and of the testing system. Several types of continuous-flow methodology are evaluated, and the advantages and disadvantages of each are discussed. Fail-safe devices, measured concentrations, and as much care and expertise as one would expect with measurements by various types of analytical instruments are essential to obtaining the best bioassay data.

KEY WORDS: water pollution, bioassay, water quality, continuous-flow, tests

To discuss various techniques and equipment for conducting continuous-flow bioassays in depth, it is necessary to develop a foundation of basic aquatic toxicology and the applications of bioassay results. This paper will not attempt to go into the details of operation of continuous-flow bioassays, since each procedure warrants a paper on its own merit. Instead the different procedures and their advantages and disadvantages will be discussed in general, and appropriate literature citations will be given. Thus, a starting point will be provided for the person who wishes to carry out this type of study.

[1] Assistant for Water Quality Criteria, U.S. Environmental Protection Agency, National Water Quality Laboratory, Duluth, Minn. 55804.

Conditions of Bioassay

If a bioassay with aquatic organisms is considered essentially an analytical tool to be used to answer specific questions, the use of such a test will be meaningful and the data generated will be applicable to specific problems. The principal difference between a bioassay and an analytical instrument is that the bioassay results are more easily affected by many different circumstances. Work with living organisms in itself creates a variety of problems and obstacles that must be considered and overcome. This approach to the technique of bioassay means that the quality-control measures, care, and other considerations used to obtain the most accurate and precise chemical or physical information are also generally applicable to bioassay work.

Many factors, environmental as well as experimental, can have significant effects on the results of a bioassay. Only the most important and common ones will be discussed. They are (1) the quality of the dilution water, (2) the sources of the dilution water, (3) the selection of a suitable test organism, (4) the condition of the test organisms, and (5) the degree of acclimation of the test organism to the test conditions.

Probably the most important condition causing unacceptable variability of bioassay results is the quality of the dilution water itself. This includes hardness, pH, dissolved solids, dissolved organic compounds, dissolved oxygen, temperature, and other characteristics. The toxicity of several metals can be affected as much as two orders of magnitude depending upon the pH and hardness of the dilution water. The principal cause of this variation is essentially a chemical problem in that the solubility and the chemical species of the metal are dependent upon the pH and other related factors. In essence, the total amount of metal present is not necessarily an accurate indication of its actual toxicity. It is known that various metal species do not contribute to toxicity, and the present state of knowledge concerning the toxic species of metals is in its infancy. The toxicity of various other materials can be affected by temperature. The problem is not a simple one, however, because the toxicity of some materials may be increased with increasing temperature and that of others may be decreased. Consequently, no generalization can be made about this factor. The dissolved oxygen concentration of the dilution water is important principally because an inadequate oxygen supply will create an additional stress on the test animal which can be added to the effect of the toxicant that is being tested. In such a case the results are confounded, and cause and effect cannot be accurately assigned. Organic compounds and amino acids are known to reduce the toxicity of copper, and even phosphates can complex heavy metals and reduce their toxicity. Although various materials can reduce the toxicity of metals, the degree and rate at which these compounds may themselves be reduced or removed is unknown at this time. When this occurs it may result in the return of the maximum potential toxicity of the metal. It becomes apparent that if bioassays are to be conducted over an extended period of time, a dilution water of uniform quality must be used to avoid the experimental variability caused by these conditions. Only when a biomonitoring approach is followed can the receiving stream water, with its variability, be used.

The source of the dilution water must be considered carefully. Toxic concentrations of chlorine are added to most municipal water supplies for disinfection. Chlorine is extremely toxic to aquatic life, and as a result, the use of this water in bioassays has caused many problems. Toxic concentrations of chlorine have been demonstrated that are below the usual limits of analytical measurement of chlorine. The use of surface water for bioassay dilution water is also a hazardous procedure. Since the condition of the water above the intake cannot be controlled, materials may well be present which in themselves would demonstrate toxic effects on the test species or even detoxify the material to be tested. The variability of the quality of surface waters is frequently so great that the bioassay results would certainly be affected. The use of ground water for bioassays is a common solution to these problems. However, in many places ground water has a high concentration of dissolved solids, and in some cases these will have to be partially removed. This would be true of excessively high concentrations of iron, sulfur, and other materials.

The choice of a test organism is highly important, because various species of aquatic organisms respond differently to toxic compounds. Various aquatic species demonstrate a range of sensitivity to some compounds over one to two orders of magnitude. Copper, for example, has been used as a selective piscicide, because game species, such as largemouth bass and blue-gills, are extremely resistant to copper, whereas some of the rough fish, such as goldfish and bullheads, are very sensitive. In such a use, sufficient copper is added to kill the less desirable species without affecting the desirable ones. The response of aquatic organisms to other toxicants may be essentially a constant, in which case most species would be affected at a very narrow range of toxicant concentration. One generalization that needs to be refuted at this time is that some aquatic species are resistant to pollution or toxicants. This generalization has led many people to believe that fish such as carp, suckers, etc. are very resistant animals. The opposite is true with regard to some toxic materials. A certain species may be very resistant to some toxicants, but it may also be very sensitive to others. As a consequence it is inappropriate and, in fact, erroneous to accept the generalization that some species are resistant to pollution, because they are, in fact, only resistant to certain conditions but not to all. Other factors, such as the age of the test animal or its sex, may also affect toxicity to some extent. The species and age of the test animal must therefore be standardized when a long series of bioassays is conducted.

As indicated earlier, quality control is as important in bioassays as in any other analytical method. Consequently, the condition of the test organisms must be maintained at an optimum just as one would maintain the various analytical instruments. Hunn et al[1] [2] have discussed guidelines for handling and maintaining fish for bioassay. Test animals must not be diseased or parasitized, they must be well fed, and they must be acclimated to both the test temperature and the quality of the experimental water to be used for dilution. Three excellent review papers by Sprague[2–4] discuss acclimation in detail and several of the problems previously mentioned in this paper.

Uses of Bioassay

It has been stated that the uses of bioassays are limited only by one's imagination. Admittedly, some are more important than others, but the principal uses of bioassays may have different interpretations by different people. For instance, at the National Water Quality Laboratory bioassays are primarily oriented toward developing water-quality criteria which can then be used to develop water-quality standards. The principal application of bioassays conducted by the Food and Drug Administration might be the determination of the possible effects of a new product on aquatic life in receiving waters. An agricultural chemicals company might use bioassays to determine the relative toxicity of the target organism and more desirable organisms in the aquatic environment. An industrial discharger might be principally concerned with bioassays as a monitoring tool to determine possible treatment, failures, or changes in effluent quality. The biochemist or physiologist might be interested in the modes of actions of toxic compounds and their physiological effects on various characteristics of blood, tissues, etc. Bioassays are essential in determining such changes. Bioassays may be used as an enforcement tool by regulatory agencies in their monitoring efforts to detect possible violations in water-quality standards. An industrial plant with a variety of processes and processed wastes may attempt to determine the necessary treatment required by conducting bioassays on the principal components of their wastes to determine which are in most need of treatment. Each of these purposes requires different emphasis in the bioassay and probably some modifications in the basic technique.

---

[2] The italic numbers in brackets refer to the list of references appended in this paper.

With the increase in environmental concern over the past several years, many independent companies have been formed that conduct contract bioassays for industrial and other purposes. These companies conduct the necessary bioassay work with their own equipment, experience, and necessary facilities. Such studies frequently are of short duration and determine acute lethality, but there is an increasing interest in determining chronic or long-term effects of toxicants on aquatic life. In the future, industries probably will need to assume greater responsibility for conducting their own bioassays or have the work conducted for them by someone else. The variety and complexity of many industrial effluents are such that it is unrealistic to expect various governmental agencies to provide all the toxicity information necessary to evaluate and determine the degree of treatment required or the permissible levels of discharge, or both. Instead the discharger will be responsible for evaluating the toxicity of his waste and will then work with the State or Federal government to determine the limits of discharge of these wastes. As this situation becomes more common, a variety of industries will be conducting many more bioassays under a great variety of conditions, and it is principally for these industries that this paper is presented.

Techniques of Continuous-Flow Bioassays

We shall begin this discussion with a brief summary of the potential use of static bioassays, because there is still a place and a need for such tests. Static bioassays provide generally exploratory information in terms of relative toxicities of various compounds or treatment processes. If a material is discharged periodically as slugs into the environment, it will be most appropriate in many cases to test the potential effects by use of static bioassay conditions. If, instead, the wastes are being discharged continuously or nearly so, continuous-flow bioassays will have to be conducted to simulate the conditions of these types of discharges. The results of static and continuous-flow bioassays frequently are similar, but many factors can cause different results. If the tested material is degradable, volatile, high in oxygen demand, or detoxified rapidly by one means or another, the static bioassay results will indicate a condition which is different from that which actually prevails.

The continuous-flow technique results in more constant test conditions, such as the toxicant concentration, dissolved oxygen, and other water-quality characteristics. It also permits testing for periods extensive enough to encompass the life cycle of the test organism. This latter situation is becoming more common as attempts are made to determine the life-cycle requirements or limitations to toxic conditions. Continuous-flow testing also permits feeding the test animal and therefore avoids the added stress of starvation during bioassays. Probably of greatest importance is the more constant toxicant concentration that results from the use of proper continuous-flow procedures. The data provided are more useful because the situation is typical of the usual discharge of effluents.

No attempt will be made to discuss the various specific techniques for continuous-flow bioassay. Each of these methods is reported in detail in the literature, to which the reader is referred in the following discussion.

In essence there are two general techniques for continuous-flow bioassays: (1) adjustment of two flow rates and (2) diluters. Probably the older method, but not necessarily the most commonly used, is the balancing of two flows of liquid, one the dilution water and the other the toxic material to be tested. This is most frequently accomplished by metering pumps and also by calibrated flow rates from constant head chambers. Several such procedures have been described by Jackson and Brungs[5], Burke and Ferguson[6], and Zillich[7]. In most cases, these procedures have not taken into account what is commonly referred to as a fail-safe device that would eliminate the flow of the toxic material whenever the flow of the dilution water is accidentally terminated. The necessity for such a fail-safe system is obvious when one considers the potential consequences of the toxic materials continuing to enter a test chamber with no dilution water to maintain the intended toxic concentrations.

The other type of test procedure is referred to as diluters. Several have been described by Mount and Warner[8], Mount and Brungs[9], and Esvelt and Conners[10]. Essentially, these techniques use a series of dilution systems that automatically dilute toxic materials to several concentrations, usually five or six. One of the principal advantages of these procedures is that there is no need to monitor flow rates constantly or to use metering pumps. In addition, if the dilution-water flow ceases, the toxicant is automatically also stopped. Diluters have become the most commonly used continuous-flow technique in the United States; they are used widely by various State and Federal agencies as well as by companies that perform contract bioassay studies.

A more general group of procedures used for continuous-flow testing includes those described by Alabaster and Abram[11], Alderdice[12], Betts et al[13], Stark[14], Solon et al[15], and others. Any one of these procedures may solve a particular problem, and the reader is referred to them so that he can build the continuous-flow system most applicable to his need.

Several other toxicant-delivery systems have been described that can be used separately or in conjunction with the diluter. Chadwick and Kiigemagi[16] have described an interesting system which has worked well with dieldrin. Other systems have been described by Mount and Brungs[9] and Engstrom-Heg[17]. McAllister et al[18] have recently described a system which appears to be more satisfactory than many previously used. This device has no moving parts and is adjustable to a wide range of toxicant-volume transfers. Whatever system is chosen, a fail-safe device is essential that will terminate the flow of toxicant when and if the flow of dilution water stops.

All these techniques with minor modifications are applicable for bioassays with many aquatic organisms, except possibly the microscopic organisms such as copepods and the smaller cladocerans. Some aquatic organisms such as riffle-inhabiting species may require a flow of water. This can best be accomplished by working with an oval tank with a closed center area, and either a recirculating pump or a paddle-wheel system to maintain a movement of water around this chamber. The use or organisms other than fish for bioassays has been discussed in earlier papers at this meeting. The space required for conducting bioassays and the test chambers themselves are generally dictated by the test species used. Obviously, the larger the organism, the larger the chamber, and, as indicated earlier, certain species will require special test chambers.

The greatest emphasis of bioassays in the past has been on the determination of time of death. This is a fairly crude endpoint for a bioassay, because only a lethal concentration can be determined. Such an endpoint has no direct relationship whatever to concentrations that are safe over extended periods, or to concentrations that cause effects after a short time. Direct lethal effects have been observed for some toxic materials after exposure for as long as several months. In the author's experience, it is becoming more and more necessary that the standard test for lethal concentrations be extended from 96 h to two weeks. This insures more accurate measure of lethality in that usually after 14 days no further significant direct lethality occurs. Warner[19] has discussed a wide variety of responses that could be studied other than death. Examples include changes in behavior or physiology, biochemical or ecological changes, embryological and growth changes, or changes in histology. Each of these has its own specific purpose, and several of them may be necessary at times. This would be especially true in some type of in-plant monitoring system. Once death has occurred, it is usually too late to accomplish much in remedial action.

It is essential that some thought be given to the materials of which continuous-flow systems are constructed. The diluters or other systems are generally made of glass or plastic. The latter may have a tendency to sorb significant quantities of certain organic materials during one test and lose these materials back to the test system when a different toxic material is used. Test chambers can be made in a variety of ways with glass, stainless steel, fiberglass, and at times resin-coated plywood. Most commonly glass is used for small chambers to hold small test animals, and stainless steel is used for large chambers. Stainless steel is desirable in many locations, such as industrial plants, where breakage may be a problem. The lines carrying the test material from the diluter to the test tanks must be made of glass with plastic connections that expose as little plastic to the water as possible. Problems have been observed frequently during the conduct of bioassays, because the dilution water is passing through copper or certain other metallic pipes. It is not uncommon that enough copper is introduced into the dilution water to give it a toxic reaction.

Several methods are used for calculating the final bioassay data in terms of TL50 values. The graphical interpolation procedure is generally acceptable, but more intensive calculations as described by the American Public Health Association[20] will provide confidence limits and more complete data. This reference also provides a good general discussion of static and continuous-flow procedures.

Several other factors contribute greatly to the quality of the final bioassay data. It is advisable to measure the concentrations of the toxicant in the water. For unknown or very complex wastes this is, of course, impractical, but whenever possible it is recommended. If measurements cannot be made, frequent checks of the delivery volumes or flow rates of the effluent or toxicant should be made to insure accurate operation of the continuous-flow system. Because of the potential variability of bioassay results, as discussed earlier, the frequency of conducting continuous-flow bioassays of industrial or municipal effluents will be determined by the degree of variability of this waste. The more frequently the quality of the waste changes, the more frequently will be the necessity of conducting bioassays. This leads to the recommendation that batches of waste discharges not be combined before bioassay, because this practice tends to result in a mean toxicity rather than a range from low to high toxicity. Certain data indicate that chronic toxicity may be a reflection of the maximum observed toxicity in acute tests over an extended period of time. If this observation is accurate, frequent bioassays are definitely necessary when the quality of the waste is variable.

In addition to quality bioassay data, it is just as important to have quality interpretation of the data when applied to the goal of determining discharge concentrations. Essentially, all the ideal qualities of bioassays, such as uniform conditions, absence of chlorine and copper, and disease-free organisms, result in an unnatural set of conditions which must be considered when applying the bioassay results. Natural stresses of fluctuating temperature, disease, predation and competition for food and space may be additive to the toxicant stress. In addition, it should be repeated that data from acute, or short-term, bioassays to determine lethality cannot be directly used to estimate long-term safe concentrations. Application factors applied to these data may estimate a safe level, but experimentally derived application factors have varied from 1/7 to 1/300, and no single generalization can be made.

Summary

The results of bioassays with aquatic organisms are subject to a great degree of variability depending on the quality of the dilution water, the test species, and the quality of the organisms and of the testing system itself. All these must be understood and accounted for before bioassays are conducted to insure that the most accurate and useful data are obtained.

Several general types of techniques are used in continuous-flow testing. The particular problem under investigation will determine to some extent the precise techniques to be used. Fail-safe devices, measured concentrations, and as much care and expertise as one would expect with measurements by various types of analytical instruments are essential to obtaining the best bioassay data.

Sprague[2–4] has contributed a very worthwhile series of publications that are of great use to investigators new to the field of aquatic toxicology. In addition, there are several general literature reviews of toxic effects by McKee and Wolfe[21], the Federal Water Pollution Control Administration[22], and the U. S. Environmental Protection Agency[23].

References

[1] Hunn, J. B., Schoettger, R. A., and Whealdon, E. W., *Progressive Fish Culturist,* Vol. 30, 1968, pp. 164–167.

[2] Sprague, J. B., *Water Research,* Vol. 3, 1969, pp. 793–821.

[3] Sprague, J. B., *Water Research,* Vol. 4, 1970, pp. 3–32.

[4] Sprague, J. B., *Water Research,* Vol. 5, 1971, pp. 245–266.

[5] Jackson, H. W. and Brungs, W. A., *Proceedings,* 21st Purdue Industrial Waste Conference, Part I, Vol. 50, 1967, pp. 117–124.

[6] Burke, W. D. and Ferguson, D. E., *Transactions,* American Fisheries Society, Vol. 97, 1968, pp. 498–501.

[7] Zillich, J. A., *Journal Water Pollution Control Federation,* Vol. 44, 1972, pp. 212–220.

[8] Mount, D. I. and Warner, R. E., "A Serial-Dilution Apparatus of Continuous Delivery of Various Concentrations of Materials in Water," U. S. Public Health Service Publ. No. 999–WP–23, 1965.

[9] Mount, D. I. and Brungs, W. A., *Water Research,* Vol. 1, 1967, pp. 21–29.

[10] Esvelt, L. A. and Conners, J. D., "Continuous-Flow Fish Bioassay Apparatus for Municipal and Industrial Effluents," Sanitary Engineering Research Laboratory, University of California, Berkeley, SERL Report No. 71-3, 1971.

[11] Alabaster, J. S. and Abram, F. S. H., *Advances in Water Pollution Research Procedures,* 2nd International Conference, Tokyo 1964. Pergamon Press, Oxford, Vol. 1, 1965, pp. 41–54.

[*12*] Alderdice, D. F., "Detection and Measurement of Water Pollution—Biological Assays," Canada Dept. Fisheries: Canadian Fisheries Report No. 9, 1967, pp. 33–39.
[*13*] Betts, J. L., Beak, T. W., and Wilson, G. G., *Journal Water Pollution Control Federation,* Vol. 39, 1967, pp. 89–96.
[*14*] Stark, G. T. C., *Laboratory Practice,* Vol. 16, 1967, pp. 594–595.
[*15*] Solon, J. M., Lincer, J. L., and Nair, J. H., *Transactions,* American Fisheries Society, Vol. 97, 1968, pp. 501–502.
[*16*] Chadwick, G. G. and Kiigemagi, V., *Journal Water Pollution Control Federation,* Vol. 40, 1968, pp. 76–82.
[*17*] Engstrom-Heg, R., *Progressive Fish-Culturist,* Vol. 33, 1971, pp. 227–231.
[*18*] McAllister, W. A., Jr., Mauck, W. L., and Mayer, F. L., Jr., *Transactions,* American Fisheries Society, Vol. 101, 1972, pp. 555–557.
[*19*] Warner, R. E., *Bulletin,* World Health Organization, Vol. 36, 1967, pp. 181–207.
[*20*] "Standard Methods for the Examination of Water and Waste Water," 13th ed, American Public Health Association, New York, 1971.
[*21*] McKee, J. E. and Wolfe, H. W., "Water Quality Criteria," 2nd ed, California State Water Quality Control Board, Sacramento, Publication 3A, 1963.
[*22*] Report of the National Technical Advisory Committee on Water Quality Criteria to the Secretary of the Interior, Federal Water Pollution Control Administration, Washington, D. C., 1968.
[*23*] *Water Quality Criteria Data Book,* Vol. 3, "Effects of Chemicals on Aquatic Life, 1971," U. S. Environmental Protection Agency, Project 18050 GWV.

John Cairns, Jr.,[1] *R. E. Sparks,*[1] *and W. T. Waller*[1]

A Tentative Proposal for a Rapid In-Plant Biological Monitoring System

REFERENCE: Cairns, John, Jr., Sparks, R. E., and Waller, W. T., "A Tentative Proposal for a Rapid In-Plant Biological Monitoring System," *Biological Methods for the Assessment of Water Quality, ASTM STP 528,* American Society for Testing and Materials, 1973, pp. 127–147.

ABSTRACT: Preliminary tests of a rapid biological monitoring system which measures changes in the movement and breathing of fish in order to provide an early warning of developing toxicity in the wastes of an industrial plant are reported. The system is designed to provide a continuous assessment of the toxicity of complex mixtures which vary through time, and it has been tested in the laboratory with simulated spills of copper and zinc. Fish detect potentially lethal zinc concentrations (8 mg/liter) rapidly enough so that they survive if zinc is removed at the time of detection, and they also detect sublethal concentrations (2 to 3 mg/liter).

KEY WORDS: indicator species, industrial waste treatment, toxicity, fishes water pollution, heavy metals, bioassay

From 1945 through 1960 there were few laboratories in the United States carrying out bioassays to determine the effects of industrial wastes on aquatic organisms. In the late 60s and early 70s the number of bioassay laboratories increased markedly. Nevertheless, the number of waste dischargers who have performed a bioassay on their waste is probably still very low. Of the few bioassays that have been done, most probably used a single grab sample or a short-term composite sample of the waste mixed with dilution water to provide a series of concentrations. Most of the test

[1] Director and professor, research associate, and research associate, respectively, Biology Department and Center for Environmental Studies, Virginia Polytechnic Institute and State University, Blacksburg, Va. 24061. Dr. Sparks is presently at the Illinois Natural History Survey, Havana, Ill. 62644, and Dr. Waller is at New York University, Tuxedo, New York 10987.

concentrations probably were prepared at the beginning of the bioassay and not renewed during the test. A few test concentrations may have been renewed every 24 h, and fewer still may have been continuously renewed.

It is highly probable that the number of waste dischargers who perform bioassays will increase substantially in the near future, and it is also likely that the procedures and standards for bioassays will become more stringent. The costs and logistics of increasing the number of bioassays may become formidable. For example, there are an estimated 4000 dischargers in the Ohio River Basin.[2] If each discharger were to have a single sample of waste tested each year on one species of fish, approximately 720 000 liters of dilution water would have to be collected and transported in the Ohio Basin.[3] More water would be required if the fish were acclimated to the dilution water prior to the test and if the test solutions were renewed.

Industries which may substantially affect the quality of the receiving river because of the high volume or high toxicity of their discharge will find it in their enlightened self-interest to continually assess the biological effects of their waste, particularly if the characteristics of the waste vary over time. A continuous biological monitoring system may be cheaper in the long run than repeated static bioassays, because the discharger can use the full receiving capacity of the aquatic system without degrading it. With a continuous monitoring system, the industry could take immediate corrective action if the toxicity of the waste increased. Apparatus and methods for such a continuous monitoring system, using the breathing and movement responses of fish, are described.

This is a research paper, not a "how-to" paper of a "tried and true" standard method! The method has not, in fact, been tested enough to be considered standard since (a) only one toxicant (zinc) has been tested in any depth, (b) there have been relatively few trials over a relatively brief period, and (c) only one species of fish has been used extensively. With other toxicants the method might not work as well or might work even better, but this remains to be determined.

Procedure

Monitoring Apparatus

One fish was placed into each of six test chambers (Fig. 1). The chambers were 20.8-liter (5.5-gal) aquaria with Plexiglas covers, and the fish were free-swimming (in earlier experiments the fish were wired).

---

[2] Personal communication with William Klein, Ohio River Sanitation Commission.
[3] This estimate assumes that each test would consist of an 18-liter control tank containing dilution water alone and nine 18-liter tanks containing waste mixed to various concentrations with dilution water.

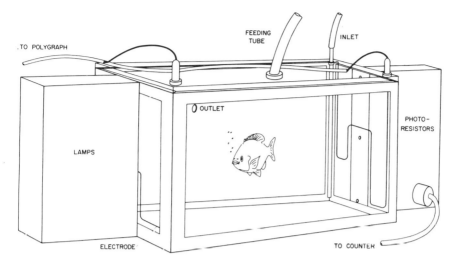

FIG. 1—*Test chamber for monitoring fish activity and breathing.*

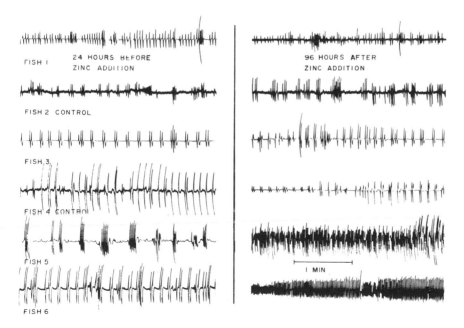

FIG. 2—*Breathing signals recorded before and after Fish 1, 3, 5, and 6 were exposed to 3 mg/liter zinc (a sublethal concentration). Fish 2 and 4 were controls and were not exposed to 3 mg/liter zinc. All six fish had been exposed to .075 mg/liter zinc for eight months.*

The sides of the aquaria were painted black to keep the fish from seeing, and being influenced by each other. Breathing signals were picked up by stainless steel electrodes located at the ends of the aquaria (Fig. 1) and were recorded by a polygraph and tape recorder. The type of results obtained is shown by polygraph records obtained before and after four fish were exposed to 3 mg/liter zinc (a sublethal concentration) in Fig. 2. The breathing rates of Fish 5 and 6 increased noticeably after zinc addition. Fish 2 and 4 were controls and were not exposed to 3 mg/liter zinc.

Light beams traversed each tank at the top, middle, and bottom, and were detected by photoresistors. When a fish swam in front of a light beam, a counter for that beam advanced one unit. An automatic camera took pictures of the counter dials every hour or every half hour (Fig. 3). Therefore, the fish activity data consisted of cumulative light beam interruptions for each fish at three levels in the aquarium during intervals of one hour or one half hour, recorded on 35 mm film. The light beams were approximately the thickness of a pencil "lead," and the wavelength was approximately 650 millimicrons, which the fish perceived dimly, if at all.

The six test chambers rested in a box of sand in a sound-proof 8 by 8

FIG. 3—*Fish activity counter, with timer-controlled camera in foreground.*

FIG. 4—*Test chambers in vibration—damping sandbox.*

by 8 ft isolation room to minimize the transmission of noise and floor vibrations that might have disturbed the fish (Figs. 4 and 5). The fluorescent room lights approximated the spectrum of natural light, and a dimmer simulated dawn and dusk. Metering pumps or gravity-fed diluters of the type described by Mount and Brungs[1] [4] and Brungs and Mount[2] mounted outside the isolation room continuously delivered test solutions or dechlorinated tapwater alone to the test chambers, and water samples were collected outside the room from the overflow drains of each tank (Fig. 5).

This monitoring system required a highly-trained person to analyze the data from the polygraph, and the minimum lag between toxicant addition and detection ranged from 1 to 9 h because a human operator cannot continuously analyze data at a faster rate. In the near future, we hope to add an analog-to-digital converter, a minicomputer, and a teleprinter to automate and speed the analysis of data, as shown in Fig. 6. This should substantially reduce the operator training necessary to successfully use the apparatus. Breathing signals from some current experiments have been recorded on tape and analyzed on an analog computer.

[4] The italic numbers in brackets refer to the list of references appended to this paper.

FIG. 5—*The room for acclimating the fish is shown on the left, and the room where the breathing and movement of the fish are monitored is on the right. Gravity-fed diluters are mounted on the front of each room, and the polygraph and tape recorder for recording fish breathing are in the foreground. Samples of water for chemical analysis are obtained from drains outside the experimental room (small arrow), and temperatures in the test chambers are continuously recorded (large arrow).*

Baseline Data

Because of variation in activity and breathing rates from fish to fish, it was necessary to obtain baseline patterns for each fish at the beginning of the experiments. Later patterns were compared to baseline patterns to determine whether a fish showed a significant response to some material in the water. At an industrial site, it would be desirable to expose fish to water known to be free of toxicants to establish the baseline before the fish were exposed to the industrial effluent. However, if toxicant-free water is not available, it is highly probable that an adequate baseline can still be established because, as shown in Fig. 2, bluegills retain their ability to respond to sublethal zinc concentrations after chronic exposure to a very low concentration. If the fish do become desensitized after chronic exposure to a waste, due to impairment of sensory organs or development of resistance, they will have to be replaced regularly.

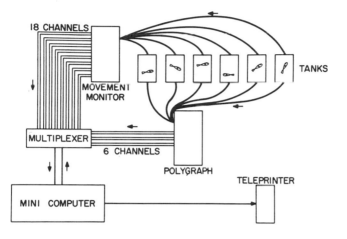

FIG. 6—*A computerized system for monitoring fish movement and breathing.*

The baseline for a fish is normally different during different periods of the day. The cumulative light beam interruptions and the breathing rate of the test species, the bluegill, are generally greater during the light period than the dark period and peak at dawn and dusk. Therefore, each day was divided into four periods, and the baseline determined during each period. The periods used for analysis of breathing rates were: Dawn (6 a.m. to 8 a.m.), Light (9 a.m. to 5 p.m.), Dusk (6 p.m. to 8 p.m.), and Dark (9 p.m. to 5 a.m.). The periods used for analysis of fish activity were: First Half-Day (7:30 a.m. to 1 p.m.), Second Half-Day (2 p.m. to 7:30 p.m.), First Half-Night (8 p.m. to 1 a.m.), and Second Half Night (2 a.m. to 7 a.m.).

Definition of "Response"

An increase in breathing rate during a particular period of the day was considered to be a response, if the rate exceeded the maximum rate recorded during the corresponding period of the first day. This definition of "response" was based on the observation that although no toxicant was in the water on the first day, the breathing rates of the fish were high because the fish were still recovering from being netted and transferred to the unfamiliar environment of the test chamber. If no toxicants were introduced to the water on succeeding days, the fish settled down and the breathing rates rarely exceeded the rates recorded on the first day. Any increase in a fish's breathing rate, that exceeded the maximum recorded during a corresponding period of the first day, was regarded as a response to a stimulus greater than the stimulus of being netted and transferred to the test chamber.

For example, in one experiment, the maximum breathing rates for Fish 1 were 44, 44, 57, and 27 during the Dawn, Light, Dusk, and Dark periods, respectively. The maximum rates are shown as heavy lines in Fig. 7. The breathing rates of Fish 1 on Day 2, when no toxicant was in the water, did not cross the heavy line, so no response was recorded. On Day 7, zinc sulfate ($ZnSO_4 \cdot 7H_2O$) was added to the water starting at 10 a.m., and the concentration in the test chamber gradually increased over a period of 9 h to 4.16 mg/liter as zinc. On Day 7 the breathing rate of Fish 1 crossed the heavy line at 2 p.m. and remained above the heavy line during the dark period. Therefore, Fish 1 responded at 10 a.m. and at every hour during the dark period.

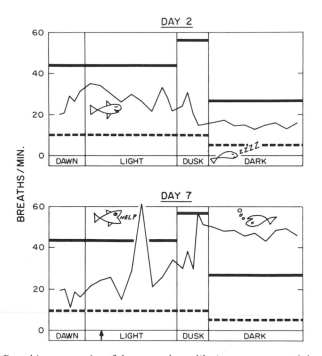

FIG. 7—*Breathing rate of a fish exposed to dilution water containing no added zinc on Day 2 and to dilution water containing 4.16 mg/liter zinc starting at 10 a.m. (arrow) on Day 7. The solid upper line is the maximum breathing rate recorded for the fish during each period of Day 1. The dashed lower line represents a minimum breathing rate (see text).*

The dashed line in Fig. 7 indicates that a lower danger limit could also be set for the breathing rate, so that a poison with anesthetic properties could be detected. The lower limit might be established by briefly exposing the fish to a concentration of an anesthetic, such as tricaine methane sulfonate (MS-222), that was a fraction of the lethal concentration.

A different definition of response was used for the movement data. In order to obtain a baseline pattern in activity, it was necessary to allow the fish to acclimate to the test chamber for at least three days and to record baseline activity for at least three additional days before the fish were exposed to a toxicant or an effluent. Therefore, on Day 1 of the experiment, the fish had actually been in the test chambers for at least three days. The variance (s^2) in number of light beam interruptions was computed for each fish for each period of the day. The variance for the data recorded during each period of Day 1 was then compared to the variance for the corresponding period of Day 2, the largest variance being divided by the smaller, to produce a value called the sample F-value (F_s). If F_s was larger than the critical F (with degrees of freedom = sample size -1, and $\alpha = 0.002$) obtained from a statistical table, then the two sample variances were significantly different, and the fish was considered to have shown a response on Day 2. For example, when comparing s^2 for the First Half-Day, Day 1 to s^2 for the First Half-Day, Day 2, the critical F, with the appropriate degrees of freedom in brackets, was:

$$F_{0.002\ [6,6]} = 20.0$$

F_s for Fish 3 was computed as follows:

$$s^2, \text{first half-day, Day 1} = 1467$$

$$s^2, \text{first half-day, Day 2} = \ \ 440$$

$$F_s = \frac{1467}{440} = 3.3$$

Since 3.3 is less than the critical F, the variances were not significantly different, and Fish 3 did not show a response on Day 2.

Each period of Day 2 was compared in turn with the same period of Day 1. If there were no significant differences in variance, Day 3 would be compared to Day 2, Day 4 compared to Day 3, Day 5 to Day 4, and so on.

If the variances had been significantly different, the variance for the last recorded day would be dropped and the preceding day would be compared to the next day. In the above example, if F_s were greater than

F, then s^2 for the First Half-Day, Day 2, would be considered abnormal and dropped, and Day 3 would be compared to Day 1.

Since the statistical test measured the difference between two variances but not the direction of difference, a marked decrease or marked increase in variance from one day to the next would register as a response. Therefore, it is likely that the activity monitoring system would detect toxicants with anesthetic properties.

Figure 8 shows the F_s values for a fish with the critical F shown as a broad dashed line. The bottom of the dashed line represents the critical F for variances computed from seven cumulative light beam interruptions (First Half-Day, Second Half-Day), and the top of the dashed line represents the critical F for variances computed from six cumulative light beam interruptions (First Half-Night, Second Half-Night). When no toxicant was present in the water (Days 2 through 6) F_s did not go above the critical value. On Day 7, zinc was added to the water from 1 p.m. until 7:30 p.m., reaching a maximum concentration of 11.39 mg/liter at 7:30 p.m. F_s did go above the critical value at the end of Day 7, but returned to a normal value at the beginning of Day 8 when the zinc concentration had dropped to less than 0.30 mg/liter. F_s remained below the critical value until zinc was again added to the water, starting at 1 p.m. on Day 13 and continuing until 1 a.m. on Day 14. The zinc concentration reached a maximum of 7.49 mg/liter at 9 p.m. on Day 13, and remained near that value until addition of zinc was stopped at 1 a.m. on Day 14. The fish showed responses during the Second Half-Day and First Half-Night on Day 14. At 10 a.m. on Day 15 the zinc concentration was down to 0.62 mg/liter. The fish showed a response on Day 16 and F_s values close to, but not exceeding, the critical values on Day 17 and Day 19.

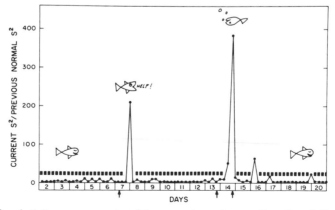

FIG. 8—*Activity response of a fish exposed to zinc on Day 7 and Days 13 and 14. The heavy dashed line represents the critical value.*

In summary, a response in fish breathing was defined as a breathing rate greater than the maximum rate recorded on the first day, and a response in fish activity was defined as a significant difference in the variance of light beam interruptions.

Definition of "Detection"

Since no more than one fish ever showed an activity response when there was no toxicant in the water, "stress detection" was defined as the occurrence of two or more responses in activity during the same time period.

Various criteria were used for stress detection by fish breathing in order to determine empirically how many false detections would be obtained with each criterion and what the lag time would be. A false detection was defined as a detection that occurred when no toxicant was in the water. The lag time was the time between the addition of toxicant and the first detection. The effect of defining detection as an increase in the breathing rate of one, two, and three fish during the same time interval was determined.

Method for Simulating Normal Plant Operation and Spills

Once a baseline activity and breathing record was obtained for each fish, they were exposed to water containing no toxicants for several days in order to simulate normal operation of an industrial or waste treatment plant.

A spill of toxic material was simulated by switching the flow to some of the test chambers from dilution water alone to dilution water containing a measured concentration of zinc (added as $ZnSO_4 \cdot 7H_2O$). Although the monitoring system was designed for use with complex mixtures, it seemed best initially to use a single toxicant that was easily dosed and measured, for the purpose of developing the monitoring technique. Because of the retention time of the test chambers, it took 9 h for the zinc concentration in the effluent from the chambers to reach the concentration in the in-coming water. In every experiment, some of the fish were never exposed to zinc, to determine that the experimental fish were responding to the zinc and not to some extraneous disturbance such as a loud noise.

Method for Relating In-Plant Biological Monitoring to Water Quality Standards for Chronic Exposure

The relationship between the lower detection limits of the monitoring system and the maximum permissible concentrations for chronic exposure of fish in the stream can be determined by growth and reproduction studies. The lowest zinc concentration used in the monitoring experiments was

2.55 mg/liter. The effects on reproduction and growth of bluegills, of zinc concentrations that were approximately 1/10, 1/34, and 1/75 of 2.55 mg/liter were determined.

Results

Simulation of Normal Plant Operation

The absence of a breathing response by an individual fish to water containing no toxicants has already been shown in Fig. 7, Day 2, and the absence of a significant activity response by an individual fish during simulated normal conditions has been shown in Fig. 8, Days 2 through 6.

Table 1 summarizes activity results obtained from six fish during a six-day initial period simulating normal plant operation. "Ex" refers to four experimental fish that were later exposed to a toxicant, and "Con" refers to two control fish that were never exposed to a toxicant. The total number of experimental or control fish showing activity responses during each time period is shown. No more than one fish ever showed a response during simulated normal operation; therefore, no detections were recorded.

TABLE 1—*Illustration of recovery following short-term exposure.*[a]

		Period						Period			
Day		1	2	3	4	Day		1	2	3	4
2	Ex	0	1	0	0	11	Ex	0	0	0	0
	Con	0	0	0	0		Con	0	0	0	0
3	Ex	0	0	0	0	12	Ex	1	0	0	0
	Con	0	0	0	0		Con	0	1	0	0
4	Ex	0	0	0	0	13	Ex	1	1 ↓	0	0
	Con	0	0	0	0		Con	0	0	0	0
5	Ex	1	0	0	1	14	Ex	0	1	2	2
	Con	0	0	0	0		Con	0	0	0	0
6	Ex	0	0	0	0	15	Ex	3	1	0	1
	Con	0	0	0	0		Con	0	0	0	0
7	Ex	1 ↓	0	0	1	16	Ex	1	1	0	1
	Con	0	0	0	0		Con	0	0	0	0
8	Ex	1	1	0	1	17	Ex	1	1	0	1
	Con	0	0	0	0		Con	0	0	0	0
9	Ex	0	0	0	0	18	Ex	0	0	0	1
	Con	0	0	0	0		Con	0	0	0	0
10	Ex	0	0	0	0	19	Ex	0	0	0	0
	Con	0	0	0	0		Con	0	0	0	0
						20	Ex	0	0	0	0
							Con	0	0	0	0

[a] See Fig. 8 for graphic illustration.
↓ Zinc introduced as a continuous flow. Zinc exposure period underlined.
NOTE—There were four experimental fish (Ex) and two control fish (Con).

TABLE 2—*Number of fish showing increased breathing rates, before and after exposure to 4.16 mg/liter zinc.*

Day								Time																	
		6 am	7	8	9	10	11	12	1 pm	2	3	4	5	6	7	8	9	10	11	12	1 am	2	3	4	5
2	Ex	0	0	0	0	0	0	0	0	0	0	0	0	0	0	0	0	0	0	0	0	0	1	0	0
	Con	0	0	0	0	0	0	0	0	0	0	0	0	0	0	0	0	0	0	0	0	0	0	0	0
3	Ex	0	0	0	0	0	0	0	0	0	0	0	0	1	0	0	0	0	0	0	0	0	1	0	0
	Con	0	0	0	0	0	0	0	0	0	0	0	0	0	0	0	0	0	0	0	0	0	0	0	0
4	Ex	0	0	0	0	0	0	0	0	0	0	0	0	0	0	0	0	recorder off					:	:	:
	Con	0	0	0	0	0	0	0	0	0	1	0	0	0	0	0	1	0	0	0	2	0	1	0	0
5	Ex	:	:	:	0	0	0	0	0	0	1	0	0	1	0	1	1	1	0	0	0	1	1	1	0
	Con	recorder off			0	0	0	0	0	0	0	0	0	1	0	0	0	1	1	0	1	0	0	0	2
6	Ex	recorder off			0	0	0	0	0	0	0	0	0	0	0	0	recorder off				1	1	0	1	2
	Con	0	0	0	0	0	0	0	0	1	0	0	0	0	0	0	3	3	4	3	3	3	3	2	2
7	Ex	0	0	0	1→	0	0	0	0	1	1	0	0	0	1	0	4	3	4	3	4	3	4	3	1
	Con	2	0	0	1	2	0	0	0	1	1	1	1	1	1	0	4	4	3	3	4	3	3	3	0
8	Ex	0	0	0	1	2	1	3	1	1	2	1	0	1	2	2	2	3	3	3	3	3	2	2	2
	Con	0	2	0	0	0	0	0	0	0	0	0	0	0	0	0	0	2	2	2	3	3	0	0	2
9	Ex	0	0	0	0	0	0	0	1	0	0	0	0	0	0	0	0	0	0	0	0	0	0	0	0
10	Con	0	0	0	0	0	0	0	0	0	0	0	0	0	0	0	0	0	0	0	0	0	0	0	0
11	Ex	0	0	0	0	0	0	0	0	0	0	0	0	0	0	0	0	0	0	0	0	0	0	0	0
	Con	0	0	0	end of experiment																				

→ Measured zinc concentration of 4.16 mg/liter introduced as a continuous flow. Responses obtained during zinc exposure are underlined.

Note—There were four experimental fish (Ex) and one control fish (Con.)

Table 2 shows the number of breathing rate responses obtained each hour from four experimental fish and one control fish during six days of simulated normal plant operation. The recorder was off from 10 p.m., Day 4, to 9 a.m., Day 5. There were 16 occasions when a single fish showed a response and three occasions when two fish responded at the same time. At no time during simulated normal plant operation did three fish respond at a time. These results indicate that there would be many false detections if detection were defined as a single response; few false detections if two simultaneous responses counted as a detection; and probably no, or very few false detections if detection were defined as three simultaneous responses.

Simulation of a Spill

On Day 7 of the experiment shown in Table 1, zinc was introduced to five test chambers from 1 p.m. until 7:30 p.m. The concentration of zinc in the effluent from the five chambers ranged from 11.39 to 13.32 mg/liter at 7:30 p.m. By 8:30 a.m. on Day 8 the zinc concentrations were less than 0.3. This short-term exposure did not cause a detection (two or more simultaneous responses) during the period of zinc addition nor in the following periods. Zinc was introduced a second time to the same five test chambers at 1 p.m. on Day 13. Between 8 and 9 p.m. on Day 13 the zinc concentration reached a maximum of approximately 7.5 mg/liter, and remained at that concentration until detection occurred during the First Half-Night of Day 14. When the detection occurred, the flow was returned to dilution water containing no zinc. At 10 a.m. on Day 15 the zinc concentrations ranged from 0.09 to 0.70. Detections (two or more responses) continued to be registered for two consecutive time intervals following the initial detection, but after that no detection was registered and the number of responses per time period returned to pre-stress levels within 48 h. To determine how the variances of light beam interruptions recorded for Day 1 compared to those after the two stress periods, a comparison was made between Day 1 and Day 20. There were no significant differences in variances between the two days, indicating a complete recovery. The significance of these results is that the warning of toxic conditions occurred soon enough so that the exposed fish recovered when the toxicity was removed. Almost certainly, a fish kill could be prevented in a stream receiving a waste of this type, if provision were made to shunt the waste into holding ponds or recycle it for further treatment as soon as stress detection occurred. It might be desirable to introduce a safety factor by metering proportionally more waste to the test fish in the monitoring system than is delivered to the receiving stream.

Table 2 gives the breathing responses of four fish exposed to 4.16 mg/liter zinc and one control fish exposed to dilution water alone. After the zinc was introduced, all four of the exposed fish showed responses simultaneously on five occasions, and three fish showed responses during the same time interval on 19 occasions. If the definition of detection were two or more responses during the same time period, then 4.16 mg/liter zinc was correctly detected 8 h after it was introduced, but three false detections occurred before any zinc was added. However, if detection were defined as three or more responses during the same time period, the zinc spill would still have been correctly detected after 8 h, and there would have been no false detections.

Table 3 summarizes results on fish breathing from three experiments, and shows that changing the criterion for detection from one to three responses per time period generally increases the lag time and decreases the number of false detections. Table 3 shows that if three simultaneous breathing rate increases counted as a detection, no false detections would occur in the three experiments reported, but the highest zinc concentration (5.22 mg/liter) would not have been detected before the experiment ended. As only three fish were exposed to zinc in this experiment, it is likely that one unusually zinc-tolerant individual determined the outcome of the test for detection. Therefore, it would be better to define detection as simultaneous responses by some proportion of the experimental fish, rather than by all of them.

The lowest concentration tested while monitoring fish breathing was 2.55 mg/liter, and this was reliably detected after 52 h, with detection defined as simultaneous responses by three fish. The detection limit of the method for analyzing fish activity, with detection defined as two responses during the same period of the day, lies between 3.64 and 2.94 mg/liter zinc for a 96-h exposure. Since the zinc concentration that is

TABLE 3—*Effectiveness of zinc detection using increases in fish breathing rates.*

Zinc (mg/liter)	Number of fish exposed to zinc	Detection criterion, minimum number of fish showing response at one time	Lag time hours from addition of zinc	False detections
5.22	3	1	0	12 in 100 h
		2	4	1 in 100 h
		3	not detected after 45 h	0 in 100 h
4.16	4	1	0	19 in 123 h
		2	11	3 in 123 h
		3	11	0 in 123 h
2.55	3	1	0	2 in 4 h
		2	8	0 in 4 h
		3	52	0 in 4 h

TABLE 4—*Bluegill reproduction and growth in four zinc concentrations.*

Zn, mg/liter	Zn, as fraction of 2.55 mg/liter	Total eggs spawned	Spawnings	Eggs per spawning [a]	Percent hatch [a]	Length of fry, mm Days			
						30	42	60	90
0.021	no added Zn	13 264	13	1046	65	8	...[b]	18	30
0.035	1/75	14 476	8	2037	80	...[b]	14	19	31
0.076	1/34	23 797	16	1367	64	...[b]	15	22	32
0.235	1/10	1 009	1	1009	43	...[c]	...[c]	...[c]	...[c]

[a] Number of eggs and percent hatch were not determined for all spawnings because of premature hatching, fungus infestation, etc.
[b] Fry were not measured.
[c] None of the fry exposed to 0.235 mg/liter zinc survived 30 days.

lethal to 50 percent of the exposed fish in 96 h (96-h LC50) is 8 mg/liter in the dechlorinated municipal water we used, the monitoring system detects sublethal zinc concentrations, in addition to detecting lethal concentrations rapidly enough to prevent irreversible damage to the exposed fish.

In practical application the monitoring system should probably receive a new set of test fish after stress detection, so that the problems of increased or decreased resistance to stress need not become a serious consideration. If the new fish were added two a day until a complete exchange had been made, the monitoring system would not have to be shut down.

Relating In-Plant Biological Monitoring to Water Quality Standards for Chronic Exposure

One tenth of the lowest concentration used in the monitoring experiments inhibited spawning in ripe bluegills and caused complete mortality of bluegill fry, whereas 1/34 and 1/75 of the lowest concentration did not have these effects (Table 4).

Based on these results, a safety factor for zinc could be introduced to the monitoring system by metering at least 34 times more waste into the dilution water delivered to the test fish than is delivered to the stream, thus giving an earlier warning than would be possible with a lower concentration. If the effluent from the industry is diluted 100-fold on entering the stream, then the test fish should be exposed to waste diluted 1/100 times 34, or approximately a three-fold dilution. The use of a safety factor is not a handicap—by metering proportionally more waste to the test fish than is delivered to the stream, the lag time inherent in the biological portion of the monitoring system would be reduced. In general, the higher the toxicant concentration, the faster the toxicant is taken up by the organism and the sooner the response appears. For the same reason, it would be desirable to use as small a test container or as high a flow rate as possible, without affecting the activity pattern of the fish, to reduce the retention time of the test chamber itself. It is quite likely that in the developmental period for this type of biological monitoring each industrial situation will require a series of trial runs to determine particular problems related to waste quality and to determine the operational limits of the testing system. During this period a range of concentrations well beyond those expected should be tested.

Conclusions

Biological Monitoring at an Industrial Site

Figure 9 shows how test fish in the in-plant biological monitoring system would be exposed to waste diluted with upstream water and the

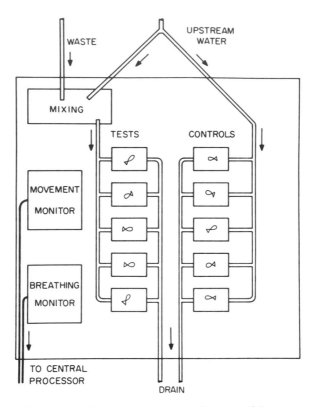

FIG. 9—*An in-plant monitoring unit, showing how test fish are exposed to waste diluted with upstream water and the control fish are exposed to upstream water alone.*

control fish would be exposed to upstream water alone. It would be desirable to have control fish to evaluate the effects of upstream conditions and detect extraneous effects such as noises that continue for several hours and disturb the fish.

Most large industries in the United States already use computers for manufacturing process control, bookkeeping, inventory, etc., and the same computers could service several biological monitoring units. Thus, the principle of information feedback and process control used in the manufacturing process would be extended to the waste treatment process. If a monitoring unit were placed on each waste stream in an industry as well as on the combined waste stream (Fig. 10), the source of toxicity could be more easily located. If the toxic waste were diverted to a holding pond, chemical analyses on the waste or a check of the manufacturing process could determine precisely the cause of trouble.

The degree of protection afforded by the in-plant monitoring units should

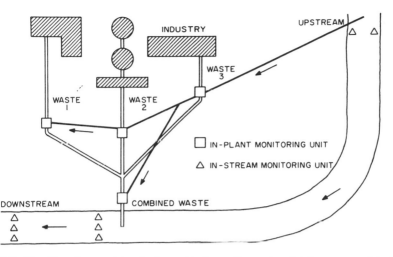

FIG. 10—*Use of several in-plant monitoring units to pinpoint the source of toxicity at an industrial site and use of in-stream monitoring units to check the performance of the in-plant units.*

be evaluated by in-stream monitoring units, since the goal of biological monitoring is to maintain vigorously functioning aquatic ecosystems[3]. An in-stream monitoring program which generates biological information quickly has been described by Cairns and Dickson[4]. An automated in-stream monitoring unit is described in another chapter of this book.[5]

Biological Monitoring in a River Management System

In-plant and in-stream [5] biological monitoring units developed for industries could be combined in a river system to increase the capability for management of the entire system and prevention of ecological disasters (Fig. 11)[3]. Quality control would not only be extended from the manufacturing process in each industry to the waste treatment process, but also to the river itself.

In-plant monitoring units would be located at each potential, major, or high impact source of industrial or municipal waste, and the information would not only go to each plant but also to a control center. In-stream monitoring units would be located above and below each potential source of pollution, including tributaries from agricultural and mining areas, and would also supply information to the control center.

If warnings of a toxic discharge came from the monitoring units at Industry 3 (Fig. 11), Industry 3 might undertake its own control measures, but several additional control measures are available if a river management

[5] See pp. 148–163.

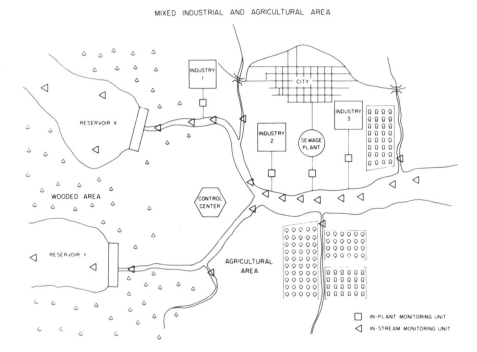

FIG. 11—*Use of in-plant and in-stream units to provide biological information in a river management system.*

system is in operation. The control center might request Industry 1 and Industry 2 to hold their waste, or reduce the discharge rate so as not to overload a system already strained by the toxic discharge from Plant 3. Alternatively, the control center could call for a release of water from Reservoirs X and Y to dilute the waste from Industry 3.

If industrial and other users of a river basin cooperated in a river management system which incorporated biological monitoring units, then full industrial and municipal use could be made of the river without endangering other uses that depend on a healthy aquatic ecosystem.

Acknowledgments

The research on in-plant monitoring using fish as sensors was initially supported by a grant from the Manufacturing Chemists Association and then by the U.S. Environmental Protection Agency (Projects 18050 EDQ and 18050 EDP), and is currently supported by the U.S. Department of the Interior, Office of Water Resources Research, administered by the Water Resources Research Center as Project A-039-VA.

References

[1] Mount, D. I. and Brungs, W. A., *Water Research,* Vol. 1, 1967, pp. 21–29.
[2] Brungs, W. A. and Mount, D. I., *Transactions,* American Fisheries Society, Vol. 99, 1970, pp. 799–802.
[3] Cairns, John, Jr. in *River Ecology and Man,* R. T. Oglesby, C. A. Carlson, and J. A. McCann, Eds., Academic Press, New York, 1972, pp. 421–430.
[4] Cairns, John, Jr. and Dickson, K. L., *Journal of the Water Pollution Control Federation,* Vol. 43, 1971, pp. 755–772.

John Cairns, Jr.,[1] *K. L. Dickson,*[1] *and Guy Lanza* [1]

Rapid Biological Monitoring System for Determining Aquatic Community Structure in Receiving Systems

REFERENCE: Cairns, John, Jr., Dickson, K. L., and Lanza, Guy, "**Rapid Biological Monitoring Systems for Determining Aquatic Community Structure in Receiving Systems,**" *Biological Methods for the Assessment of Water Quality, ASTM STP 528,* American Society for Testing and Materials, 1973, pp. 148–163.

ABSTRACT: Biological monitoring plays an important role in a pollution monitoring program providing information not available through conventional physical and chemical monitoring. The saprobic system and the use of structural and functional changes in aquatic communities are two approaches utilized in assessing the effects of pollutants on aquatic communities. The feedback of information from conventional instream biological monitoring has been too slow for the most effective management of an aquatic system. Two rapid biological monitoring systems (the Sequential Comparison Index, and an automated community structure analysis using laser holography) have been developed to increase the speed of data collection and data analysis.

KEY WORDS: water pollution, lasers, holography, aquatic biology, environmental surveys, monitors

Society's interest in pollution is centered on its effects on living organisms (including man); therefore, the assessment of pollution must include an integration of chemical, physical and biological monitoring. Most pollution monitoring programs have been oriented solely towards chemical and physical parameters since biological monitoring in the past has not been

---

[1] Director, assistant director, and research associate, respectively, Biology Department and Center for Environmental Studies, Virginia Polytechnic Institute and State University, Blacksburg, Va. 24061. Dr. Lanza is presently at the Smithsonian Institute, Washington, D. C.

within the capabilities of industrial pollution control personnel (usually engineers and chemists), has not been amenable to numerical expression, and has generally been more time-consuming and expensive than chemical and physical monitoring. However, biologists and engineers have been working together to overcome these problems, and it is now possible and necessary to include biological monitoring as a part of any progressive pollution monitoring program.

Why Include Biological Monitoring

Perhaps the most important reason for doing biological monitoring is that aquatic organisms act as natural monitors. During a short-term exposure to water of poor quality, organisms that cannot tolerate the stress are destroyed and the aquatic community structure changes. Since aquatic organisms respond to their total environment, they provide a better assessment of environmental damage than do the handful of chemical or physical parameters (dissolved oxygen, temperature, conductivity, pH, turbidity, etc.) that can now be continuously monitored effectively. It is important to recognize that biological monitoring does not replace chemical and physical monitoring. They all provide converging lines of information that supplement each other but are not mutually exclusive.

A biological monitoring program is essential in determining the synergistic or antagonistic interactions of waste discharges and the receiving system.

If one considers the waste assimilative capacity of a river as a natural resource then it is only logical to make use of that capacity along with other uses such as water supply, recreation, and asthetics to derive maximum beneficial use from the system. In order to make maximum beneficial use of the system, biological monitoring is essential so that other beneficial uses will not be harmed.

The State of the Art in Biological Monitoring

At the present time a biological monitoring program has four basic components consisting of in-stream monitoring, in-plant monitoring, bioassays, and systems simulation. Obviously, no biological monitoring program is routine; none can be established on a "cookbook" basis, nor does one necessarily have to include all of the above components. However, each of the components provide valuable and useful information.[2]

Historically, one of the most important parts of an in-stream biological monitoring program has been the ecological survey. An ecological survey of an aquatic system should be carried out by a team of chemists, ecologists,

[2] A discussion of in-plant monitoring and bioassays can be found on pp. 127–147.

engineers, and taxonomists to get a complete picture of the chemical, physical, and biological condition. If complete background data are to be generated, the team should consist of one or more chemists, a bacteriologist, an algologist, a protozoologist, one or more invertebrate zoologists (including an aquatic entomologist), an ichthyologist, and a sanitary engineer. Certain members of the team will utilize dredges, nets, traps and artificial substrate [3] to collect aquatic organisms. Since this involves a number of well-trained people, it can be moderately expensive (although the cost is quite small compared to the cost of even a modest waste treatment plant). The exact cost would depend on a number of factors including the size and structure of the river and the number of species likely to be encountered. Obviously, the lower Mississippi is a more difficult river to survey than a small river that one can throw a rock across. In addition, a stream already degraded by pollution is likely to have fewer species resulting in less cost for identifying the various organisms collected than an unpolluted stream with a very high number of species. Before such a survey is contemplated, it is necessary to have a preliminary survey by an ecological generalist who can make a firm estimate of the costs involved and place reliable time estimates on completion of the project.

A survey of this nature will provide a wide variety of information valuable in a pollution monitoring program. It will establish a baseline of biological, chemical, and physical water quality which can be useful in determining the waste assimilative capacity and other beneficial uses of the system. In addition, a river survey will determine pre-existing man-made or natural stresses on the receiving system. River survey biological data which document the water quality are extremely valuable particularly in receiving systems which are already partially under stress from other waste discharges.

Evaluating the Effects of Pollution on Aquatic Life

Basically, there are two major approaches in evaluating the effects of pollution on aquatic life: (1) listing the species found in a system together with some notes on the areas in which they occur as a sort of biological inventory and (2) determining the structure and function of various components of the biological community present. Each of these approaches has merit and is useful in certain situations. The first of these methodologies is particularly important where there is an interest in protecting rare or commercially valuable species or where the system is one which changes relatively slowly.

The first approach utilizes the saprobic system of Kolkwitz and Marsson

---

[3] See pp. 227–241.

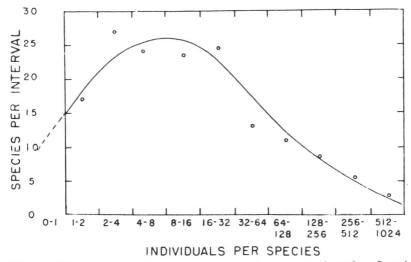

INDIVIDUALS PER SPECIES

FIG. 1—*Diatom community structure in a stream not adversely affected by pollution* [9].

[1,2] [4] which was modified and used by Richardson[3], Gaufin[4,5], Hynes[6], and Beck[7,8]. It depends upon a taxonomic grouping of organisms in relation to whether they are found in clean water, polluted water, or both. This approach requires a precise identification of organisms and is based on the fact that different organisms have different ranges of tolerance to the same stress. Patrick[9] and Wurtz[10], using a system of histograms, have developed elaborate systems to report the results of stream surveys based on the differences in tolerance of various groups of aquatic organisms to pollution (Figs. 1 and 2). Beck[7] developed a biotic index as a method of evaluating the effects of pollution on bottom fauna organisms. His biotic index is calculated by multiplying the number of intolerance species by two and then adding the number of facultative organisms. Beck considers a biotic index value greater than ten to indicate clean water and a value less than ten polluted water. Other techniques based on the tolerance of aquatic organisms to pollution have been reported by Beak[11].

The breakdown of an assemblage of organisms into pollution tolerant, intolerant, and facultative categories is somewhat subjective, since tolerance for the same organism may vary under a different set of environmental conditions. Needham[12] observed that environmental conditions other than pollution may influence the distribution of organisms. Pollution-

---

[4] The italic numbers in brackets refer to the list of references appended to this paper.

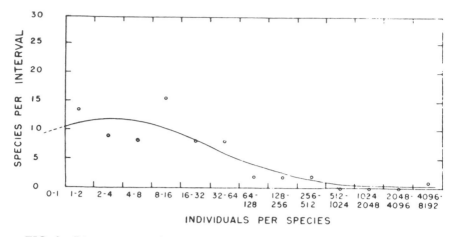

FIG. 2—*Diatom community structure in a stream adversely affected by pollution* [9].

tolerant organisms are also found in clean water areas[13,14]. Therefore, the concept of the use of indicator organisms to evaluate biological water quality has certain difficulties and is not commonly accepted today.

The second approach is to use the community structure and functions (respiration, photosynthesis, etc.) of associations or populations of aquatic organisms to evaluate pollution. Hairston[15] defined community structure in terms of species frequency, species per unit area, spatial distribution of individuals, and numerical abundance of species. Gaufin and Tarzwell[14] found that the total community structure of benthic invertebrates provides a more reliable criterion of organic enrichment than presence of any single indicator species.

All biological communities are energy-nutrient transfer systems, and the geometry of these systems is such that they can only vary within certain limits regardless of the kinds of species present. To oversimplify the situation, the basic food supply is determined by the number of photosynthetic organisms transforming the sun's energy into a state that is useful to other members of the biological communities not capable of the photosynthetic process. The number of species or kinds of plants doing this is determined by the way in which the environment is fractionated into suitable habitats for these various species. This fractionation occurs all the way up the food chain and is determined by a variety of factors among which the most important is the ability to survive in a particular habitat.

All organisms in natural habitats are subjected to a continuum of variable stresses. Many of these stresses occur simultaneously rather than sequentially. However, organisms are usually able to survive, as a result of selection, stresses of the kind for which their genetic information system has accumulated appropriate data. In this context, pollution might be defined as a form of environmental stress for which the organism of that particular locale have not accumulated appropriate genetic information and are incapable of doing so in a relatively short period of time. A natural stress such as a seasonal temperature change is one which may be expected to occur in a given place as a result of the normal processes of nature. A pollutional stress, on the other hand, usually has reference to some act of man, such as the discharge of warmed water from a plant. Nature has provided a variety of species such that when a natural stress occurs or exists, some species capable of enduring that stress will move in or multiply and take over a given community function such as serving as a food supply for fish. When a cultural (man-made) pollutional stress is introduced, however, nature may not have a suitable species available to take over that function, and so the aquatic community is thrown out of balance.

Pollutional stress usually involves two changes in community structure: (1) a reduction in the total number of species present and (2) an increase in number of specimens of those species which can survive the stress. Another way of expressing this latter point is to say that there is a greater disproportion in the numbers of individuals per species in the entire community (Figs. 1 and 2). However, one might ask why an industry should be interested in maintaining diversity and protecting the structure of aquatic community. The rapid loss of diversity in the entire world is a serious general phenomenon. Loss of diversity or simplification of natural ecosystems is both deliberate as a result of agricultural utilization of land and inadvertent due to pollutional stresses of many kinds. The basic argument for the maintenance of diversity is that it enhances stability of a system, thereby making its performance characteristics more predictable. The desirability of diversity in natural systems (ecosystems) is in some ways comparable to the reasons which make diversification in industry worthwhile. For a single corporation, diversification insures that the loss of a single product will not cause the demise of the corporation, because it is only one out of many, whereas an industry with only a single marketable product or even a few marketable products is likely to be seriously and perhaps even fatally affected by the loss of one of these. The presence of many species in a natural community insures the likelihood of "redundancy of function" so that the loss of one species does not mean that the functional capacity of the community in some particular regard is fatally jeopardized. In other words, spreading the risk in natural communities is no different from spreading the risk in industrial operations. The stability of performance is more likely to be predictable if the system has a large number of elements and, therefore, more homeostatic feedback loops. Therefore, an adjustment caused by a new set of conditions is likely to cause less oscillation in a complex system than in a simplified system with relatively few feedback loops.

We will not discuss in detail assessments of function for two reasons. (1) Because out of the vast array of functions carried out by aquatic communities, there are only a few for which appropriate methodology and assessment techniques are available. These tell only part of the picture, and it is our feeling that a more complete body of information should be available before functional changes are used as criteria and standards for protecting aquatic life. (2) Although scientific evidence is not available to show that maintenance of structure is synonymous with maintenance of all the functional cause-effect pathways, one intuitively feels that since organisms are clearly interdependent and continually interacting that it would be very difficult to substantially change the structure of a community without also markedly changing the function. Therefore, protection of structure is quite likely to protect function despite the fact that firm evidence supporting this statement is not currently available.

The interest in the effects of pollutants on the functions of aquatic communities has lead to a limited body of methodology dealing with such things as primary production, energy transfer, and others. For practical purposes, studies dealing with the useful and functional aspects of communities in pollution assessment have been generally restricted to determinations of photosynthesis to respiration ratios (P/R) which gives an index relation to the oxygen cycle in the receiving system[16]. Nutrient enrichment (carbon, nitrogen, phosphorus, etc.) generally cause a shift in community structure and often stimulate growths of algae which have a direct effect on the oxygen cycle in the receiving system.

Diversity Indices

Diversity indices are useful in monitoring changes and detecting shifts in water quality. As engineers, chemists, and biologists began working together to solve environmental problems, it became apparent that classical biological information (species lists) needed to become more quantitative. Diversity indices which summarize large amounts of information about community structure were developed and are currently becoming more and more accepted in pollution assessment.

These diversity indices result in a numerical expression which can be used to make comparisons between two communities of organisms. Gleason[17] developed a diversity index based on the species accumulated versus the logarithm of the area sampled. Other diversity indices to describe community structure have been developed by Fisher et al[18], Preston[19], Patten[20], Margalef[21], Cairns et al[22], and Cairns and Dickson[23].

Diversity indices derived from information theory were first used by Margalef[21] to analyze natural communities. This technique equates diversity with information. Maximum diversity, and thus maximum information, exists in a community of organisms when each individual belongs to a different species. Minimum diversity exists when all individuals belong to the same species. A community in which all individuals belong to the same species is high in redundancy. Thus, mathematical expressions can be used for diversity and redundancy which describe community structure.

Wilhm[24], Mathis[25], and Wilhm and Dorris[26] have used diversity indices derived from information theory to describe bottom fauna community structure. They have found that the indices for diversity per individual ($\bar{d}$) and redundancy (r) possess features which make them reasonable measures of community structure. They are dimensionless equations which are sample size independent.

As pointed out by Wilhm and Dorris[26], natural biotic communities typically are characterized by the presence of a few species with many individuals and many species with a few individuals. An unfavorable limiting factor such as pollution results in detectable changes in community structure. As it relates to information theory, more information (diversity) is contained in a natural community than in a polluted community. A polluted system is simplified, and those species that survive encounter less competition and therefore are usually able to increase in numbers. Redundancy in this case is high since the probability that an individual belongs to a species previously recognized is increased, and the amount of information per individual is reduced.

The application of the diversity per individual ($\bar{d}$) and redundancy (r) to describe community structure requires only that organisms be recognized and the number of individuals per taxon be determined.

Rapid In-Stream Systems

Management of aquatic ecosystems requires a clear understanding of the goals to be achieved, the types of environmental information that are necessary, and development of the means to achieving the goals. As stated in the Water Quality Act of 1965, the national management goal for most of our aquatic ecosystems is multiple use: use for public water supplies, propagation of fish and wildlife, recreational purposes, and agricultural, industrial, and other legitimate uses. We already have some means for achieving those goals, such as storage and diversion of water, the rearing and stocking of fish, low flow augmentation, etc. Precise control depends upon feedback of information. Control measures applied to aquatic ecosystems, in the absence of information on the condition of the system, are apt to be inappropriate and thus may overprotect the receiving system at times and underprotect it at other times, since the ability of ecosystems to assimilate wastes is not constant. The precision and efficiency of environmental quality control and the lag time in the information feedback loop are related. If the lag time is too great, the control measures may repeatedly overshoot and undershoot the desired goal, as a thermostat with too slow a response will cause first underheating and then overheating of a house.

Present techniques for measuring the responses of aquatic organisms and communities require days or weeks. These techniques are useful in before and after studies (before and after construction of an impoundment, a power plant, or an industry) or after an environmental disaster (following an oil spill, a fish kill, etc.) to document the extent of damage. However, in order to institute meaningful quality control of aquatic ecosystems and prevent crises, we must have the means of assessing the condition and responses of aquatic organisms and communities in hours or minutes, rather than in days or weeks.

There are two principal sources of delay in obtaining biological data about the effects of a pollutant on the aquatic life in the receiving system-data collection and data analysis. The automation of collecting biological data in the receiving system has not progressed as rapidly as the continuous chemical and physical monitoring systems. In addition, biologists have been reluctant to simplify the analysis of biological data so that water pollution personnel who often have very little biological expertise can be aware of the effects of their discharges on the receiving system. In the sections which follow we would like to describe the Sequential Comparison Index which is a rapid technique for nonbiologists and biologists to determine changes in aquatic community structure and also discuss the use of laser holography for diatom pattern recognition as an automatic monitoring system.

The Sequential Comparison Index—A Community Structure Analysis

The Sequential Comparison Index (SCI) is a simplified method for estimating relative differences in biological diversity. It was developed to fill the need for a rapid numerical method of assessing the biological consequences of pollution. The SCI method requires no taxonomic expertise on the part of the investigator and is based on differences in the shape, color, and size of the organisms.

A detailed explanation of how to perform the SCI was published by Cairns and Dickson[23]. Briefly, the SCI uses a modification of the sign test and theory of runs to derive a diversity index. It utilizes the innate ability of the investigator to recognize differences in shape, color, and size of organisms such as algae and bottom fauna. The SCI is an expression of community structure since it is dependent not only upon the compositional richness of the community but upon the distribution of individuals among the taxa. Since taxonomic determinations (Latin names) are not needed to perform the SCI, considerable time is saved in analyzing an aquatic community (algae, invertebrates, etc.). For the SCI method, only two specimens are compared at a time. The current specimen need only be compared with the previous one. If it is similar, it is part of the same "run"; if not, it is part of a new run. The greater the number of runs per number of specimens examined, the greater the biological diversity. A healthy community is characterized by being highly diverse (a high number of different kinds of organisms). A numerical diversity index DI_T can be calculated for each community and statistically analyzed. The SCI diversity index is equal to the number of runs divided by the number of specimens times the number of kinds of organisms present.

$$SCI = \frac{\text{Number of Runs}}{\text{Number of Specimens}} (\text{Number of kinds of organisms})$$

The number of kinds of organisms (taxa) is determined by the investigator after he determines the number of runs. Obviously, the greater the taxonomic training on the part of the investigator, the greater the accuracy in determining how many taxa are present in a sample. Nevertheless, experience has shown that untrained investigators can detect relative differences between the community structure from different stations, since they are consistent in their bias. Some people are "lumpers" others are "splitters". However, if the same person analyzes two samples to be compared, then relative differences can be detected. The SCI has been used by industrial groups to monitor the effects of waste effluents. Nalco Chemical Company offers an aquatic monitoring service utilizing the SCI. The Environmental Protection Agency, Manufacturing Chemists, and American Institute of Chemical Engineers all currently utilize the SCI in their training sessions, although it has yet to be accepted as a "standard" method.

Laser Holography in Pollution Monitoring

We are presently developing an in-stream monitoring system based on the coherent optical spatial filtering of diatoms. Ideally, a workable apparatus of this type could function as a segment of a computer-based network of in-stream monitoring stations measuring deviations from established "normal" communities of microorganisms. These deviations could provide an alert prior to severe ecological degradation resulting from pollutional stress in the aquatic system.

Our initial studies have been directed toward diatoms because of (1) their obvious critical significance as primary producers and (2) their rigid and durable silicon dioxide shell which is well suited for pattern recognition studies. The concepts present here, however, are not limited to any one particular group of aquatic microorganisms, and applications to other essential microorganisms should be possible.

The system is based on the utilization of Fourier transform holograms as spatial frequency filters designed to select diatoms of one particular structure from a mixture of diatoms of varying structure; that is, to "identify" the type of diatom which "matches" that particular filter[27]. The actual filtering process resembles the technique used in reconstructing hologram images; however, a dot of light in lieu of the reconstructed image results on the output screen. Light dots will only appear if the sample under consideration contains the diatom type or species for which the filter was produced. A mechanical system fitted to a reference "library" of spatial filters could then rapidly scan a sample and greatly reduce the time required for data output from the monitoring system. Light dots are measured by the electronics sensor portion of the system. The x and y coordinate position of the light dot on the output screen corresponds to the same relative position of the individual of a diatom species on a slide containing various other species of diatoms. The intensity of the light dot is also provided and measured; the ratio between the intensity and the background determines the signal to noise ratio. Each filter and specimen has identification codes which are recorded for each dot produced. In addition, a computer can perform many related functions of the system, such as data storage and analysis and the operational control of the system itself.

In-Stream Monitoring System

A schematic drawing of the present design of the proposed laser system is given in Fig. 3. The first objective involves the establishment of a reference "library" composed of a series of matched spatial filters, ideally one for each diatom species in the aquatic ecosystem under surveillance. This is accomplished by using the laser system to produce a special type of hologram, a Fourier transform hologram, of the diatom which serves as a matched spatial filter for that particular species. The matched spatial filter (Fourier transform hologram), in effect, represents the modified image of the diatom species and carries the various spatial frequencies associated with the details of that particular species. The microscopic size of the organisms under study requires magnification of a few hundred times in order to produce well defined Fourier transform holograms for use as matched spatial filters. To accomplish this, samples are collected from the in-stream monitoring sites (using various types of artificial substrates or free water samples) and prepared for examination using standard procedures[28].

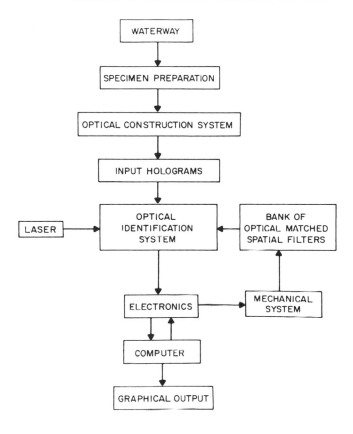

MONITORING SYSTEM

FIG. 3—*Proposed in-stream monitoring system using laser holography.*

Figure 4 provides a simple diagram of one process used in the production of our matched spatial filters. The symbol O is used to represent a particular diatom species. Because an average slide community from a "healthy" stream could contain about 25 000 diatoms representing about 165 species, any field of view will probably contain several diatoms. This necessitates the use of an optical stop to block the light from all but the diatom of interest; by switching the stop position a different diatom receives illumination and is transformed to produce another matched spatial filter. The result is a series of matched spatial filters characterizing diatom community structure.

In preliminary studies, slides were prepared from fresh and brackish water sources on standard 75 by 25-mm glass slides and selected for the presence of several different types of diatoms with a dominance of two

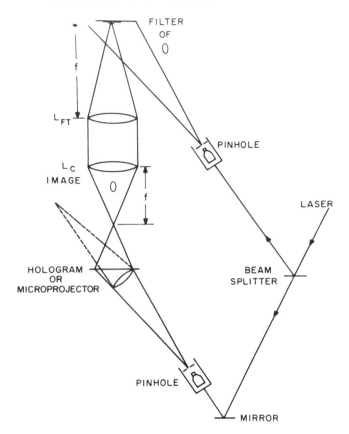

PRODUCTION OF MATCHED SPATIAL FILTERS

FIG. 4—*Production of matched spatial filters.* $L_c = $ *collimating lens;* $L_{FT} = $ *Fourier transform lens.*

common species with grossly different morphological characteristics. The types initially made into filters were (1) a pennate (linear) type, for example, *Navicula* sp., and (2) a centric type, for example *Cyclotella* sp. A Bausch and Lomb microprojector was modified and coupled to a He-Ne-CW gas laser and used as the optical construction system. The diatoms were imaged to a magnification of ×250 and recorded on a negative, a Kodak 649-F spectroscopic plate, which served as the signal source in the construction of the matched spatial filter. This same plate containing a mixed sample of various different types of diatoms later served as the source for the unknown signal input used to measure the response of the filters constructed for *Navicula* sp. and *Cyclotella* sp.

Figure 5 provides a simple diagram of the optical identification process involving the production of correlation dots. In this hypothetical example, the field of view contains a total of eight diatoms comprising five species. A matched spatial filter for one of the five species, again represented by the symbol *O*, is orientated into the filter plane and illuminated with the Fourier transform of an unknown diatom signal from a water sample. Because the sample contains four individuals of the species matching the filter (*O*), the output will have four corresponding bright dots and four

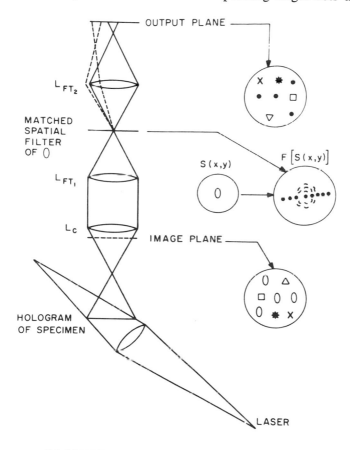

PRODUCTION OF CORRELATION DOTS
(OPTICAL IDENTIFICATION SYSTEM)

FIG. 5—*Production of correlation dots (optical identification system. $L_c=$collimating lens; $L_{FT1} =$ Fourier transform lens 1; $L_{FT2} =$ Fourier transform lens 2.*

images of the species not matching the filter (the four bright output dots correspond to the four input signals, O). A vidicon tube located at the output plane allows a scanning electron beam to sense the presence of bright spots; coupled with proper electronic counting equipment, the number of diatoms of a given species, their relative positions on the area scanned, and the intensity of the spot could all be recorded. Automatic rescanning of the same area with the filter rotated to search for diatoms at various angles in the input beam would also occur. Data accumulated in the electronic counting bank during one complete cycle is forwarded to the computer, and the process begins again with a different specific filter used with the same input images (hologram or microprojector). When all species have been identified and classified in slide area, the process is repeated on a different area of the same slide with different input images (hologram or microprojector). The percent of the slide or number of slides which must be surveyed to obtain a reliable estimate of the diversity and density of the diatom population in the stream could be empirically determined. Because of the flexibility of the computer, numerous approaches to data analysis and evaluation would be possible, culminating in various graphical outputs including species diversity plots. Completely new statistical approaches, previously not feasible due to inadequate sample size, could be investigated. Multiphase approaches to data evaluation, such as a preliminary measurement which could indicate the need for subsequent, more detailed study of a given sample, would greatly enhance the time-efficiency factor. Feedback from one or several data storage computers in a centralized locale with a monitoring capacity for an entire water basin could also be considered (Cairns, in press).

As mentioned previously, we have produced matched spatial filters (Fourier transform holograms) for *Navicula* sp. and *Cyclotella* sp. in our laboratories. In addition, we have subjected these filters to preliminary testing. By using an input plane signal composed of a mixed diatom sample, bright dots appeared wherever the filter signal appeared on the input plane. Preliminary results of these experiments are discussed in Cairns et al[27].

References

[1] Kolkwitz, R. and Marsson, M., *Berichte der Deutschen Batanischen Gesselschaft,* Vol. 26, 1908, pp. 505–519.

[2] Kolkwitz, R. and Marsson, M., *Internationale Revue der Gesamten Hydrobiologie und Hydrographie,* Vol. 2, 1909, pp. 126–152.

[3] Richardson, R. E., *Bulletin,* Illinois Natural History Survey, Vol. 17, 1928, pp. 387–475.

[4] Gaufin, A. R., *Ohio Journal of Science,* Vol. 58, 1958, pp. 197–208.

[5] Gaufin, A. R., *Sewage and Industrial Wastes,* Vol. 28, 1956, pp. 906–924.

[6] Hynes, H. B. N., "The Significance of Macroinvertebrates in the Study of Mild River Pollution," *Biological Problems in Water Pollution,* U. S. Public Health Service Report 235, Washington, D. C., 1962.

[7] Beck, W. M., *Quarterly Journal of the Florida Academy of Sciences,* Vol. 17, 1954, pp. 211–227.

[8] Beck, W. M., *Sewage and Industrial Wastes,* Vol. 27, 1955, pp. 1193–1197.

[9] Patrick, R., *Proceedings,* Academy of Natural Sciences of Philadelphia, Vol. 101, 1949, pp. 277–341.

[10] Wurtz, C. B., *Sewage and Industrial Wastes,* Vol. 27, 1955, pp. 1270–1278.

[11] Beak, T. W., "Biotic Index of Polluted Streams and its Relationship to Fisheries," Second International Conference on Water Pollution Research, Tokyo, Japan, 1964.

[12] Needham, P. R., *Trout Streams,* Comstock Publishing Co., Inc., New York, 1938, p. 233.

[13] Hynes, H. B. N., *The Ecology of Running Water,* University of Toronto Press, Toronto, 1970, p. 555.

[14] Gaufin, A. R. and Tarzwell, C. M., "Aquatic Invertebrates as Indicators of Stream Pollution," Public Health Report 67, Washington, D. C., 1952.

[15] Hairston, N. G., *Ecology,* Vol. 40, 1959, pp. 404–416.

[16] Odum, E. P., *Japanese Journal of Ecology,* Vol. 12, 1962, pp. 108–118.

[17] Gleason, H. A., *Ecology,* Vol. 3, 1922, pp. 158–162.

[18] Fisher, R. A., Corbet, A. S., and Williams, C. B., *Journal of Animal Ecology,* Vol. 12, 1943, pp. 42–58.

[19] Preston, F. W., *Ecology,* Vol. 29, 1948, pp. 254–283.

[20] Patten, B. C., *Research,* Vol. 20, 1962, pp. 57–75.

[21] Margalef, R., "Diversidad de especies en les communidades naturales," *P. Inst. Biol.,* Apl. Vol. 9, 1951, p. 5–27.

[22] Cairns, J., Jr., Albaugh, D. W., Busey, F., and Chaney, M. S., *Journal of the Water Pollution Control Federation,* Vol. 40, 1968, pp. 1607–1613.

[23] Cairns, J., Jr. and Dickson, K. L., *Journal of the Water Pollution Control Federation,* Vol. 42, 1971, pp. 755–772.

[24] Wilhm, J. L., "Species Diversity of Benthic Macroinvertebrates in a Stream Receiving Domestic and Oil Refinery Effluents," Ph.D. thesis, Oklahoma State University, 1965.

[25] Mathis, B. J., "Community Structure of Benthic Macroinvertebrates in an Intermittent Stream Receiving Oil Field Brines," Ph.D. thesis, Oklahoma State University, 1965.

[26] Wilhm, J. L. and Dorris, T. C., *Bioscience,* Vol. 19, 1968, pp. 477–481.

[27] Cairns, J., Jr., Dickson, K. L., Lanza, G. R., Almeida, S. P., and Del Balzo, D., *Archiv Fuer Mikrobiologie,* Vol. 83, 1972, pp. 141–144.

[28] Patrick, R. and Reimer, C. W., "Diatoms of the United States," *Monographs,* Academy of Natural Sciences of Philadelphia, 1966, p. 688.

C. E. Stephan[1] *and D. I. Mount*[2]

Use of Toxicity Tests with Fish in Water Pollution Control

REFERENCE: Stephan, C. E. and Mount, D. I., "**Use of Toxicity Tests with Fish in Water Pollution Control,**" *Biological Methods for the Assessment of Water Quality, ASTM STP 528,* American Society for Testing and Materials, 1973, pp. 164–177.

ABSTRACT: The recent growth of interest in water pollution control programs has fostered the development of applied fish toxicology. One of the functions of applied fish toxicologists is to make the best possible decisions concerning the effects of pollution on fish based on existing data. A second function is to help make available the additional data most needed for the protection of important species of fish. A third function is to evaluate the usefulness of specific toxicity tests and ways of using them to fulfill needs that have been identified and to suggest improvements in existing tests or new tests that should be developed. The acute mortality test provides data that are useful in some situations, but the chronic test which studies effects of a toxic agent on survival, growth, and reproduction is probably the most useful toxicity test for estimating long-term safe concentrations. Other important adverse effects that should be studied include avoidance, flavor impairment, and the accumulation of toxic residues.

KEY WORDS: fishes, toxicity, toxicology, water pollution, tests

Fish toxicology deals with the interaction of toxic agents and fish and with the practical problems that result from such interactions. Since all areas of toxicology face similar problems, such as those associated with nomenclature, methodology, interpretation of data, and use of results, each area should be able to learn from and contribute to the others. Unfortunately in the past, fish toxicology has not maintained good contacts with other areas of toxicology.

[1] Research chemist, Newtown Fish Toxicology Laboratory, Environmental Protection Agency, Cincinnati, Ohio 45244.

[2] Director, National Water Quality Laboratory, Environmental Protection Agency, Duluth, Minn. 55804.

The two main divisions of toxicology are experimental and applied. Basically, experimental toxicology is concerned with developing and conducting toxicity tests, whereas applied toxicology is concerned with applying the results of the tests to real-life situations. Although this separation is convenient for the sake of discussion, in practice the two often overlap. Until about ten years ago, the basic concern of most fish toxicologists was an academic interest in experimental toxicology, but in the last decade interest in applied toxicology has increased markedly as a result of a growing interest in water pollution control programs. In turn, the development of applied fish toxicology has emphasized the importance of and given direction to experimental fish toxicology by identifying the most significant research needs.

Both experimental and applied toxicology have their own inherent problems. For instance, experimental toxicologists must constantly strive to achieve or maintain an acceptable balance between the biological, chemical, statistical, and toxicological considerations. A more serious problem in applied toxicology is that decisions relating to real-life situations nearly always have to be made on the basis of incomplete information. Therefore, applied toxicologists must often employ subjective judgment.

Critics constantly say that more research needs to be done. This is always true, but it does not help solve the immediate problem. Existing legislation has provided the legal means for protecting fish. If this legislation is to be utilized in an intelligent manner, applied fish toxicologists should be involved in making the necessary toxicological decisions. One can criticize the legislation, the decisions that are made by the toxicologists or the philosophies upon which the decisions are based, but toxicologists must make such decisions because that is one of their jobs. If they do not do it, someone less qualified will. It is unfortunate that decisions must be based upon incomplete information and sometimes opinions and unproven assumptions. However, even though critics might not be happy with some of the decisions, it is just as likely that fish might not be happy either. One of the basic functions of applied toxicologists is to make the best possible decisions concerning the effects of toxic agents on the basis of the information that is available.

A second function of applied toxicologists is to help make available the most needed additional information by publicizing the need for more data and by identifying the most critical needs for experimental toxicologists. Just to say that more data are needed offers no guidance. The practical needs of applied toxicologists must guide experimental toxicology, not the whims of experimental toxicologists. Therefore, applied fish toxicologists must develop a detailed concept of their goals. The primary goal must be to protect the important species of fish for whatever reasons they are considered important. Some species are commercially or recreationally important; some are important as food for commercially or recreationally important species; and some are important because they are rare and endangered species. Normally, the protection of a species of fish requires protection of the population and a harvestable crop of quality fish suitable for various uses, such as food for man. Not only are fish important in their own right, but they also serve as sensitive indicators of water quality. A body of water that is unacceptable for fish is likely to be unacceptable for other desirable uses also.

Applied fish toxicologists must decide what specific data are needed the most on the basis of the goals, the legislation, and the most pressing problems. Once the needed information has been identified, then it must be determined whether existing toxicity tests can supply the information or whether new tests must be developed. Since almost any agent can cause an adverse effect if too much is present, the purpose of a toxicity test is to determine how toxic an agent is, not whether or not it is toxic. Because toxicity can be affected by many things, toxicity tests must be matched to specific needs and to individual kinds of situations.

Short-Term Exposures

Information regarding the effects of short-term exposures of fish to toxic agents is urgently needed. Such exposures can arise from a spill of a chemical or the application of a pesticide to a body of water. Some such information can be supplied by the acute mortality test. Several methods and many variations of each are in use, but most of them determine the level of a toxic agent which kills 50 percent of the subjects in two to seven days. This test has achieved widespread acceptance among fish toxicologists because it is easier, quicker, less costly, and more dramatic than any other kind of test. In addition, the acute mortality test has shown that great differences in sensitivity can exist between different species of fish and that water quality and temperature can have an important effect on the results of toxicity tests. However, short-term exposures can cause obviously important adverse effects other than death, such as flavor impairment and accumulation of toxic residues in fish tissue, and other kinds of acute toxicity tests are necessary to study these kinds of problems.

Long-Term Exposures

At least as important as the effects of short-term exposures are the effects of long-term exposures of fish to toxic agents. As the human population increases, the quantity and sources of pollutants are growing. As water pollution control becomes a reality, discharges of high levels of toxic agents are more and more being replaced by long-term discharges of low levels.

Thus, fish are being increasingly exposed to low levels of pollution for long periods of time, and applied fish toxicologists are becoming more and more concerned about the effects of long-term low-level exposures. Although fish are probably rarely exposed to a constant low level of a toxic agent continuously over a long period of time in a field situation, this is a practical and useful way to approach the problem from both legal and toxicological viewpoints.

Because of the advantages and acceptance of the acute mortality test, the first attempts to determine long-term safe concentrations were based on it. The test is severely limited for this use because first, a level that kills 50 percent of the subjects cannot be considered safe, and second, the test ignores all of the possible adverse effects other than death. However, two ways have been suggested to overcome these limitations. One involves the use of application factors. Hart et al[1][3] proposed a formula for the calculation of a safe concentration from results of acute mortality tests. Later, Henderson and Tarzwell[2] suggested that an application factor of one tenth might estimate the safe concentration in some cases. Such application factors are essentially arbitrary attempts to extrapolate from a toxicity test to a real-life situation.

The second way that has been suggested for using the acute mortality test to estimate long-term safe concentrations is to determine what is sometimes called a lethal threshold and to assume that the lethal threshold is the same as the long-term safe concentration. Unfortunately, a wide variety of terms, definitions, and methodologies have been used in connection with the lethal threshold concept, as evidenced by the articles of Chen and Selleck [3], Gersdorff[4], and Sprague[5]. The lethal threshold determined from an acute mortality test will almost never be the same as the safe concentration. Some other age group of the species will sometimes be more sensitive than the one tested or some other life process, such as reproduction, will almost certainly be more sensitive than survival. Arbitrary application factors could be used with the lethal threshold concept, but this again would be an arbitrary extrapolation. Even though these means of using the acute mortality test to estimate long-term safe concentrations for fish are not necessarily very accurate, sometimes they are the only means available.

Some fish toxicologists have suggested that the problems associated with using the acute mortality test for estimating long-term safe concentrations can be avoided by using other acute toxicity tests and making the assumption that any toxicant-induced change from normal in a species is deleterious to the species. Warner[6] has discussed this approach and many physio-

---

[3] The italic numbers in brackets refer to the list of references appended to this paper.

logical, biochemical, histological, and behavioral effects that could be studied in order to detect a change from normal. However, this approach is faced with the problem that different toxicants will cause different effects to greatly different extents. A given effect may be caused by one toxicant but not by others, and so to use this approach, numerous effects would have to be studied.

Even if a practical method were developed based on this approach, many fish toxicologists do not accept the basic hypothesis. Physiological, biochemical, histological, and behavioral studies of fish have not achieved importance in pollution control work because experimental evidence of their biological significance is lacking. The philosophy that any change from normal in a species is deleterious to the species can be extended to apply to whole aquatic ecosystems, which would imply that any man-caused change in the biological structure of an aquatic ecosystem should be considered detrimental. Investigators have little trouble showing that a change from normal will occur in a species or an ecosystem under specified conditions, but they have much trouble showing the significance of the change. Fish and aquatic ecosystems can adapt to some changes from normal, and certain changes may even be beneficial, as has been discussed by Smyth[7] and Haydu[8]. Changes from normal should not be considered detrimental to aquatic life until such changes can be shown to cause adverse effects on important organisms. Species diversity is a good thing, but it is not an end in itself. Thus, we do not agree with those who believe that all changes in aquatic ecosystems constitute damage or that the highest species diversity is the ultimate goal, just as we do not agree with those who believe in management of aquatic ecosystems in large natural bodies of water to the point of approaching monoculture.

Chronic Toxicity Tests

In 1967 Mount and Stephan[9] described a chronic toxicity test which was specifically designed to be useful for estimating long-term safe concentrations. Although many different kinds of tests have been called chronic tests, for our purposes a chronic test with fish consists of exposing different groups of one species to different specified levels of a toxic agent throughout a complete life cycle in order to study the effect of the toxic agent on the survival, growth, and reproduction of the species. To insure that all life stages and life processes are exposed to the toxic agent, the test is begun with eggs or fry younger than 20 days old and continued until the offspring of these fish are at least 30 days old. A similar test, called a partial chronic test, is conducted with some species that take a long time to reach sexual maturity. Partial chronic tests are begun with immature fish that are several months old so that the test can be completed in less than 15 months. The distinguishing feature of these tests is that the fish are exposed to the toxic agent before and during reproduction and the eggs and fry produced are exposed for at least 30 days. Despite the problems that have been encountered, successful chronic or partial chronic tests have already been conducted with fathead minnows, bluegills, brook trout, flagfish, bluntnose minnows, green sunfish, and longear sunfish. Chronic tests have also been conducted with three aquatic invertebrates, amphipods, daphnids, and midges, and methods for other aquatic organisms are being developed. Detailed instructions for conducting chronic and partial chronic tests with some of these species are available from the National Water Quality Laboratory in Duluth, Minn.

If the first important characteristic of the chronic test is the length of the exposure, the second is the nature of the effects that are studied. Since results of the test should be readily relatable to real-life situations, the results should be determined on the basis of effects that are obviously important and obviously adverse. Therefore, effects on survival, growth, and reproduction are used. These include, but are not necessarily limited to, effects on hatchability of eggs, survival of fry and adults, growth of fry and adults, maturation of adults, and successful spawning. By studying growth and spawning success, the chronic test can detect beneficial effects in addition to adverse ones, which most toxicity tests cannot do, as pointed out by Haydu[8].

In spite of its advantages, the chronic test by no means replaces all other toxicity tests because fish can be adversely affected in many ways. Other obviously important adverse effects which can be studied rather easily by means of toxicity tests are avoidance, flavor impairment, and accumulation of toxic residues. A toxic agent which renders fish useless due to flavor impairment or the accumulation of toxic residues in fish tissue can be just as destructive as one that interferes with survival, growth, or reproduction. Which toxicity test will be most appropriate in a given situation will often depend on the nature of the toxic agent. Undoubtedly, some toxicants will produce adverse effects due to avoidance, flavor impairment, or accumulation of toxic residues in short-term exposures at concentrations that will not adversely affect survival, growth, or reproduction in long-term exposures. Thus in some situations, acute toxicity tests will be more important for estimating long-term safe concentrations than chronic toxicity tests will.

Mixing Zones

Information is needed by applied fish toxicologists concerning the special problem of mixing zones. Here many considerations other than the toxicological ones are important, and these will have a bearing on the kind of toxicological information that is needed. The problem of mixing zones must be attacked on an interdisciplinary basis, but as a beginning, fish toxicologists should make a list of all the ways mixing zones might adversely affect fish to try to insure that all probable problems are adequately considered in mixing zone standards. Only then can the kinds of toxicity tests that are important be selected.

Toxicological Data Bank

A toxicological data bank of basic information about the toxicity of individual chemicals to fish is much needed. Such a bank should include not only information on relative toxicity, but also information on symptoms and rate of effect. To be most useful for comparative purposes, data should be collected using one test conducted according to a detailed methodology under defined conditions in an aqueous solution whose composition is completely specified with a specified age of one species of fish originating from a prescribed stock raised under known conditions. Data from more than one kind of toxicity test and more than one species of fish would be advantageous, but the information collected according to one test procedure with one species of fish in one water under one set of conditions would be much more useful than the mass of unrelated information that is now available. Such information could be used for classifying individual chemicals and mixtures of chemicals on the basis of toxicological properties toward fish and for making a first estimate of the potential hazard of new chemicals in real-life situations by reference to chemicals with similar chemical and physical properties. Specifically, a toxicological data bank should be useful for estimating what kinds of effects are likely to be most important for untested chemicals. Much of this kind of information can probably be obtained from one or more acute toxicity tests.

A third function of applied toxicologists is to evaluate the usefulness of toxicity tests and ways of using them to fulfill the needs that have been identified and, on the basis of the evaluations, to suggest improvements in existing tests or new tests that should be developed. The toxicity tests themselves and the ways they are used are equally important, and both must be evaluated in terms of their ability to provide useful information about what happens in real-life situations. Several different hypotheses have been used to make extrapolations from what does happen in a toxicity test to what will happen in a real-life situation. The simplest and most widely used hypothesis is the one-to-one correlation hypothesis that what happens in a real-life situation will be the same as what happens in a toxicity test, all other things being equal. The basic problem with this hypothesis is that it is often used when all other things are not equal or not even approximately equal. A second problem is the criteria that are used to determine if the same thing happened in the two different situations. For the purposes of water pollution control, whether or not exactly the same thing happened is not necessarily too important. One possible criterion is whether or not a level of a toxic agent which was found to be unsafe to a particular species in a toxicity test was also found to be unsafe to that same species in a comparable real-life situation. If so, then the one-to-one correlation hypothesis might be considered valid for that toxicity test and the test might therefore be considered useful. However, since this hypothesis can be used with any toxicity test, its validity must be tested with each individual kind of test, and any toxicity test for which the one-to-one correlation hypothesis is valid must be considered useful. No toxicity test should be used to determine water quality criteria unless there is good reason to believe that the test is useful, namely, that the test provides accurate information about what will happen in a real-life situation.

Direct, Indirect, and Induced Effects

One consideration that can have an important bearing on whether a toxicity test is or appears to be useful is whether the effect studied is direct, indirect, or induced. Direct effects are those caused only by a direct action of the toxic agent on fish. Indirect effects are those caused by an action of the toxic agent on something other than fish which, in turn, causes an effect on fish. The classic example of an indirect effect is the toxic agent that adversely affects fish because it destroys the food supply. Induced effects are those brought about by a direct action of the toxic agent on fish but which can only occur in the presence of another agent. For example, a toxic agent might increase the susceptibility of a species to a disease or a predator, but this effect will only occur if the disease or predator is present. Direct effects that occur in a laboratory exposure are much more likely to occur in a field exposure than indirect or induced effects. Thus, toxicity tests based on direct effects are much more likely to be useful than those based on indirect or induced effects. It is good common sense to emphasize direct effects first and make some immediate progress before attention is concentrated on the more difficult indirect and induced effects. Fortunately, most toxicity tests conducted with fish are based on direct effects.

Applied fish toxicologists cannot ignore indirect and induced effects just because extrapolations based on them are more difficult, since such effects can be just as important as direct ones. Again, the classic example is the toxic agent that adversely affects a food organism through a direct effect. Thus, it can be accurately predicted that the food organism will be destroyed in certain situations. However, species of fish that utilize that organism extensively may or may not be adversely affected. They may just switch to another food, in which case it would not be necessary to protect the food organism to protect the fish. If, on the other hand, an important species of fish that was not affected directly by the toxic agent was adversely affected indirectly because of the destruction of the food organism, then it would be necessary to protect the food organism in order to protect that species of fish.

Few people question the usefulness of the acute mortality test, but many question the usefulness of the chronic test, probably because it is fairly new and rather sensitive, even though both of these tests are based on direct effects. From the beginning, we have emphasized the necessity of testing the usefulness of the chronic test in a field situation[9], and this is the purpose of the Shayler Run Copper Toxicity Study being conducted by the Newtown Fish Toxicology Laboratory in Cincinnati, Ohio. This study was designed to be a side-by-side comparison of the results of acute and chronic laboratory exposures and long-term field exposures under comparable conditions. Effects other than those studied in the chronic test can occur and be observed in the field exposure. Not only do we want to know if the effects observed in the laboratory test occur in the field test, but we also want to know if effects that do not occur in the laboratory occur in the field. This one study with a few species of fish and one toxic agent in one water cannot answer all questions about the usefulness of the chronic test, but it is an important beginning. In addition to providing some information about the usefulness of and possible improvements in the chronic test, it will provide some information about what other toxicity tests might be important and about how future studies of this kind should be conducted. Unfortunately, such studies are high-risk ventures and require a lot of money and man-power, but even more of them are needed to determine the usefulness of the chronic test and other toxicity tests used in water pollution control.

If a toxicity test is assumed or proved to be useful, it may be used in several different ways to estimate water quality criteria using various hypotheses for extrapolating from one species of fish to another, one water to another, one set of conditions to another, or various combinations of these. In addition, relationships between toxic agents have been hypothesized. The accuracy of an extrapolation often depends on the validity of the hypotheses on which it is based, and in general, the broader the hypothesis, the less likely it is to be valid.

The broadest hypothesis is that the toxicity of a particular toxic agent is the same for all species of fish in all waters under all conditions. This hypothesis is often used to obtain a first estimate of toxicity when only one piece of information is available. Even though this hypothesis may be valid for some toxic agents, extrapolations based on this hypothesis are rarely believed to be very meaningful. A slightly more limited hypothesis is that the toxicity of a given toxic agent is the same for all closely related species of fish in all waters under all conditions. A more limited hypothesis is that in a specific water under a given set of conditions, the toxicity of a specific toxic agent is the same for closely related species. Such an hypothesis is likely to be valid for some toxic agents and some closely related species, but not for others. Another limited hypothesis is that the toxicity of a given toxic agent to any one species of fish is the same in all waters under all conditions. This hypothesis seems to be valid for some kinds of toxic agents and is often used as a basis for making extrapolations.

Because of the great differences that have been found between species of fish, extrapolations are more likely to be accurate if the same species is involved on both ends of the extrapolation. If important species are to be protected, these same important species should be used in the toxicity tests if at all possible. Acute tests and especially chronic tests are much easier to conduct with smaller species, because they are easier to obtain and handle in the laboratory and they have shorter generation times. However, most of the important species are larger ones. We believe that the need for accurate extrapolations is a compelling reason to conduct toxicity tests with important species whenever possible, even though this may require more effort. One of the major advantages of acute tests is that they can be conducted with a much greater variety of important species than can chronic tests.

Because toxicity can vary greatly with water quality, conditions, and species of fish, and because of the advantages of the acute mortality test, the most popular extrapolation procedure is the application factor hypothesis which states that the ratio between the long-term safe concentration and a specified LC50 is the same for all species of fish in all waters under all conditions. This hypothesis was widely used in spite of the fact that very little evidence was available to support its validity and very little evidence was available concerning the numerical value of the ratio. Generally, the ratio or application factor has been arbitrarily set at one tenth. To use this hypothesis, the specified LC50 of the toxic agent is determined with the species and water of concern under the appropriate conditions. The long-term safe concentration is then estimated by multiplying the LC50 by one tenth. Although many people were undoubtedly unhappy with arbitrary application factors, Warren and Doudoroff[10] were possibly the first to propose the use of experimentally-derived application factors. They suggested the use of 30-day toxicity tests in artificial streams to determine application factors for pulp mill wastes. Mount and Stephan[9] proposed that an application factor be calculated from the results of a chronic test and an acute mortality test conducted with the same species of fish and the same toxicant in the same water. This experimentally determined application factor would be much more useful for estimating water quality criteria than arbitrary application factors, if it could be shown that this application factor is nearly identical for a given toxicant for a variety of species of fish in a variety of waters under a variety of conditions. Laboratory tests are being conducted to test the validity of this hypothesis, and improvements in the original formulation have been suggested by Mount and Stephan[11] and Eaton[12].

Application factor hypotheses using the acute mortality test can be based on field data rather than laboratory data[13,14]. Such approaches generally derive an average application factor for all toxicants. However, such average application factors will undoubtedly be too high in some cases and too low in others, but the advantages of this kind of approach may more than compensate for this disadvantage. In addition, other application factor hypotheses can be formulated by replacing the acute mortality test with other acute toxicity tests, such as those based on physiological effects. Of special interest is the equivalent concentration hypothesis that for a toxic agent an acute toxicity test exists such that the ratio of the results of the chronic test and the acute toxicity test is unity for all species of fish in all waters in which and under all conditions under which the individual species can survive, grow, and reproduce acceptably. The major problem with this hypothesis is finding the right acute test, but often the chronic test will provide useful clues. Obviously, any acute test that makes up part of the chronic test can be used to place an upper limit on the long-term safe concentration. If the validity of the equivalent concentration hypothesis can be established for a given toxic agent, the acute toxicity test can be used as a short-cut test for estimating the long-term safe concentration. The equivalent concentration hypothesis may have more general validity than an application factor hypothesis, because it is not limited to one specific acute toxicity test and both the acute and chronic tests are conducted at the same levels of the toxic agent. This also means that synergism and antagonism can be studied at the level of the long-term safe concentration without conducting chronic tests. Of course, even without the equivalent concentration hypothesis, this is possible for those toxic agents whose long-term safe concentrations depend on avoidance, flavor impairment, or the accumulation of toxic residues.

A wide variety of toxicity tests and hypotheses are available, and a multitude of combinations are possible. Theoretically, the best procedure for making decisions about real-life situations would be to use only the one-to-one correlation hypothesis, but this would mean that for a given toxic agent and body of water the toxicity tests would have to be conducted in that water with the species of fish that were important in that body under ambient conditions. Although this can be done in many cases, it is usually considered more work than it is worth when dealing with individual toxic agents. However, toxicity tests on aqueous effluents are usually based on the one-to-one correlation hypothesis and generally utilize indigenous species and unaltered receiving water at existing conditions. Most often the biological testing of aqueous effluents is also based on the acute mortality test and an essentially arbitrary application factor. Basing effluent testing on the one-to-one correlation hypothesis and the chronic test would offer some distinct advantages. In testing effluents with the chronic test, fish would be exposed continuously to dilutions of the effluent in its receiving water throughout a whole life cycle. Thus, the test would be conducted with the water of concern under ambient conditions with one or more important species.

Since the test would have to be conducted under flow-through conditions with continuous sampling of the effluent, the problem of obtaining a representative sample of the effluent would be eliminated. An added advantage of this kind of test is that it would provide continuous biological monitoring of the effluent. Acutely toxic slugs of toxicants, which might be missed by monitoring systems based on grab samples, would be detected. Another advantage is that the fish themselves would be used to integrate the effects of various levels of various agents over a long period of time, rather than trying to do this in some arbitrary manner. Used in this way, the chronic test would provide a continuous biological monitoring system that would test the effluent using the sensitive, important end points of survival, growth and reproduction. The use of large fish would permit checking for problems related to flavor impairment and accumulation of toxic residues.

Because of the unique capabilities of biological testing of aqueous effluents, it should be a useful complement to physical and chemical testing. Chemical and physical water quality standards and effluent standards for the protection of fish are usually determined on the basis of biological measurements but promulgated and enforced on the basis of chemical and physical measurements. This kind of approach has its drawbacks. The identity and toxicity of each toxic agent must be known, and each sample be analyzed for each agent. In addition, the possibility of synergism or antagonism between toxic agents is usually ignored. Biological water quality and effluent standards can overcome these problems, but to be most useful, biological effluent testing should be based on the chronic, flavor-impairment, accumulation, and avoidance tests in addition to the acute mortality test. The obvious drawback of such tests for effluent testing is cost, but in many cases the advantages might outweigh the disadvantages.

Safety Factors

Regardless of what kinds of standards are set for the protection of fish, they all are based on decisions made by toxicologists on the basis of the best available information and all such decisions are to some degree subjective. Traditionally, applied fish toxicologists have not been allowed to use safety factors. Application factors are one means of making an extrapolation, whereas safety factors acknowledge the imprecision of extrapolations and allow a margin of safety to help insure protection. If standards are set only on the basis of extrapolations, a small error could be very detrimental to the fish. The decision as to whether or not to use safety factors should take into account the inherent imprecision of toxicological extrapolations and the appropriate risk-benefit ratio on a case-by-case basis. In many cases, it may be more appropriate to provide a margin of safety in some way other than through the use of a safety factor.

Water quality standards and effluent standards based on toxicological extrapolations must always be subject to change, not only because of the inherent imprecision and subjective nature of such extrapolations, but also, and more importantly, because of the possibility of new information becoming available from other kinds of toxicity tests. Standards based on the results of only one kind of toxicity test should especially be considered only first estimates, but standards based on obviously important adverse direct effects on important species will rarely be overly protective. A more basic problem is the changes that are likely to occur in fish toxicology as new information becomes available. Therefore, it is important to test various philosophies and hypotheses that are being used and to look for better alternatives. Furthermore, in any water pollution control program, the toxicological considerations must interact with the political, economic, social, and legal considerations to define the practical goals of the program and the best means of achieving them under the existing conditions. However, decisions about water pollution control should always take into account the nature of toxicology whenever standards are based on the results of toxicity tests.

References

[1] Hart, W. B., Doudoroff, P., and Greenbank, J., "The Evaluation of the Toxicity of Industrial Wastes, Chemicals, and Other Substances to Fresh-water Fishes," Waste Control Laboratory, Atlantic Refining Co., Philadelphia, June, 1945.
[2] Henderson, C. and Tarzwell, C. M., *Sewage and Industrial Wastes,* Vol. 29, No. 9, Sept. 1957, pp. 1002–1017.
[3] Chen, C. W. and Selleck, R. E., *Journal of the Water Pollution Control Federation,* Vol. 41, No. 8, Part 2, Aug. 1969, pp. R294–R308.
[4] Gersdorff, W. A., *Journal of Agricultural Research,* Vol. 50, No. 11, June 1935, pp. 881–891.
[5] Sprague, J. B., *Water Research,* Vol. 3, No. 11, Nov. 1969, p. 793–821.
[6] Warner, R. E., *Bulletin of the World Health Organization,* Vol. 36, No. 2, March 1967, pp. 181–207.
[7] Smyth, H. F., *Food and Cosmetic Toxicology,* Vol. 5, No. 1, Jan. 1967, pp. 51–58.
[8] Haydu, E. P., *Industrial Water Engineering,* Vol. 5, No. 7, July 1968, pp. 18–21.
[9] Mount, D. I. and Stephan, C. E., *Transactions,* American Fisheries Society, Vol. 96, No. 2, April 1967, pp. 185–193.

[*10*] Warren, C. E., and Doudoroff, P., *TAPPI,* Vol. 41, No. 8, Aug. 1958, pp. 211A–216A.

[*11*] Mount, D. I. and Stephan, C. E., *Journal of the Fisheries Research Board of Canada,* Vol. 26, No. 9, Sept. 1969, pp. 2449–2457.

[*12*] Eaton, J. E., *Water Research,* Vol. 4, No. 10, Oct. 1970, pp. 673–684.

[*13*] Armstrong, N. E., Storrs, P. N., and Pearson, E. A., in *Advances in Water Pollution Research,* Vol. 2, S. H. Jenkins, Ed., Pergamon Press, New York, 1971, pp. III–1/1 to III–1/15.

[*14*] Alabaster, J. S., Garland, J. H. N., Hart, I. C., and de L. G. Solbé, J. F., *Symposia/Zoological Society of London,* No. 29, 1972, pp. 87–114.

N. A. Thomas [1]

Assessment of Fish Flesh Tainting Substances

REFERENCE: Thomas, N. A., "**Assessment of Fish Flesh Tainting Substances,**" *Biological Methods for the Assessment of Water Quality, ASTM STP 528,* American Society for Testing and Materials, 1973, pp. 178–193.

ABSTRACT: Increased use of lakes and rivers for sport and commercial fishing in the vicinity of large municipal and industrial discharges has led to the realization that fish in many bodies of water are not palatable. The discharge of organic compounds has led to the contamination of fish flesh to such an extent that fishing is curtailed more because of poor eating quality rather than the lack of fish.

To evaluate the magnitude of the tainting of fish flesh in a large river, studies were conducted on the flavor of channel catfish (*Ictalurus punctatus Rafinesque*) flesh from the Ohio River from Pittsburgh, Pa., to Cairo, Ill. Tasting of fish flesh determined that a panel could differentiate between fish held upstream and downstream from a wastewater discharge. Caged test fish exposed for three days acquired a minimum of 70 percent of the off-flavor of native fish.

KEY WORDS: rivers, water pollution, organic compounds, fishes, taste, flavor, tainting substances

The quality of fish, as measured by their flavor, has not received the amount of public attention as compared to some of the other effects from pollution. The need to protect public health and aquatic life from toxic conditions has been the impetus for most of the pollution control programs. Fish flavor has only been noted in a passing way during the last 40 years.

Today, however, in recognition of the importance of fish flavor, many states have separate water quality standards protecting the quality of fish flesh. The State of Indiana is one of these where the standard reads, "There shall be no substance which imparts unpalatable flavor to food fish. . . ." All state standards include certain conditions which provide for a minimum level

---

[1] Chief, Large Lakes Program, Environmental Protection Agency, Grosse Ile Laboratory, Grosse Ile, Mich. 48138.

of protection. These are called the four freedoms, because a waterway is to be free of four types of pollutants. Many of the states feel that the four freedoms also include the flavor of fish, particularly number three, which states that the fish shall be "Free from materials attributable to municipal, industrial, or other discharges that: . . . produce color, odor, or other conditions in such degree as to create a nuisance."

In assessing water quality, fish flavor becomes important in that many compounds will impart an undesirable flavor to fish flesh at a lower concentration than is lethal to the organism.

The suitability of fish for consumption by humans is now becoming important, as well as the protection of aquatic life against adverse environmental conditions. A few examples of the seriousness of the problem will be shown later in greater detail.

The problem of the flavor of fish from San Francisco Bay reached such a magnitude that the San Francisco Bay Council awarded a contract to have the flavor of fish assessed and to extract compounds in order to identify the causative agents[1].[2] Rivers where off-flavors are a problem include stretches of the Mississippi from St. Louis downstream to New Orleans, and the Missouri River which contains a few sites where fish have an off-flavor[2]. Estuaries along the Gulf contain shrimp and oysters that contain undesirable flavors. Chemical compounds either singly or in combination with sewage discharged in large quantities usually produce off-flavors in fish (Ohio and Missouri River data).

Off-flavor in fish flesh does not necessarily signify a toxic or harmful condition for the consumer. On the other hand some highly toxic materials, such as mercury, do not impart off-flavor in fish flesh.

The group of compounds causing off-flavors in fish appears to be more related to the organic compounds, particularly the chlorinated compounds.

A wide variety of materials that can cause off-flavor in fish are listed in Water Quality Criteria[3]. These are hydrocarbons, phenolic compounds, sodium pentachlorophenate, coal-tar wastes, gas wastes, sewage containing phenols, coal-coking wastes, outboard motor exhaust wastes, petroleum refinery wastes, kraft paper mill wastes, wastes from synthetic rubber, explosives manufacturing wastes, algae, resins, and resin acids. A summary of literature is presented in Table 1.

Industry, for the major part, has limited fish flavor studies to very short-term investigations. These studies were either on a particular compound or a particular effluent that might contain many compounds. Dow Chemical of Midland, Mich., is one of the few companies that has a continuing program

[2] The italic numbers in brackets refer to the list of references appended to this paper.

TABLE 1—*Compounds imparting off-flavor to fish flesh.*

Compound	Threshold Odor Concentration mg/l	Reference [a]
Acetophenone	0.5	4
Benzkatechin	2.5	6
o-*sec* butylphenol	0.3	9
p-*tert.* butylphenol	0.03	9
p-Chloride Phenol	0.06	12
Chlorophenol	0.01	8
o-Chlorophenol	0.015	9
o-Chlorophenol	0.015	12
p-Chlorophenol	0.05	9
Coal-Coking Wastes	0.02	6
Coal-Tar Wastes	0.1	6
Cresylic Acid ("meta para")	0.2	4
Cresols	10.0	6
Cresol	10.0	7
"Cutting" Oil (Emulsifiable)	15.0	4
o-dichlorobenzene	0.25	4
B,B-dichlorodiethyl Ether	1.0	4
2,4-dichlorophenol	0.01	15
2,4-dichlorophenol	0.005	9
Diphenyl Oxide	0.05	4
Ethylbenzene	0.25	4
Gasoline	0.005	10
Simple petroleum hydrocarbon	1.0	10
"Insecticide" Oil (Heavy Aromatic Naphtha)	0.1	11
Isopropylbenzene	0.25	4
Kerosene	0.1	4
Kerosene	0.5	10
Kraft Mill Effluent—raw	1.0 (percent by volume)	26
Alpha-methylstyrene	0.25	4
Naphthaliene	1.0	6
α-Naphthol	0.5	6
B-Naphthol	1.0	6
α-Naphthylamine	3.0	6
Outboard Motor Exhaust Wastes	0.5	13
Petroleum Refinery Effluents	0.25 (threshold odor number)	14
Aromatic, neutral substances of phenols	2.6–3.4	5
Phenols in Polluted River	.02–.15	6
Phenol	.02–.1	11
Phenol	1.0	9
Phenol	15–25	6
Phenol	25.0	7
o-Phenyl phenol	1.0	9
Phloroglucin	100.0	6
Pyridine	5.0	6
Pyrogallol	20–30	6
p-quinone	0.5	6
Quinoline	.5–1.0	6
Resorcin	30.0	6
Sewage containing phenols	0.1	6
Styrene	0.25	4

TABLE 1—*Continued*

Compound	Threshold Odor Concentration mg/1	Reference [a]
Toluene	0.25	4
p-Toluidine	20.0	6
Xylenols	1–5	6

Type of Industry	Off Flavor	Reference [a]
Petroleum	none	2
Paper	present and toxic	2
Municipal sewage	severe	2
Chemical—general	severe and toxic	2
Type of Manufacture		
Synthetic detergents	none	2
Acetylene	none	2
Carlude	none	2
Glycol	present	2
Synthetic elastomer	present	2
Fluoridated hydrocarbons	present	2
Methylene	present	2
Chloronal	present	2
Chloroform	present	2
Hydrogenchloride	present	2
Synthetic rubber	severe	2
Metal	present and toxic	2

[a] Numbers in italics refer to the list of references appended to this paper.

to determine the lowest concentration of compounds that impart off-flavor to fish flesh, threshold odor number, for most of the products they manufacture[9].

Historically, three approaches have been used in the study of the production of off-flavor and odors of fish. Addition of materials to laboratory test tanks containing fish has provided much of the information on the mechanics of this phenomenon. From data on phenolic substances presented by the Aquatic Life Advisory Committee of ORSANCO in its Third Progress Report[16], it is evident that various compounds produce off-flavors in fish at concentrations that vary from 1/50 to almost equal that of the harmful or lethal concentration. Schulze[12] reviewed the work of Albersmeyer and Von Ericksen[5] and concluded that some phenolic compounds can produce an off-flavor in fish in 15 min, whereas others may require as long as 20 h. Mann[17] indicated that the entry avenue for an off-flavor producing substance is through the gills and skin. These studies also revealed that flesh near the lateral line in the abdominal region is most readily contaminated by tainting materials. The Dow Chemical Company[9] used the production of off-flavors in fish to monitor sewers and to determine the degree of removal required for specific compounds.

A second approach has been to test native fish. Fetterolf[18] determined that fish collected in the vicinity of industrial discharges did not have as desirable a flavor or aroma as fish captured from other sources. Boyle[10] used gas chromatography to analyze fish from the Ohio River and concluded that simple petroleum hydrocarbons in the flesh at concentrations even less than 1 ppm caused off-flavors. He also concluded that a taste panel could detect petroleum hydrocarbons in fish at concentrations less than the sensitivity of analytical techniques.

A third method to study off-flavor and odor is to expose caged fish to the contaminants. Surber et al[13] studied the effect of outboard motor exhausts and found that an off-flavor in fish was produced when the total fuel consumption of outboard motors was between 6.6 and 10.5 ml of fuel per cubic meter of pond water. One pond in his studies produced fish with a severe off-flavor when the total fuel consumption was 17.7 ml/m^3. They concluded that to avoid fish tainting, total fuel consumption should be restricted to 7.8 ml/m^3. Both native and caged fish did not possess an off-flavor prior to the operation of outboard motors, whereas after motor operation both types of fish samples possessed an off-flavor.

Results of studies in Muskegon Lake, Mich.[19] demonstrated that wastes from a petroleum refinery imparted an off-flavor to caged trout and that trout held within 0.8 km (0.5 miles) of the waste discharge of a bleached kraft pulp and paper mill acquired an off-flavor. In a study by Union Carbide[20], fish held in cages downstream from an effluent had an off-flavor after three weeks exposure. Chromatograms of these fish and of waste effluents led to the identification of the waste stream that produced the off-flavors.

Work by Newton and Fetterolf[21] indicated that even with a dilution of 1 to 440 of a chemical company's discharge, fish placed in the receiving stream acquired an off-flavor in four days. In additional work by Newton [22], he demonstrated that caged fish could be used to identify waste sources that produced off-flavors in fish. His results were the same for both four and seven day exposures. The caged fish method for the identification of the waste source that produces off-flavors in fish has proved very successful.

Methods

In May and October 1968, a series of off-flavor studies of the Ohio River on caged catfish were conducted. These studies incorporated the use of uncontaminated catfish placed in cages immediately upstream and within 100 to 1,500 m (109 to 1640 yd) downstream from waste discharges. The reach of river between Louisville, Ky., and Leavenworth, Ind., included 25 test sites. In July and October 1968 and 1969, cooperative surveys were conducted on the entire river to determine the general quality of the Ohio River fish. The States of West Virginia and Kentucky, the Federal Water Quality Administration, Bureau of Commercial Fisheries, and the Ohio River Valley Water Sanitation Commission participated in these studies. As a result of these studies, a total of 43 sites were evaluated.

Channel catfish from Lake Erie were used in all studies. The weight of the fish was 500 to 800 g. No attempt was made to identify the sex, as Baldwin et al[23,24] did not find any trend for higher or lower ratings for the same species of fish from any one season or any difference attributable to sex, weight, length, or body section. To ensure a uniform quality before exposure, the fish were held in 15° C running well water for a period of three weeks. After the fish were transferred to the test site, two fish each were placed in collapsible fish baskets. The baskets were 30 cm (12 in.) in diameter and 45 cm (18 in.) high. Two baskets were tied beneath the water surface where pilings were available. Otherwise, a float was placed in the basket which was tied so that it was 1 m below the surface, and a marker float was attached to the anchor. Where toxicity was suspected to be a problem, cages were placed at various depths farther downstream. Downstream from some of the municipal outfalls, slime covered the baskets in sufficient quantity to suffocate the fish. At these sites, wooden boxes with 4 cm (1.5 in.) holes were used as cages. In the cooperative study, the baskets were suspended from the wingwalls of locks and dams. During the initial studies, the baskets were allowed to remain in the river for 96 h. Subsequently, it was determined that a 48-h exposure was sufficient to produce off-flavors in fish.

After exposure, the fish were either frozen whole on dry ice or filleted, wrapped, and frozen. Whole fish were shipped to the Bureau of Commercial Fisheries Laboratory in Ann Arbor, and filleted samples were shipped to the Department of Food Science and Technology, Oregon State University, Corvallis, Ore. In both laboratories, the fish were thawed at 3.3° C, and the whole fish were cleaned and then wrapped in aluminum foil. Both laboratories baked the fish at 204° C for 40 min. After baking, the fish were removed from the ovens and meat from each sample was flaked and subdivided for the taste panel. At Oregon State University eight to ten experienced judges served on the flavor panel. Panelists were given a known reference along with the test samples. "Blind" references were also included in the testing. As indicated in Table 2, Oregon State University used a scale ranging from 1 to 7, whereas the Bureau of Commercial Fisheries used a scale from 1 to 9. However, it was noted in analysis of the four samples that

TABLE 2—*Fish odor and flavor rating system.*

Oregon State University Overall Desirability		Off-Flavor		Bureau of Commercial Fisheries Flavor and Odor	
				9	like extremely
				8	like very much
7	very desirable	7	none	7	like moderately
6	moderately desirable	6	slight	6	like slightly
5	slightly desirable	5	moderate	5	neither like or dislike
4	neutral	4	strong	4	dislike slightly
3	slightly undesirable	3	very strong	3	dislike moderately
2	moderately undesirable	2	extremely strong	2	dislike very much
1	very undesirable	1	very extreme	1	dislike extremely

NOTE—A rating of 5.0 to 7.0 is acceptable.

the Bureau of Commercial Fisheries Laboratory did not utilize the upper portion of their scale. The average difference of the duplicate samples between laboratories was 0.125 with a maximum difference of 0.6.

At Oregon State University the data was analyzed by analysis of variance. This provided for a statistical difference of samples from a reference.

Since 1968, the method used on the Ohio River has not changed appreciably except that the catfish are now obtained from commercial fish hatcheries which makes the holding no longer necessary.

Fish flavor assessment has been conducted on many river systems; however, the Ohio River has been studied in the greatest detail. It is difficult to pinpoint the beginning of complaints about the off-flavor of Ohio River fish, but it is evident from test results the problem is severe. Sportsmen have sought new uncontaminated fishing waters and commercial fishermen have had to sell their catches at reduced prices. Many commercial fishermen have lost their dressed fish markets and must now hold their catch live for use in private pay fishing lakes. Even with the impaired fish quality, there remains an important sport and commercial fishery on the Ohio River. Eliminating off-flavor, by improving water quality, could substantially increase these fisheries.

A survey by Jackson et al[25] estimated that sport fishermen in the Kentucky section of the Ohio River spent $746 434 in 1958 to capture fish and commercial fishermen marketed $410 000 worth of fish. They also estimated that this section of the river provided recreation to 287 090 fishermen a year. The Kentucky sector of the river is the downstream 1068 km (662 miles) of the total 1578 km (978 miles).

Complaints of fish possessing an off-flavor came mainly from fishermen that use two reaches of the Ohio River. Jackson et al[25] reported that

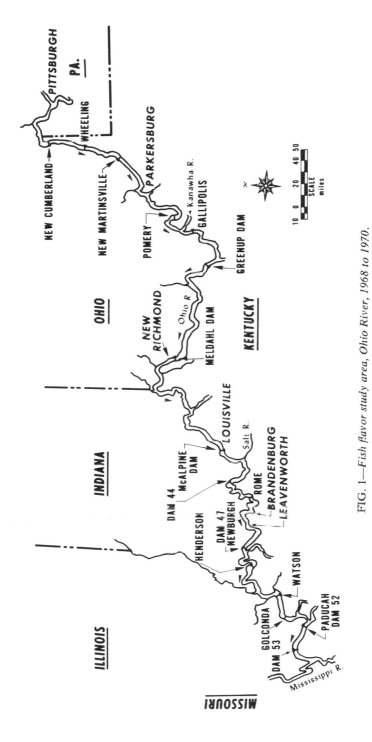

FIG. 1—*Fish flavor study area, Ohio River, 1968 to 1970.*

during the summer of 1958 complaints were received that fish downstream from Pittsburgh were unfit to eat because of a strong oily taste and odor. Jackson's survey revealed that fishes from the Ohio River at Louisville, Ky., possessed a disagreeable taste and odor. Residents in the area were asked to answer a questionnaire after eating native fish. Results indicated that fish from the Ohio River at Ashland and Louisville, Ky., were generally considered to have a poor taste. Jackson et al also reported a commercial fisherman complaint at Leavenworth, Ind., where fish were not marketable because of a taste resembling "slaked carbide."

Initially, the present study was to identify waste discharges that produced off-flavor in channel catfish (*Ictalurus punctatus Rafinesque*) downstream from Louisville. A later phase of the study identified the reaches of the entire Ohio River that contained fish of a poor flavor and odor quality. Intensive studies of May and October 1968, were conducted from Louisville (river mile (RM) 600) to Brandenburg, Ky. (RM 645). Studies covering the entire Ohio River were conducted in July and October 1968, and July and October 1969 (Fig. 1).

The Ohio River receives wastes from almost every type of industry. From Pittsburgh, Pa., to Wheeling, W. Va., the Ohio River receives wastes from numerous large steel mills. Along the reach from Wheeling to Huntington, W. Va., there are numerous steel mills and chemical industries. The reach from Huntington, W. Va., to Cincinnati, Ohio, is bordered by a mixture of textile, chemical, and metal industries. The reach from Louisville, Ky., to Evansville, Ind., was intensely studied because of the presence of a wide variety of industries which produced chemical, petroleum, metal, and paper products. The Ohio River downstream from Evansville, Ind., to its confluence with the Mississippi River has little industrial development except for the production of electrical power.

1968 Results

The investigation of the off-flavor of fish flesh in May 1968 revealed that a taste panel could differentiate between fish exposed to wastes in the Ohio River as compared to fish held upstream from the waste sources. In July 1968, caged fish acquired an off-flavor in the 320 km (200 mile) reach downstream from Pittsburgh and the 320 km reach downstream from Louisville. Native fish were collected from four of the test sites. This study revealed that both caged and native fish from sites in West Virginia generally possessed an off-flavor and that caged fish can be used to reflect the off-flavor caused to native fish of the same reach. The caged fish had at least 70 percent of the off-flavor score given to native channel catfish. In one case the caged catfish had a much lower degree of off-flavor which may have resulted from "native" fish migrating into the area just prior to capture. The use of caged fish has several advantages in that they are not subjected to migration, are not difficult to capture, and are of uniform quality at the beginning of the test.

The testing at Oregon State University included the rating of the fish for the overall desirability and flavor. The Bureau of Commercial Fisheries rated the fish as to their odor and flavor in the July test and added an evaluation of appearance and an overall rating for the October test. Between laboratories, the flavor rating of duplicate samples was very consistent. The lower flavor scores as compared to the odor score indicate that the detection of off-flavor producing substances was more pronounced when the panelists placed the sample in their mouth as compared to smelling the sample.

In the October 1968 study, a period of increased flows and lower water temperatures, the test fish did not acquire as strong an off-flavor. The average flavor score increased from 3.0 in July to 4.4 in October at the four stations downstream from Pittsburgh. In October, fish from two of these stations (New Cumberland and New Martinsville, W. Va.) were of an acceptable quality (flavor rating exceeding 5.0). From Pomeroy, Ohio, to Cairo, Ill., the same pattern of off-flavor existed; unacceptable fish flavors were found in the Louisville reach with acceptable fish flavors downstream to the confluence with the Mississippi River. Test fish from the upstream station at Louisville were of an acceptable quality with an average score of 5.2. In all studies the most downstream 320 km (200 miles) of the Ohio River (Evansville, Ind., to Cairo, Ill.) produced fish of an acceptable quality except at Golconda.

During the most popular fishing season (July) in 1968, only fish from the most downstream 290 km (180 miles) had acceptable flavor. During the October study, fish from three reaches totalling 600 km (372 miles) of the river had an acceptable flavor. These reaches were New Cumberland, Pa., to Wheeling, W. Va., upstream from Louisville, and the downstream reach to the confluence with the Mississippi River. The difference between the July and October surveys was that downstream from Pittsburgh the off-flavor producing substances had been dissipated sufficiently within 80 km (50 miles) to produce fish of an acceptable quality. Farther downstream, in the reach from Parkersburg to Huntington, W. Va., the fish were still of an unacceptable quality. In the Louisville area unacceptable flavors developed in the test fish; however, recovery took place within 240 km. During this study, test fish were exposed for both 48-h and 14-day periods. The fish that had been exposed for only 48 h obtained a minimum of 73 percent of the off-flavor of fish exposed for 14 days.

1969 Results

Fish flavor studies conducted in July and October of 1969 indicate the same general areas of fish flavor degradation as were documented in 1968. Severe degradation of fish flavor occurred downstream from Pittsburgh (3.7), the Kanawa River confluence (3.4), Huntington (3.4), Cincinnati (3.9), Louisville (4.6), and Galconda, Ill. (3.8). Similar flavor ratings for July and October 1969 were obtained for the fish samples from Pittsburgh to New Martinsville, W. Va. (3.7 to 4.7). For the remainder of the river (New Martinsville, W. Va., to Cairo, Ill.), the exposed samples from the October survey were of lower quality (3.0 to 5.5). During the July survey, fish from Meldahl Dam and Dam 47 had acceptable flavor (5.0) (Fig. 1). Samples downstream from Dam 47 were lost. High flows during the July survey probably diluted the wastes causing the undesirable flavors.

During the October survey, fish downstream from the Kanawha River to Greenup Dam had the lowest flavor ratings (2.8). During the October survey, samples from Dams 52 and 53 had an acceptable flavor.

Even with a large difference (4.7 in July and 5.5 in October) in the rating of fish flavor before they were placed in the river, the results indicate that fish can improve or deteriorate in flavor quality during the four day exposure period.

1970 Studies

During 1970, the flavor of caged catfish was assessed in four reaches of the Ohio River: (1) Pittsburgh—RM 0 to 43.0, (2) Wheeling—RM 54.4 to 129.1, (3) Huntington—RM 264.9 to 361.5, and (4) Cincinnati—RM 450 to 530. These surveys indicated that all but two test sites acquired unacceptable flavors. Industries responsible for the most serious problems produced chemicals, steel products, railroad drainage, etc. All of the large municipal discharges in the Pittsburgh reach produced severe off-flavors. Caged fish held in the Ohio River in West Virginia acquired unacceptable flavors as the result of discharges in Pennsylvania.

In the Wheeling reach, four of five samples were rated unacceptable. The samples downstream from the steel industry received the lowest ratings (2.2 to 3.6). The results from 1970 approximated those of 1968 and 1969 and indicated little or no improvement in the quality of the flavor of fish from the Wheeling reach.

The assessment of effluents causing undesirable flavors in fish flesh was studied in great detail from Huntington to Portsmouth, Ohio. These studies showed that discharges from chemical and steel industries, along with municipal wastes, severely degraded the flavor of fish. The flavor of fish held along the Ohio bank was the most severely degraded. Water currents in the Ohio River prevent lateral mixing for several miles downstream, thus confining the effects to near shore. The average quality was less than 0.5 units higher in 1970 as compared to the 1968–1969 average.

Analysis of the data from the Cincinnati reach indicates that the effluents from both sewage treatment and industrial plants in Kentucky and Ohio taint fish flesh. The municipal wastes in this reach contained both domestic sewage and industrial wastes which probably account for the severe off-flavor in the fish held downstream from Cincinnati.

Discussion

A comparison of all the results (Fig. 2) indicates that fish of acceptable quality occur in the downstream 320 km (200 miles), Newburg, Ohio, to Cairo, Ill. During periods of higher flows, fish had an acceptable quality at New Cumberland, Ohio, and Louisville, Fish from the remainder of the river had an unacceptable flavor.

In the intensive study of the Louisville area from RM 600 to 665, the taste panel noted that various types of industries produced noticeable differences in the flavor of caged fish. The main problem encountered in the testing of individual waste discharges was that of toxicity. The short distances between the discharges often did not provide sufficient dilution of a waste to less than its toxic level before the next downstream discharge entered the river. The degree of off-flavor caused by an individual outfall can be ascertained by the difference between the values obtained upstream and downstream from the discharge.

In the Louisville reach at the time of the studies, the petroleum related industries did not discharge substances that produced off-flavors in fish. In the paper industries, the discharges produced an off-flavor in fish flesh and were toxic. The average flavor score was 1.6 units lower at a distance of 100 m (330 ft) downstream from the discharge. Test fish placed in surface cages 100 m downstream from the paper products discharge were killed in 48 h. Fish placed an additional 160 m (525 ft) downstream had an off-flavor score 0.8 units higher than those fish immediately downstream from the discharge.

The discharge from the Louisville sewage treatment plant (STP) caused caged catfish 255 m (738 ft) downstream to have an off-flavor score of 0.8 units lower than fish held immediately upstream. This discharge was sufficient to produce extreme off-flavor in test fish 1.6 km (1 mile) downstream. The degradation in flavor of fish probably extended farther downstream, but other discharges that lowered the flavor score even more prevented the determination of the total distance downstream that the STP effluent caused off-flavors.

The waste discharge from industries producing chemicals and related

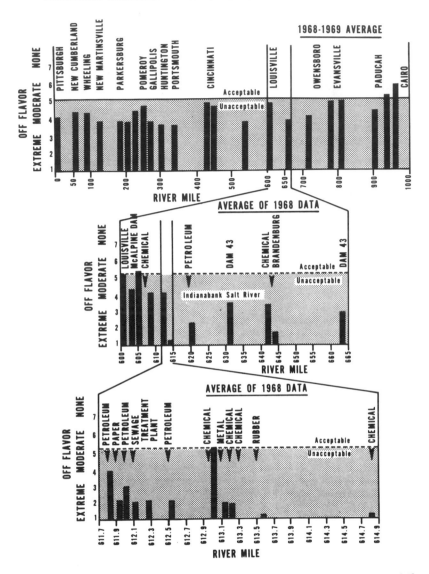

FIG. 2—*Degree of off-flavor of caged channel catfish, Ohio River, 1968 to 1969.*

products caused off-flavors to occur for the longest distances downstream. Synthetic detergents, acetylene, and carbide manufacturing waste products did not produce off-flavors or toxicities during this survey. The industries producing glycol synthetic elastomer, fluoridated hydrocarbons, methylene, chloronal, chloroform, and hydrogen chloride discharged wastes that caused severe off-flavors in test fish and were lethal to some test fish. The off-flavor of fish in the reach of the river receiving discharges from chemical companies was quite high, thus making the individual score decreases minimal.

In the Louisville to Brandenburg, Ky., reach of the Ohio River, there are waste discharges from five chemical plants and one synthetic rubber manufacturing plant that produced extreme off-flavors in fish as far as 13 km (8 miles) downstream. Three of the chemical waste discharges and the synthetic rubber waste discharge caused off-flavors so severe as to average only 1.3 on a 7 unit scale (1.0 is the lowest possible score). These were the lowest ratings assigned to any fish in the entire river from Pittsburgh to Cairo, Ill. The toxicity of these chemical waste discharges was a particular problem in waters near the surface and persisted for 160 to 450 m (525 to 1475 ft) downstream. Toxicity occurred at all depths at a point 145 m (475 ft) downstream from one of the chemical discharges.

In the metals and related products industry group, the effluents from industries manufacturing aluminum were toxic to test fish in surface waters 130 m (426 ft) downstream. Fish held beneath the surface waters acquire an unacceptable flavor. The wastes from the production of synthetic rubber and related products produced an off-flavor in the test fish.

Intense studies of the Pittsburgh, Wheeling, Huntington, and Cincinnati reaches reflect the same type of results that were observed in the Louisville study; namely, that the degradation of fish flavor could be attributed to individual discharges. Fish held several miles downstream would accumulate wastes in sufficient quantities to render the flesh unpalatable.

Conclusions

The quality of fish flesh can be assessed through a panel testing fish that have been held in cages. Test fish acquire nearly the same undesirable flavor as fish collected from the test site. It has also been found that fish acquire the undesirable flavor with only 48 h exposure. However, the off-flavor is only partially lost in 7 days, and the undesirable flavor can persist an additional week. Individual effluents can be assessed for their capability of producing an off-flavor several miles downstream. The test does not delineate the compound causing the off-flavor; however, threshold concentrations of individual components of a suspected effluent could be determined using the same procedure. The main purpose of the test is to delineate those effluents that cause fish to have off-flavors and allow the industry to test that discharge to determine which component is the causative agent.

Selection of an acceptable concentration of a substance must protect the flavor of fish flesh as well as being non-toxic. If fish are present in sufficient quantities to support a sport and commercial fishery, the concentrations of materials in discharges must be reduced so the flavor of fish is not impaired.

Acknowledgments

Acknowledgment is given to Lois Sather McGill, Department of Food Science and Technology, Oregon State University, and to the Bureau of Sport Fisheries and Wildlife (formerly the Bureau of Commercial Fisheries), Ann Arbor, Mich., who conducted the flavor panel studies.

References

[1] "Fish Taste Study Program," North Bay Water Advisory Council, San Pablo, Calif., 1967.
[2] Thomas, N. A. and Hicks, D. B., "Effects of Waste Water discharges on the Flavor of Fishes in the Missouri River (Sioux City, Iowa to Waverly, Missouri)" in *Everyone Can't Live Upstream*, EPA, Office of Water Programs, Kansas City, Mo., 1971.
[3] "Water Quality Criteria," Federal Water Pollution Control Administration, USDI, Washington, D. C., 1968.
[4] Winston, A. W., "Test for Odor Imparted to the Flesh of Fish," presented at 2nd Seminar on Biological Problems, Cincinnati, Dow Chemical Co., Midland, Mich., 1959.
[5] Albersmeyer, W. and Von Ericksen, L., *Zeitschrift Fuer Fischerei und Deren Hilfswissenschaften*, No. 8, 1959, pp. 44–46.
[6] Bandt, H. J., *Wasserwitrsch-Wassertech*, Vol. 9, 1955, p. 1.
[7] Ebeling, G., *Vom Wasser*, Vol. 14, 1940, pp. 81–91.
[8] Boetus, J., *Meddelelser Fra Danmarks Fiskeri—Og Havundersogelser*, Vol. 1 No. 4, pp. 1–7; also, *Water Pollution Abstracts*, Vol. 28, Jan 1954, p. 358.
[9] Teal, J. L., "The Control of Waste through Fish Taste," presented at American Chemical Society, National Meeting, 1959.
[10] Boyle, H. W., "Taste/Odor Contamination of Fish from the Ohio River near Tell City, Indiana," Cincinnati Water Research Laboratory, FWPCA, USDI, 1967.
[11] Knop, E., *Technische Mitteilungen*, Vol. 38, 1955, p. 132.
[12] Schulze, E., *Internationale Revue Der Gesamten Hydrobiologie*, Vol. 46, No. 1, 1961, pp. 81–90.
[13] Surber, E. W., English, J. N., and McDermott, G. N. in *Transactions*, Third Seminar on Biological Problems in Water Pollution, HEW, Public Health Service, Cincinnati, 1963, pp. 170–176.
[14] Krishnaswami, S. K. and Kupchanko, E. E., *Journal of the Water Pollution*, Vol. 41, Part 2 of No. 5, 1969, pp. R189–R196.
[15] Shumway, D. L., "Effects of Effluents on Flavor of Salmon," Department of Fisheries and Wildlife, Agricultural Experiment Station, Oregon State University, 1966.
[16] "Aquatic Life Water Quality Criteria," 3rd Progress Report of the Aquatic Life Advisory Committee of the Ohio River Valley Water Sanitation Commission, *Journal of the Water Pollution Control Federation*, Vol. 32, 1960, pp. 65–82.
[17] Mann, H. in *Transactions*, Pollutions Marines Par Les Microorganismes Et, hes Produits Petroliers, section of dela Commission, Paris 16, 1965, pp. 371–374.
[18] Fetterolf, C. M., Jr., "Taint Tests of Lake Run Rainbow Trout, Spring 1967," Michigan Water Research Commission, 1967.
[19] Fetterolf, C. M., Jr. in *Proceedings*, 18th Industrial Waste Conference, 1963, Purdue University Engineering Bulletin, Engineering Extension Series 115, 1964, p. 174.

[20] Wright, R. L., *Oil and Gas Journal,* Vol. 12, 1966, p. 135.
[21] Newton, M. and Fetterolf, C., "Follow-Up Fish Taint Tests, Little Bear Creek Muskegon County, Mich.," Report to the Michigan Water Research Commission, 1966.
[22] Newton, M., "Fish Taint Test, Manistee Lake, Manistee County, Michigan," Report to the Michigan Water Research Commission, 1967.
[23] Baldwin, R. E., Strong, D. H., and Torrie, J. H., *Transactions,* American Fisheries Society, Vol. 90, 1961, p. 2.
[24] Baldwin, R. E., Sides, K. G., and Robinson, J. W., *Transactions,* American Fisheries Society, Vol. 3, 1969, pp. 533–537.
[25] Jackson, D. F., Weise, J. G., Krumholz, L. A., Charles, J. R., Minckley, W. L., Clay, W. M., and Carter, B. T., "Aquatic Life Resources of the Ohio River," Ohio River Valley Water Sanitation Commission, 1962.
[26] Shumway, D. L. and Chadwick, G. C., *Water Research,* Pergamon Press, New York, Vol. 5, 1971, pp. 997–1003.

D. E. Hinton,[1] *M. W. Kendall,*[1] *and B. B. Silver* [1]

Use of Histologic and Histochemical Assessments in the Prognosis of the Effects of Aquatic Pollutants

REFERENCE: Hinton, D. E., Kendall, M. W., and Silver, B. B., **"Use of Histologic and Histochemical Assessments in the Prognosis of the Effects of Aquatic Pollutants,"** *Biological Methods for the Assessment of Water Quality, ASTM STP 528,* American Society for Testing and Materials, 1973, pp. 194–208.

ABSTRACT: Application of histologic and histochemical techniques to the determination of effects of aquatic pollutants upon fish tissues is discussed. Definition of terms and techniques associated with appropriate preparation of tissue specimens are given. Illustrations include examples from control and altered tissues. A summary of our work with methyl mercuric chloride in channel catfish illustrates the use of both techniques in assessing the prognosis of the effects of aquatic pollutants upon fish tissues.

KEY WORDS: water pollution, histology, histochemistry, histopathology, cytochemistry

Histology is an area of science which has to do with the study of the microscopic structure of body tissues. The techniques associated with histology are concerned with appropriate preparation of tissue specimens which permit microscopic examination of cells and cellular components.

Preservation of the Specimen

The initial step in tissue preparation is "fixation" or preservation of the specimen to be studied. Once an organ is deprived of its oxygen and blood

---

[1] Assistant professor of anatomy, Office of Water Resources Research predoctoral trainee in anatomical science, and assistant professor of physiology and biophysics, respectively, Departments of Anatomy, and Physiology/Biophysics, University of Louisville, School of Medicine, Louisville, Ky. 40202.

supply, the cells degenerate very rapidly (that is, they decay). This process is halted by fixation methods which preserve the tissue in a near-living state. Once tissues are properly fixed, water is removed by dehydration with alcohols. Tissues are then infiltrated with paraffin to permit the slicing of thin sections (5 to 10 microns). These sections are then spread on microscopic glass slides, the paraffin is removed and the tissues are then stained with dyes. Certain dyes demonstrate affinity for particular cellular components, usually through ionic attraction. Therefore, we are able to describe tissue structure and any peculiar alterations of cells which may indicate the presence of disease.

Fish Tissues

For illustrations of routine histologic preparations let us look at fish tissues prepared by common histologic techniques. In the gill (Fig. 1), lining cells of the organ are seen to have a single nucleus. The cells are flattened in appearance and blood vessels can be seen extending into each of the secondary lamellae. The kidney (Fig. 2) is seen as a bag of tubules without apparent arrangement. Inspection at higher magnification (Fig. 3) shows that the cells lining the tubules in one portion of the kidney differ in shape and size from those cells of other regions. By study of the special functions of each region, we learn the correlation between structure and function. Typical representation of liver tissue can be seen (Fig. 4). In this organ the cells are arranged in cords. Each cord is separated from the adjacent cord by a blood space. Nutrient material has abundant time to diffuse into the liver cells from the blood. Connective tissue (Fig. 5) lines the blood spaces of the liver. If this connective tissue becomes too numerous or increases in thickness or both (Fig. 6), the passage of nutrient material may be hampered and disease will result.

Desiring to go beyond the description of structure without regard for function, histologists have developed a large number of so-called histochemical methods. In simple terms, histochemistry is the study of chemicals found in tissues. By utilizing appropriate histochemical techniques, we are able to demonstrate fat (Fig. 7) and carbohydrates (Fig. 8) in tissue sections. In these instances we are localizing chemicals within tissues (namely, histochemistry).

Why go to all this trouble for histologic and histochemical examination? The external effects of toxins on fish (loss of equilibrium, death) occur after significant damage to internal organs. Histology can give useful data concerning tissue changes prior to external manifestation. Thus, examination of fish tissues should give us early indications of pollution. Examination after fish kills may serve to identify the causative agent. We need to become

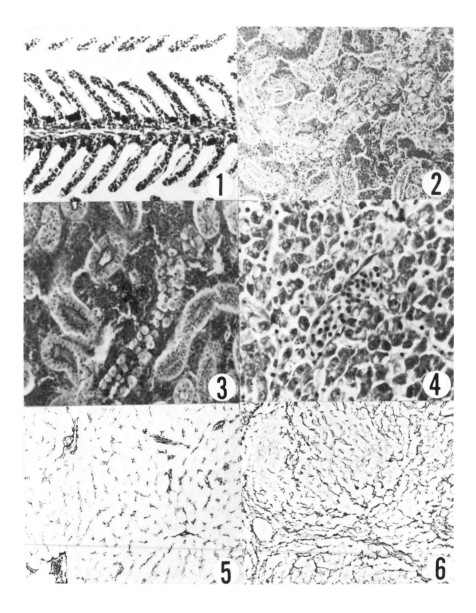

aware of the baseline of normalcy in fish histology, so that subsequent identification of toxic alteration can be accurately accomplished.

Depression of respiration, a common feature in acute poisoning, may be reflected by changes in the tissues of the respiratory organ. The respiratory organ of fishes is the gill, and certain features of the gill histology, such as amount and functional state of mucus glands, and thickness and cellularity of respiratory epithelium, deserve special attention.

Nerve transmission and brain function are altered in acute toxic conditions[1].[2] The brain is also the site of deposition of copper and mercury in heavy metal intoxication in humans. Special stains can demonstrate copper in affected tissues.

Assessment of Toxicity of Substances

The liver, the primary organ of detoxification[2], should receive special attention because of its role in the partial metabolism of chlorinated hydrocarbon pesticides[3]. Numerous investigations of intoxication in mammalian systems by chlorinated hydrocarbons have been undertaken[2,4–10]. The following criteria have been used extensively in assessing toxicity of substances (drugs, food additives, etc.) prior to approval for human consumption, and these criteria may serve as a working approach for assessing toxicity in aquatic pollution.

1. Fat accumulation in liver cells (hepatic liposis) often follows periods of starvation, poisoning, and extreme stress. Chlorinated hydrocarbon pesticide residues are found in liver and body fat of fishes[11–13] indicating that

---

[2] The italic numbers in brackets refer to the list of references appended to this paper.

FIG. 1—This section of gill is from a bluntnose minnow. The horizontal bar supports respiratory structures called secondary lamellae (vertically oriented). A single layer of epithelium separates blood cells from surrounding water. Periodic acid-Schiff's reagent and Hematoxylin, × 400.

FIG. 2—A low power view of channel catfish kidney reveals numerous tubules in cross section with abundant intertubular tissue. Pollak's Polychrome, × 200.

FIG. 3—At higher magnification, the cells lining the channel catfish kidney tubules are seen to differ. Large, rounded cells of the distal tubules are in center of photograph. Toward the sides, more proximal segments with darkly stained brush borders can be seen. Periodic acid-Schiff's reagent, × 400.

FIG. 4—In liver of largemouth bass, a small vein can be seen containing nucleated red blood cells. The liver cells are separated from adjacent cells by abundant blood spaces (white areas). Hematoxylin and Eosin, × 325.

FIG. 5—Connective tissue of liver from largemouth bass exists in a regular netlike pattern. Silver impregnation, × 325.

FIG. 6—In this section from mouse liver extensive scarring of connective tissue is shown. There is an increase in thickness and amount of connective tissue fibers. Silver impregnation, × 200.

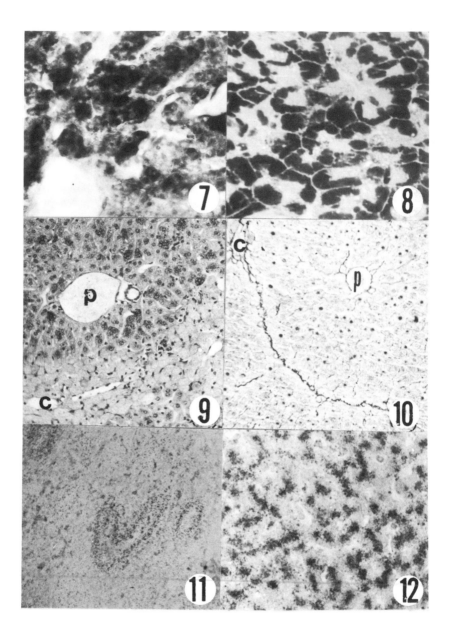

partial metabolism of these substances occurs in the liver followed by binding to fat molecules and transport to peripheral fat depots. Variations in total liver fat, concurrent with seasonal changes, have been demonstrated in catfish[14]. We feel, then, that study of the normal seasonal fat content of the liver is necessary to establish the dilution factor for chlorinated hydrocarbon pesticides.

2. Necrosis (death) of liver cells in areas adjacent to central veins. This is a reaction in response to more severe stimuli or chronic exposure to stimuli (as in 1). Necrosis of liver cells in areas adjacent to portal veins has been seen in our mercury studies. Thus, the location of dead cells serves to identify the responsible toxin.

3. Increase in connective tissue of the liver (hepatic fibrosis). This condition is illustrated (Figs. 9 and 10) in sections from mouse liver. Carbon tetrachloride injection caused centrolobular necrosis (Fig. 9) which was followed by fibrosis (Fig. 10).

4. Presence of regenerative nodules (hepatomas) in liver. This reaction is indicative of massive hepatic necrosis following repeated hepatic insults. The occurrence of hepatoma in trout liver was reported[15]. These tumors arose in response to aflatoxin. It is reasonable to expect that changes similar to the above sequence occur in other fish and are suitable to detailed histologic and histochemical analysis.

Enzyme Histochemistry

Not only does histochemistry concern location of fat and carbohydrate, but also protein, particularly enzymes; thus, the subdiscipline termed enzyme histochemistry.

FIG. 7—*This liver section has been stained to show lipid (fat). Black areas represent sites of neutral lipid. The normal fish liver would not reveal this abundance of lipid. Sudan black stain,* × *400.*

FIG. 8—*Black areas represent glycogen deposits. This section was taken from largemouth bass liver. This amount of glycogen is seen frequently in livers of normal fishes. Technique employed oxidation with H_2O_2 [29]. Schiff's reagent,* × *950.*

FIG. 9—*This figure shows necrotic cells staining a light grey in color, in bottom of photograph surrounding central veins of liver. A portal vein, just above the center of field, surrounded by unaltered liver cells which stain more darkly and contain glycogen. Periodic Acid-Schiff's reagent and Hematoxylin,* × *200.*

FIG. 10—*Connective tissue septum is seen as a black line extending from central vein at upper left corner. Portal vein (p) and surrounding area show no connective tissue changes. In normal liver sections no connective tissue septa are seen. Silver impregnation,* × *200.*

FIG. 11—*Acid phosphatase reaction product in kidney tubule of channel catfish. This represents a normal location and amount of the enzyme,* × *500.*

FIG. 12—*Acid phosphatase reaction product in liver of channel catfish. The reaction product is seen as droplets overlying bile canaliculi. Both pattern and amount of reaction product are within the normal range,* × *400.*

Several hundred protein enzymes are known. Each year new enzymes are added to the list. Enzymes are named by the reactions they catalyze. Thus, oxidases, hydrolases, reductases, dehydrogenases, and esterases are general names for biologic enzymes. In enzyme function the following factors are of extreme importance: pH, enzymes have optimum pH's at which they operate, some are acid and some are alkaline; temperature, increases in temperature increase the speed of reactions, although excessive temperatures denature enzymes; inhibitors, enzymes have reactive sites that are small in comparison to the size of the overall protein, these reactive sites may become bound to metals with inhibition of enzyme activity resulting. Enzymes, then, become extremely important as we consider heavy metal aquatic pollutants.

Localization of enzymes is made possible by introducing tissue enzyme to synthetic substrate. A reaction occurs in which a colored reaction product is formed. The reaction product and, thus, the locale of the enzyme can be determined.

Some of the enzymes commonly assayed in biologic studies are: succinic dehydrogenase, a respiratory enzyme which catalyzes the conversion of succinate to fumarate within the Kreb's citric acid cycle[16,17]; acid phosphatase, a lysosomal enzyme[18,19] which breaks ester linkages in molecules; alkaline phosphatase and adenosine triphosphatase, enzymes mediating membrane transport[20]; carbonic anhydrase, a respiratory enzyme catalyzing the formation of carbonic acid; aminopeptidase, a hydrolytic enzyme which cleaves the peptide chains of proteins at the amino terminal and is seen at sites of tissue repair[21]; acetylcholinesterase, necessary for the destruction of the neurotransmitter, acetylcholine, at neuromuscular junctions[22]; and glucose-6-phosphatase, located in the smooth endoplasmic reticulum of liver cells and in kidney, this enzyme catalyzes the breakdown of glycogen to glucose[23,24].

In the channel catfish, acid phosphatase is found in cells of proximal kidney tubules (Fig. 11) and in liver cells (Fig. 12). Alkaline phosphatase can be seen in brush border of certain tubular cells of the kidney (Fig. 13) and succinic dehydrogenase can be seen (Fig. 14) in the distal portion of kidney tubules. In the liver of largemouth bass, glucose-6-phosphatase reaction product forms a cuff around nuclei of liver cells (Fig. 15). Certain of the enzyme histochemical techniques have been adapted to electron microscopy. The increased resolution and magnification properties of electron microscopy permit intracellular localization of enzymes within cellular organelles (Fig. 16).

Enzyme histochemistry yields precise data concerning localization of enzymes, but quantitation must be accomplished through biochemical techniques of homogenization performed on whole organs; quantitation but not

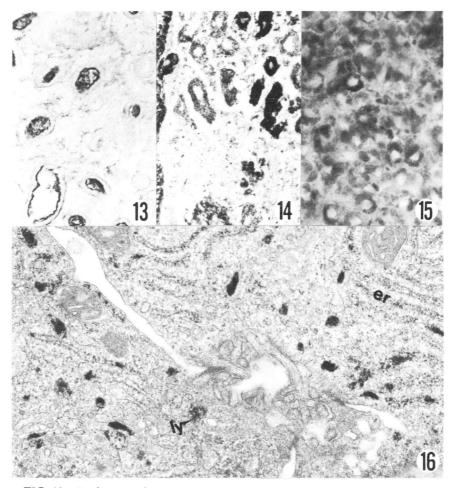

FIG. 13   Dark material is reaction product of alkaline phosphatase in brush border of proximal kidney tubules from channel catfish. This represents normal pattern and amount of reaction product, × 400.

FIG. 14—Dark material is reaction product of succinic dehydrogenase. Location is distal tubules of kidney in channel catfish. Both pattern and amount are normal, × 400.

FIG. 15—Dark material surrounding circular clear areas is glucose-6-phosphatase reaction product in liver cells of largemouth bass. This represents a normal pattern and amount, × 400.

FIG. 16—Electron micrograph showing acid phosphatase reaction product (dark material) in liver cell of channel catfish. Reaction product is localized in lysosomes (LY) and in endoplasmic reticulum (ER). Gomori's [30] acid phosphatase method with adaptations for electron microscopy, × 26 000.

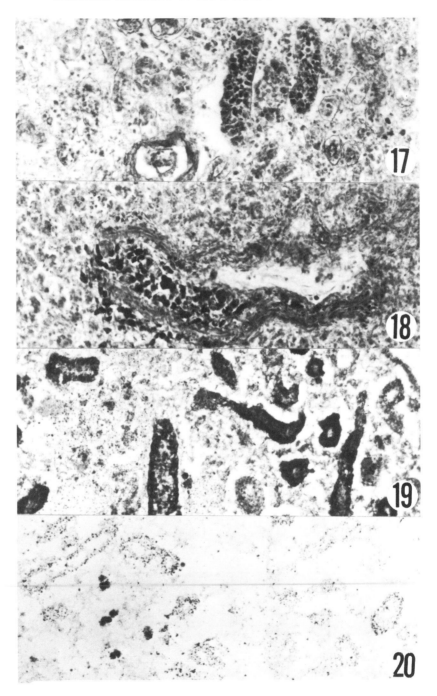

localization is possible. One can see the need for correlation of study incorporating biochemical/histochemical techniques.

Previous studies involving aquatic pollutants and enzyme alteration are due our consideration at this time. Koch[1,25] demonstrated inhibiting effects of various pesticides (aldrin, chlordane, DDT, dieldrin, lindane) on the enzyme ATPase. Animals studied were lake trout, rabbits, chickens, and cockroaches. In all animals, DDT was found to be the most effective inhibitor of adenosine triphosphatase (ATPase). This work is particularly interesting in light of the similarity of response in fish and warm blooded species (rabbit, chicken).

Hutterer et al[26], studying the effect of dieldrin on rat liver, described an early response in liver cells. This response was an alteration seen as hypertrophy of the smooth endoplasmic reticulum (SER). The SER is an organelle of cells which is active in drug metabolism. The SER response occurred prior to light microscopic alteration in liver cells and was believed to reflect the border between adaptation and toxicity. As such, this response would be useful in aquatic toxicologic consideration. We have demonstrated the glucose-6-phosphatase reaction in largemouth bass[27]. You will recall that this enzyme is associated with the SER. Therefore, spectrophotometric assay for total glucose-6-phosphatase would be useful as a measure of SER and an indirect measure of early cellular toxicity.

In vitro studies of five liver enzymes (acid and alkaline phosphatase, catalase, xanthine oxidase, and ribonuclease) in the killifish[28] revealed marked differences in enzyme activities following exposure to copper and mercury. These workers believe, as do we, that changes in liver enzyme activity and in enzymes from other tissues (brain, gills, kidney) are useful as a kind of biochemistry autopsy tool for diagnosing sublethal metal poisoning in fish.

Histologic and Histochemical Assessment in Fish Exposed to Methyl Mercury

We have studied the acute effects of methyl mercuric chloride intoxication in the channel catfish. A brief discussion of that study will serve as an

FIG. 17—*Channel catfish kidney shows death of cells (necrosis) following single exposure to 15 mg/kg body weight of methyl mercuric chloride. Tubular cells are desquammating into lumen of tubules. Basement membranes of glomeruli are thickened and stain intensely. Periodic acid-Schiff's reagent plus hematoxylin, × 400.*
FIG. 18—*Portal vein and adjacent area of liver in mercury treated catfish. Necrosis of cells and connective tissue scarring are shown. Periodic acid-Schiff's reagent, × 500.*
FIG. 19—*Succinic dehydrogenase in kidney of control catfish, × 500. This reveals normal amount and pattern.*
FIG. 20—*Section from same kidney as in Fig. 19 but incubation medium contained methyl mercuric chloride. Note decrease in reaction product and inhibition of enzyme, when compared to Fig. 19.*

example of the use of histologic and histochemical assessments in determination of the effects of aquatic pollutants.

Fish were divided into three groups. One group received 15 mg methyl mercuric chloride/kg body weight in a single intraperitoneal injection. After periods of 24, 8, 742, 96 h, fish were killed and the liver and kidneys were removed for histologic, histochemical, and biochemical analysis. A second group received one tenth the dosage of the first group in a single intraperitoneal injection, and the liver and kidneys were studied as in the first groups after identical time periods. A third group received a single injection of volume of a physiologic solution without methyl mercuric chloride.

Histologic study of the liver and kidney from controls revealed no alterations. Histologic examination of fish receiving the heavy dose (15 mg/ kg) revealed extensive pathologic alteration in kidney and liver (Figs. 17

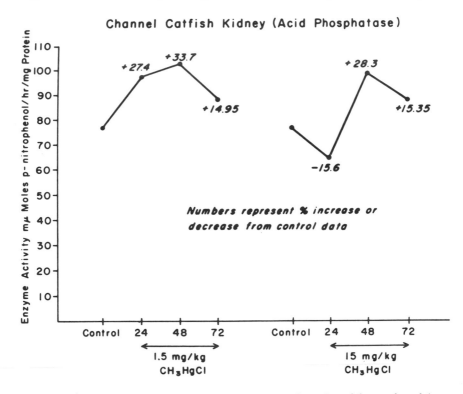

FIG. 21—*Acid phosphatase activity in kidney of channel catfish at selected intervals following exposure to methyl mercuric chloride. Line to left represents changes in enzyme activity following a single dose of 1.5 ppm. An increase, seen at 24 h, is maintained through 48 h. Subsequent levels return toward control amounts. With 15 ppm dose, an initial decrease is seen followed by a sharp rise in activity when compared to control values.*

and 18). When studied histologically, fish receiving the 1.5 mg/kg dosage revealed little or no change in kidney and only small, occasional foci of alteration in liver when compared to controls.

Enzyme histochemistry revealed marked changes in succinic dehydrogenase in kidney after the 15 mg/kg dosage (Figs. 19 and 20). Spectrophotometric analysis showed increases in kidney and liver acid phosphatase activity at both dosage levels (Figs. 21 and 22) between 24 and 48 h after injection. Succinic dehydrogenase was inhibited at both dosage levels in kidney at 24 h (Fig. 23).

From these results we can conclude that definite histologic alteration will accompany single dosage levels near the LD50 range of toxicant concentra-

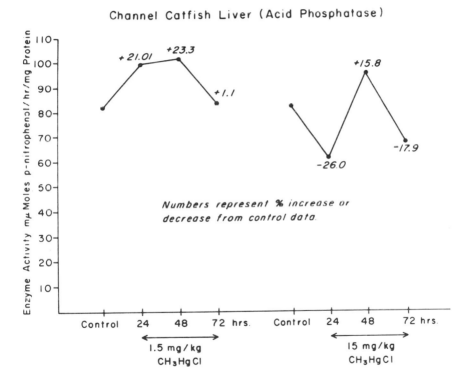

FIG. 22—*Acid phosphatase activity in liver of channel catfish at selected intervals following exposure to methyl mercuric chloride. With the 1.5 ppm dose, an increase in activity is seen through 48 h, followed by a return to normal values at 72 h. With the heavier dose (15 ppm) an initial decrease is seen followed by a sharp increase and, at 72 h, below normal values are seen. All fish treated with 15 ppm dose died. Below normal acid phosphatase values in liver accompanies massive alteration of tissue.*

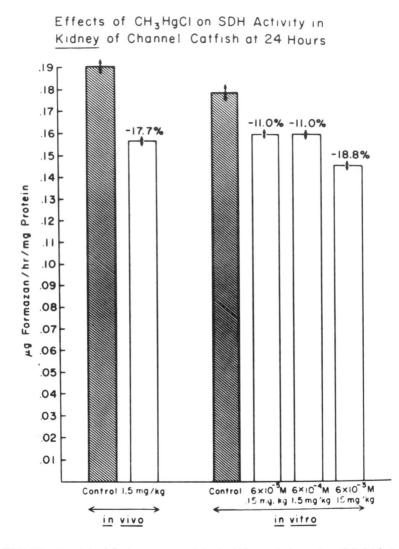

FIG. 23—*Succinic dehydrogenase activity in kidney of channel catfish 24 h following exposure to methyl mercuric chloride. At 24 h following a single injection of 1.5 ppm methyl mercuric chloride* (in vivo), *a depression of 17.7 percent is seen in succinic dehydrogenase activity.* In vitro *experiment reveals depression of activity at three dosage levels.*

tion. Chronic administration of even smaller concentrations would be expected to produce alteration. Alterations in enzymes without concurrent structural, histologic alteration characterize the administration of a single acute low concentration of methyl mercury. Electron microscopic examination coupled with enzyme histochemical techniques offer greater possibility of detection of early alteration in response to aquatic toxins.

In general, we can state the following concerning heavy metal pollutants:

1. Free metals in tissues cause enzyme alteration even in very low concentration.

2. Liver damage can be seen as necrosis in portal areas (especially with mercury) and connective tissue septum formation.

3. Pancreatic cells within walls of portal veins are subject to damage and can release injurious enzymes (lipases, proteases) into adjacent liver tissue.

4. Sequelae symptoms may appear from indirect effect upon other organs such as lenticular damage in brain.

5. External symptoms are loss of equilibrium and often edema (ascites) from inadequate kidney function.

Chlorinated hydrocarbons cause enzyme inhibition particularly in liver and at neuromuscular junctions. Enzyme alteration is accompanied by structural alteration upon continued exposure to toxin.

Summary

By demonstration of tissue alteration subsequent to exposure to aquatic pollutants, histologic and histochemical assessments prove the toxic nature of these compounds. In addition, the extent of alteration becomes the basis for prognosis of effects of various concentrations of aquatic pollutants. Following the elucidation of effects of differing levels of aquatic toxins, reasonable water quality standards can be made. Continuous bioassay of animal tissues living under these water quality conditions reveals the efficacy of our standards. Both establishment of new water quality criteria and examination of current standards can be facilitated by histologic and histochemical assessments.

References

[1] Koch, R. B., *Chemical Biological Interactions,* Vol. 1, 1969, pp. 199–209.
[2] Hutterer, F., Klion, F. M., Wengraf, A., Schaffner, F., and Popper, H., *Laboratory Investigation,* Vol. 20, 1969, pp. 455–464.
[3] Ortega, P., Hayes, W. J., and Durham, W. F., *Archives of Pathology,* Vol. 64, 1957, pp. 614–622.
[4] Anderson, P., Cohen, S., and Barka, T., *Archives of Pathology,* Vol. 71, 1961, pp. 89–95.
[5] Aterman, K., *Archives of Pathology,* Vol. 57, 1954, pp. 1–11.
[6] Gall, E. A., *American Journal of Pathology,* Vol. 36, 1960, pp. 241–271.

[7] Popper, H., Paranetto, R., Schaffner, F., and Perez, V., *Laboratory Investigation,* Vol. 10, 1961, pp. 265–290.

[8] Quinn, P. S., and Higginson, J., *American Journal of Pathology,* Vol. 47, 1965, pp. 353–369.

[9] Rubin, E., Hutterer, F., and Popper, H., *American Journal of Pathology,* Vol. 42, 1963, pp. 715–728.

[10] Kimbrough, R. D., Gaines, T. B., and Hayes, W. J., *Archives of Environmental Health,* Vol. 16, 1968, pp. 323–341.

[11] Dugal, L. C., *Journal of the Fisheries Research Board of Canada,* Vol. 25, 1968, pp. 169–172.

[12] Gakstatter, J. H., *Journal of the Fisheries Research Board of Canada,* Vol. 25, 1968, pp. 1797–1801.

[13] Duffy, J. R. and O'Connell, D., *Journal of the Fisheries Research Board of Canada,* Vol. 25, 1968, pp. 189–195.

[14] Suppes, C., Tiemeyer, O. W., and Deyoe, C. W., *Transactions, Kansas Academy of Science,* Vol. 70, 1967, pp. 349–358.

[15] Halver, J. E. and Mitchell, I. A., Trout Hepatoma Research Conference Papers, Research Report 70, USDI, 1967.

[16] Roodyn, D. B. in *Enzyme Cytology,* Academic Press, New York, 1967, p. 113.

[17] Sanadi, D. R., *Annual Review of Biochemistry,* Vol. 34, 1965, p. 21.

[18] Novikoff, A. B. in *The Cell,* Vol. 2, J. Brachet and A. E. Mirsky, Eds., Academic Press, New York, 1961, p. 423.

[19] Novikoff, A. B., *Ciba Symposium on Lysosomes,* Churchill, London, 1963, p. 36.

[20] Goldfischer, S., Essner, E., and Novikoff, A. B., *Journal of Histochemistry and Cytochemistry,* Vol. 12, 1964, pp. 72–95.

[21] Nagel, W. and Willig, F., *Nature,* Vol. 201, 1964, pp. 617–618.

[22] Nachmansohn, D. in *Modern Trends in Physiology and Biochemistry,* E. S. B. Barron, Ed., Academic Press, New York, 1952, p. 229.

[23] Pearse, A. G. E. in *Histochemistry,* Little, Brown and Company, Boston, 1953.

[24] Tice, L. W. and Barrnett, R. J., *Journal of Histochemistry and Cytochemistry,* Vol. 10, 1962, pp. 715–728.

[25] Koch, R. B., *Journal of Neurochemistry,* Vol. 16, 1969, pp. 269–271.

[26] Hutterer, F., Schaffner, F., Klion, F. M., and Popper, H., *Science,* Vol. 161, 1968, pp. 1071–1019.

[27] Hinton, D. E., Snipes, R. L., and Kendall, M. W., *Journal of the Fisheries Research Board of Canada,* Vol. 29, 1972, pp. 531–534.

[28] Jackim, E., Hamlin, J. M., and Sonis, S., *Journal of the Fisheries Research Board of Canada,* Vol. 27, 1970, pp. 383–390.

[29] Pool, C. R., *Stain Technology,* Vol. 44, 1969, pp. 75–79.

[30] Gomori, G., *Microscopic Histochemistry, Principles and Practice,* University of Chicago Press, Chicago, 1952.

V. T. Stack, Jr.[1]

Stabilization Oxygen Demand

REFERENCE: Stack, V. T., Jr., **"Stabilization Oxygen Demand,"** *Biological Methods for the Assessment of Water Quality, ASTM STP 528,* American Society for Testing and Materials, 1973, pp. 209–220.

ABSTRACT: Oxygen required in biological stabilization of organic materials is a fundamental approach in assaying the presence of such biodegradable materials. Comparative results present the status of biological stabilization reactions in natural systems and biological processes. The biochemical oxygen demand procedure (5-day incubation) has been utilized as a limited measurement of the desired data. A stabilization oxygen demand technique for more definitive examination of biological stabilization is being developed by a Task of Committee D–19 on Water. The analytical technique is based on measurements of energy oxygen utilized in support of synthesis reactions and of the resulting synthesis of microorganisms. Completion of analysis in about 1 h is an objective.

KEY WORDS: water pollution, biochemical oxygen demand, aeration, microorganism control (sewage), bioassay, stabilization oxygen demand, energy oxygen, endogenous oxygen

In 1971, the Biochemical Oxygen Demand (BOD) Task Group of Committee D-19 on Water took action to discontinue without replacement ASTM Test for Biochemical Oxygen Demand of Industrial Water and Waste Water (D 2329–68). The action was drastic considering that the BOD procedure goes back to antiquity and considering the place of importance of BOD data in many state laws concerned with quality of waste water effluents discharged to natural waters. However, the action taken, while drastic, was not sudden and rash. It was based on years of practical concern about the nature of the BOD procedure and the impracticality of preparing the method to reasonably meet the objectives asked of it.

The standard BOD procedure (5-day incubation) has been used as a

---

[1] President, Weston and Stack, Inc., Malvern, Pa. 19355.

quantitative analytical procedure while, in fact, it does not qualify because it is not intended to be a quantitative representation of biological reactions. It is best described as a bioassay procedure, in which partial completion of stabilization reactions is observed. The portion of biological stabilization represented in the observed consumption of oxygen is not defined. Therefore, if supporting data are not available to indicate the partial nature of the BOD results, the practical value of the BOD result is severely limited.

Stabilization reactions can be represented completely by utilizing extended incubation time (20 days or more). It is necessary to control nitrification during the incubation period so that carbonaceous and nitrogenous oxygen requirements can be interpreted independently. It is also necessary to have good definition of the toxicity or inhibition involved in the BOD determination and to provide precise blanking procedures for any organic materials introduced with the biological seed or in the dilution water.

The BOD Task Group has considered the introduction of a long-term procedure incorporating the indicated improvements, but decided that such a procedure is impractical because of the complexity and extended time required to obtain the results. Consequently, the BOD Task Group elected to discontinue the BOD method without replacement and to work towards other procedures which might be more practically directed to the overall objective of measuring biological stabilization of organic materials in waste water.

Biological Stabilization Reactions

Biochemical Oxygen Demand

As a starting point in the consideration of methods for measurements of biological stabilization, consider the BOD procedure and some of the problems that have been encountered. Figure 1 shows some of the "normal" abnormalities encountered when comparing the BOD of influents and effluents of biological waste water treatment systems. It is not particularly abnormal to find that the BOD curve for the untreated waste water may have a lag in the development of oxygen demand during the first few days of incubation[1].[2] In the extreme case, as illustrated, the lag may extend beyond five days of incubation, and it is possible that the 5-day value for the raw waste water might be lower than the 5-day value for the effluent. However, as incubation time passes and the oxygen demand of the influent and effluent samples develop fully, the true nature of the stabilization is reflected.

A similar problem is observed if the influent waste water has a less

[2] The italic numbers in brackets refer to the list of references appended to this paper.

extreme lag in oxygen demand, as illustarted by the dashed curve in Fig. 1. In this case, the BOD result at five days shows a degree of biological stabilization, but it is not quantatively representative. If inhibitory charac-teristics of the waste water or difficulty with the seed organisms results in BOD curves similar to those illustrated in Fig. 1, biological stabilization can be examined only through ultimate BOD values (with nitrification control) determined after extensive incubation periods of 20 days or longer.

Figure 2 illustrates the more "normal" situation for BOD development of waste waters before biological treatment. The effluent BOD, as illus-trated, develops more slowly than the influent BOD and requires a longer period of time to reach the ultimate demand. If percentage of biological stabilization is calculated based on the illustrated information, the 5-day stabilization is erroneously higher (90 percent) than the true stabilization based on ultimate BOD values (80 percent).

The basic conclusion from Figs. 1 and 2 is that any practical interpreta-tion of biological stabilization must be based on ultimate BOD values. The use of a selected incubation period such as five days would be practical only if definitive data are available to provide correlation of the selected incuba-tion time with the ultimate BOD value. If a waste water contains a single organic material, correlation of 5-day BOD and ultimate BOD would be practical.

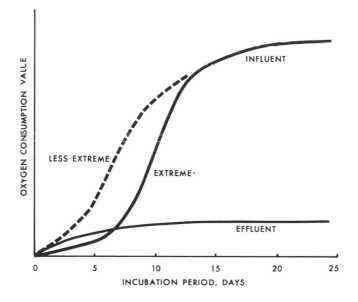

FIG. 1—*"Normal" abnormalities in relative biological stabilization.*

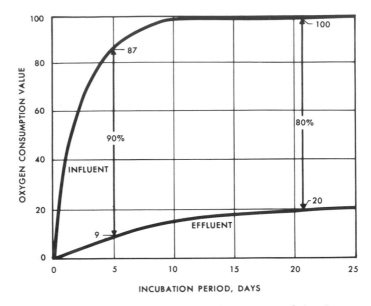

FIG. 2—*BOD curves and biological stabilization normal situation.*

The compounds in waste water have become more complex, and the response of biological activity to organic and other materials in waste water is not predictable. It has become very difficult to justify acceptance of biological stabilization results based on bottle incubation procedures.

The classical BOD curve as illustrated in Fig. 3 presents the steps involved in biological stabilization under mesophilic conditions, which are representative of most biological stabilization processes.

In the incubation bottle procedure, the wastewater sample, along with nutrients, seed organisms, and dilution water, is placed in the BOD bottle at time zero (0). For the first few days of the incubation period, the predominant overall result is the synthesis of organic material into new microorganisms. The synthesis requires energy, and a portion of the organic material present is oxidized in the energy reactions.

The end products for organic materials oxidized in energy reactions are carbon dioxide, water, or other stable materials. The energy reactions are closely coupled to the synthesis reactions so that little of the energy is lost as heat. Thus, at the end of the synthesis period, the biodegradable organic materials initially introduced with the waste water no longer exist. A portion has been consumed in energy reactions, and the remainder has been converted into new cell material.

Beyond the synthesis period, activity in the incubation bottle continues. The microorganisms go through lysis or otherwise die, and contents of the

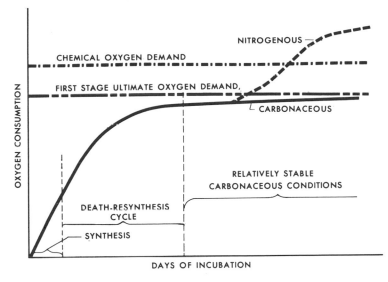

FIG. 3—*Classical BOD development.*

cells are released back to substrate. Organic materials in the release are resynthesized into new organisms. A portion of the cell, primarily the cell wall, is complex and is slow to be acted upon biologically. Therefore, it represents relatively stable organic material. As the death-resynthesis cycle continues, the number of viable organisms in the system decreases, and a residue of stable end products accumulates. After a period of time, the number of viable organisms in the system is reduced to a low level, and the oxygen consumption in the system decreases to a slow rate. In a carbonaceous sense, the BOD system has become relatively stable. The amount of oxygen consumed during the synthesis period and during the death-resynthesis period is referred to most frequently as the first stage ultimate oxygen demand (FSUOD).

The dashed curve in Fig. 3 suggests that a second stage of oxygen demand will develop, in which nitrogenous compounds are oxidized to nitrates.

The chemical oxygen demand (COD) indicated in Fig. 3 is intended to represent the oxidization of carbon to carbon dioxide and hydrogen to water. Nitrogenous materials would not be oxidized and would remain as ammonia. On this basis, chemical oxygen demand is basically equivalent to a total ultimate carbonaceous demand including oxidation of cell walls. The FSUOD does not equal the COD, differing by an amount equal to the chemical oxidation of cell walls and other stable compounds. In practical waste waters, refractory materials contribute to the difference between FSUOD and COD.

To place the stages in biological stabilization into perspective, the energy reactions in support of synthesis may consume from about 10 percent to as much as 70 percent (author's observations) of the biodegradable organic materials introduced into the system. The remaining 30 to 90 percent is synthesized into new cell material. In the death-resynthesis recycle, the weight of cell material is reduced to approximately 25 percent of the starting weight[2], representing the residual weight of cell walls.

Stabilization Oxygen Demand

A fundamental approach to the determination of FSUOD would involve measurement of the amount of oxygen, referred to as energy oxygen, consumed in energy reactions, and the resulting weight of biological cells synthesized. The total COD for the weight of cells could be calculated and about three fourths of this demand would be exerted as the cells are biologically stabilized. Oxygen involved in the stabilization of cells is referred to as autoxidation or endogenous oxygen. The total amount of oxygen included in stabilization would be calculated as the summation of energy oxygen and autoxidation oxygen and referred to as Stabilization Oxygen Demand (SOD)[3].

Figure 4 illustrates SOD calculations applied to a solution of sodium acetate. The solution contains approximately 2500 mg/liter of sodium acetate with a measured COD of 2100 mg/liter. The energy oxygen for sodium acetate is 40 percent of the COD (author's data). If the remaining COD is converted to microorganisms and 75 percent of that oxygen demand appears as autoxidation oxygen, the resulting SOD is approximately 1800 mg/liter. In Fig. 4, calculated SOD agrees with the graphical estimation of the FSUOD.

As a side light, the data in Fig. 4 show the oxygen demand for two dilutions and illustrate two problems in the application of a blank in the BOD procedure. Data from observed blanks are shown at the bottom of the graph as a straight line. The shape of a BOD curve through the data points suggests that the blank correction should be the ·dashed curve. In later stages of BOD development, there was a difference between the FSUOD values of the two dilutions which might be related to the blank.

The calculations of SOD for sodium acetate in Fig. 4 were facilitated by previous knowledge of energy oxygen for sodium acetate and by the simplifying assumption that the fraction of sodium acetate not used in energy reactions would appear as synthesized cell material. The latter assumption appears to be reasonably close to the facts. In practical systems where the organic material present is not identified (and in most cases will be a

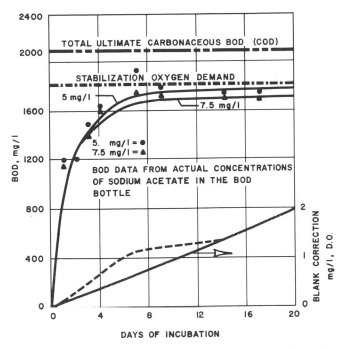

FIG. 4—*Biochemical oxygen demand sodium acetate, 2500 mg/liter solution.*

mixture of organic materials), the calculation of SOD would require determinations of energy oxygen and of synthesis.

The development and application of methodology for SOD determination is in the practical realm. The measurement of energy oxygen is practical and utilizes established respiration techniques. Methods and techniques for measurement of synthesis are much less established and require development and evaluation. The SOD Task Group of ASTM Committee D-19 is currently examining techniques which have potential applicability in SOD methodology. Much of the effort is being directed to measurements of synthesis.

Stabilization Oxygen Demand Methods

Measurements of Energy Oxygen

Figure 5 serves to define energy oxygen and to describe a procedure for measurement of energy oxygen. The starting point for the measurement requires a culture of microorganisms which have been grown on a particular waste water. The resulting growth would be relatively concentrated and essentially equivalent to mixed liquor from an activated sludge process. If the culture of microorganisms is not fed over a period of time, the reactions taking place will be primarily autoxidization, and the culture will be in an endogenous condition. In Fig. 5 the initial endogenous condition is indicated by the constant rate of oxygen consumption before waste water is added.

Shortly after wastewater containing organic material is added, the rate of oxygen uptake will increase as energy is required in the synthesis of organic material into new cell material. The oxygen uptake rate will rise to a maximum and, after a period of time, return to an endogenous condition. Since a part of the organic material added has been synthesized into new cell materials, the oxygen uptake rate associated with the second endogenous condition (after the synthesis period) will be somewhat higher than the endogenous condition before the synthesis period.

In Fig. 5 the area under the curve represents oxygen consumed. By segregating the area corresponding to endogenous oxygen, a residual area which corresponds to energy oxygen is obtained. The area is planimetered and energy oxygen is calculated as mg/liter. Energy oxygen may be compared to COD removed from the substrate during biological stabilization; the energy oxygen will be a fraction of the COD removed, ranging from 10 percent to possibly 70 percent but generally between 30 and 60 percent in the author's experience.

Procedurally, energy oxygen can be determined by examining the oxygen consumed by an active biological system which progresses, following the introduction of waste water, from an endogenous level, through synthesis

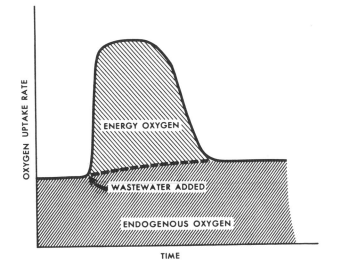

FIG. 5—*Energy oxygen from oxygen uptake rate data.*

reactions, to a second endogenous level. If the activity of the biological system and the amount of organic material added to the system are properly proportioned, the value for energy oxygen can be obtained within a relatively short period of time, probably less than 1 h.

The apparatus required for the determination of energy oxygen is not particularly complicated. The data in Fig. 5 can be obtained by utilizing an open container fitted with an air supply and diffuser stone for aeration and mixing of microorganisms and waste water. The rate of oxygen uptake can be determined by removing a sample from the aerated container into a BOD bottle. The contents of the bottle can then be mixed and the oxygen concentration in the sample observed with a dissolved oxygen (DO) probe over a period of time. The rate of disappearance of oxygen corresponds to the oxygen uptake rate. Thus, the apparatus involved is a simple aerated container and a probe suitable for measuring DO in BOD bottles. A potential disadvantage of the open system is that volatile materials in the waste water might be removed by stripping rather than by biological stabilization.

An alternative procedure for measurement of energy oxygen is to utilize a respiration apparatus such as a Warburg. Characteristic data are illustrated in Fig. 6. The initial endogenous rate would be determined by a blank on the biological culture. Cumulative oxygen consumption after the addition of waste water would be measured, and the final endogenous rate established as a relatively constant rate of oxygen consumption after synthesis has been completed. The illustration in Fig. 6 suggests that the estimation of energy oxygen should take into account the initial and final

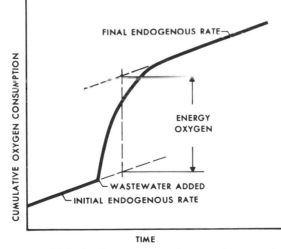

FIG. 6—*Energy oxygen from respirometer data.*

endogenous rates, because they may differ significantly and require an averaging approach to establish energy oxygen. The use of the Warburg or other respiration devices for the determination of energy oxygen provides a convenient technique, but also requires a significant investment in respiration equipment.

Another alternative respiration procedure is illustrated in Figure 7. The basic apparatus used can be any closed container, for example a BOD bottle. A culture of microorganisms (at endogenous conditions) would be aerated to establish a near-saturation level of dissolved oxygen in the system. Aeration with pure oxygen might be practical to establish a rather high concentration of oxygen (for example, 20 to 30 mg/liter). A dissolved oxygen probe would be used to monitor the rate of disappearance of oxygen and to establish the initial endogenous rate. Once the endogenous rate was established, the biological culture would be allowed to settle, and supernatant would be removed to make room for the addition of waste water. After the addition of waste water, the oxygen concentration in the system would be monitored until the completion of synthesis, as indicated by return to an endogenous rate. Oxygen utilized in energy reactions is taken from the plot of data as illustrated in Fig. 7.

The closed unaerated system provides a simple respirometer. If the oxygen supply is depleted, the system can be reaerated to replenish the supply.

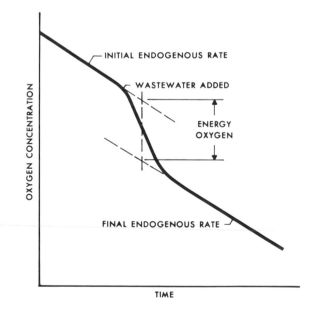

FIG. 7—*Energy oxygen from a closed unaerated system.*

By controlling the quantity of organic material added as waste water, it is possible to determine energy oxygen in a period of a few minutes. Comparisons have been made of energy oxygen determined in closed, unaerated systems, versus other procedures, with good results.

Utilizing the suggested procedures, it is practical to determine energy oxygen with good precision and in a relatively short period of time. There is no particular problem in determining energy oxygen in less than 1 hr.

Measurement of Synthesis

In order to calculate SOD, a measurement of the mass of viable organisms in the biological culture is needed before and after synthesis. In each of the three examples (in Fig. 5, 6, and 7), a measurement of the dry weight of viable organisms at the initial endogenous level and at the final endogenous level would be required. The change in total dry weight of viable organisms would represent new microorganisms synthesized during biological stabilization of organic material added in the waste water.

Any technique for measurement of synthesis must be directly related to some characteristic of the biological cell. Weight difference of suspended solids before and after synthesis can be misleading if suspended solids in the waste water are solubilized or if the materials in the waste water cause precipitation within the biological mass.

A potential approach to the measurement of synthesis is through the measurement of adenosine triphosphate (ATP), which is associated with viable organisms. If a sample of the biological culture is filtered and washed to remove extracellular ATP, the washed cells may then be lysed to release the ATP for subsequent analysis. In any procedure for energy oxygen measurement, an ATP measurement would be made prior to the addition of waste water, with a second ATP measurement when the final endogenous condition had been reached. The difference in ATP would then be used to calculate synthesized cell material. The practicality of synthesis measurement by measuring ATP change is under evaluation.

Calculation of Stabilization Oxygen Demand (SOD)

Based on energy oxygen and ATP data, the SOD value for waste water under evaluation can be calculated. The observed energy oxygen in the uptake of a respiration system is converted into an energy oxygen value related to the waste water. The energy oxygen value from the system (in milligrams per liter) is correlated to the waste water by the conversion factor of system volume divided by the wastewater volume.

The ATP measurements from the system are in micrograms of ATP per liter. The relationship of cell weight to ATP averages 0.46 milligrams of cell weight per microgram of ATP (DuPont Biometer Literature). Thus, the observed microgram change in ATP from the initial to final endogenous conditions would be multiplied by 0.46 to obtain cell synthesis as milligrams per liter. This result would be correlated to the waste water by the conversion factor of system volume divided by wastewater volume. Conversion of cell weight to oxygen equivalent utilizes a conversion factor of 1.42, which is a theoretical COD of a unit weight of cell material[2].

The SOD value is calculated as the summation of energy oxygen and the oxygen equivalent of cell material which will be stabilized biologically. If we apply the rule of thumb that approximately 75 percent of the cell material will be stabilized, the resulting summation is:

$$SOD, (mg/liter) = Energy\ Oxygen, (mg/liter) \\ + Biomass\ synthesized\ (1.42)(0.75), \\ (mg/liter)$$

Conclusions

Stabilization oxygen demand has the potential to provide within about 1 h a practical understanding of ultimate biological stabilization by examination of energy and synthesis reactions. The oxygen utilized in energy reactions (energy oxygen) in support of synthesis can be determined separately. Synthesis conceivably may be measured by determinations of changes in ATP concentrations. SOD is calculated as the summation of energy oxygen and autoxidation oxygen utilized in the stabilization of synthesized cell material.

References

[1] ReVelle, C. S., Lynne, W. R., and Rivera, M. A., *Journal Water Pollution Control Federation,* Vol. 37, 1965, pp. 1679.
[2] McCarty, P. L., *Proceedings,* 2nd International Water Pollution Research Conference, Tokyo, 1964, Pergamon, 1965, pp. 169.
[3] Stack, V. T., Jr., *Water and Water Pollution Handbook,* Vol. 3, L. Ciaccio, Ed. Marcel Dekker, New York, 1972, Chapter 15, pp. 801.

P. J. Marks [1]

Microbiological Inhibition Testing Procedure

REFERENCE: Marks, P. J., **"Microbiological Inhibition Testing Procedure,"** *Biological Methods for the Assessment of Water Quality, ASTM STP 528,* American Society for Testing and Materials, 1973, pp. 221–226.

ABSTRACT: The Microbiological Inhibition Testing Procedure was developed to determine the possible adverse effects of specific compounds or waste waters on biological treatment processes. The test procedure consists of monitoring the oxidation rate of a biological seed at various dilutions of the waste water in BOD bottles. The threshold inhibition level of a compound or waste water is defined as the lowest concentration of the compound or waste water which causes a reduction in the biological oxidation rate.

KEY WORDS: water pollution, tests, inhibitors, microorganism control (water)

Biological treatment systems, such as activated sludge units or trickling filters, treating industrial or combined municipal and industrial waste waters, receive a variety of organic and inorganic compounds over a wide concentration range. Certain groups or classifications of compounds, depending upon a number of variables such as the concentration, antagonistic effects, environmental conditions, and the concentration of biological mass, can cause the assimilation rates of these systems to be seriously impaired or even stopped.

Microorganisms can continuously remove organic matter from solution by only one method, synthesis into new protoplasm. Organic matter can be absorbed by microorganisms in large quantities, but unless this matter is assimilated into new protoplasm, the rate of absorption will approach zero.

In the synthesis of new protoplasm, a part of the organic matter absorbed is required for the formation of the building blocks of the cell, and another

[1] Group manager, Laboratory Services, Roy F. Weston, Inc., West Chester, Pa. 19380.

definite part must be oxidized to provide the energy necessary for synthesis.

It follows that biological growth can be inhibited by (1) interfering with the energy supply, (2) reducing the supply of materials, especially of the very critical elements (such as vitamins), which are required in small amounts, or (3) interfering with the synthetic process itself, especially with its most vulnerable participants, the nucleic acids.

Growth can also be inhibited less specifically by physical damage to the cell or components thereof, so that cell growth and mechanisms for taking up solutes are impaired. This type of inhibition can be caused by changes in the environmental conditions such as temperature, pH, and osmotic pressure gradients that are outside the cell's tolerance limits. The tolerance levels for these environmental conditions in biological systems have been defined and are documented in the literature.

Growth Inhibiting Compounds

Chemical compounds can inhibit growth by various mechanisms. The major groups of growth-inhibiting compounds[1][2] and the biochemical reactions are presented as follows:

Sulfhydryl Reactive Compounds—Many enzymes, as well as coenzyme A and lipoic acid, depend for their activity on the sulfhydryl radical (C-SH). They are inactivated when this radical combines with other reactive compounds. Most of the heavy metals which form insoluble sulfides (such as copper, silver, cadmium, and lead) can combine with the sulfhydryl radical and in doing so cause inactivation of the enzymes.

Surface-Active Substances—This group includes phenol and its congeners, the soaps and detergents, the salts of some organic acids, and a small group of basic peptides and amines. These compounds are strongly adsorbed onto the cell wall, and they tend to reduce the interfacial tension at the surface of the organism. This phenomenon causes the cells to leak solutes into the medium.

Dyes—It is thought that dyes react and combine with the proteins and nucleic acids of the bacterial cells. Generally, the bacteriostatic potency of dyes increases as the dissociation constant increases in any given series of dyes.

Antagonists of Essential Metabolites—This heading covers a large number of chemical materials whose reactions compete with the normal metabolic reactions within the cell. These reactions include substitution of side chains or radicals, changes in the shape or constituents of a ring, and the loss or removal of a group. Other compounds in this grouping do not

---

[2] The italic numbers in brackets refer to the list of references appended to this paper.

prevent synthesis but are incorporated into the bacterial metabolites; the product may be modified to a degree that further processes, such as enzyme formation, are repressed.

The Microbiological Inhibition Testing Procedure can detect, under a set of defined conditions, the threshold inhibition level of a compound or waste water, which is defined as the lowest concentration of the compound or waste water which causes a reduction in the biological oxidation rate. This procedure can be used as a guideline in determining the effects that a compound or waste water may have on a biological wastewater treatment system. The results of this test procedure are also useful in starting a biological system with a waste water which has growth-inhibiting tendencies. The biological system can be started with a concentration of waste water that is less than the threshold level.

Procedure for Microbiological Inhibition Test

The pH of the wastewater specimen should be measured, and if the pH is outside the range of 6.5 to 7.5, it should be adjusted. pH adjustment is necessary to eliminate the possible inhibition effects caused by extreme pH values. The pH adjustment is accomplished with a strong acid, sulfuric or base, sodium hydroxide to minimize the dilution of the sample. A series of BOD bottles should be prepared as shown in Table 1.

An aliquot of biological culture seed is added to each bottle to insure that viable organisms are available for biological oxidation of the glucose and of the organic matter that may be present in the waste water. The biological culture is a heterogeneous culture that is started with domestic sewage or with a specimen of earth inoculated in dilution water. The

TABLE 1—*Preparation of BOD bottles.*

	ml Specimen	ml Biological Culture	ml of 300 mg/ liter Glucose Solution	Dilution Water
1	0.0	5	6	289.0
2	0.01	5	6	288.99
3	0.1	5	6	288.9
4	1.0	5	6	288.0
5	3.0	5	6	286.0
6	6.0	5	6	283.0
7	10.0	5	6	279.0
8	30.0	5	6	259.0
9	60.0	5	6	229.0
10	100.0	5	6	189.0
11	200.0	5	6	89.0
12	250.0	5	6	39.0

culture should be fed on a daily basis with a mixture of biodegradable organics or domestic sewage such that the oxidation rate as measured by an oxygen consumption rate is in the range of 1 to 3 mg/liter/h.

The oxygen consumption rate is determined by removing a specimen of the biological culture from the aerated container into a BOD bottle. The contents of the bottle can then be mixed, and the oxygen concentration in the specimen observed with a dissolved oxygen probe over a period of time. The rate of oxygen disappearance corresponds to the oxygen consumption rate.

The dilution water is prepared with distilled water (ASTM Specifications for Reagent Water (D 1193–72)) and with the dilution water inorganic salts listed under the BOD procedure in Ref 2.

Glucose is added to all the bottles, including the control, in the event that the waste water under investigation does not contain biodegradable organics. The biological oxidation of the glucose will reduce the dissolved oxygen level in the BOD bottle by approximately 50 percent of the saturation value of 9.2 mg/liter at 20°C (68°F). The individual bottles should be aerated using the technique of connecting two BOD bottles together with a piece of fitted plastic pipe, and shaking. The specimen is then drained into the original bottle. This method provides a quick and simple method of aerating the specimen to a saturation value. If the waste water has an immediate oxygen demand, this should be satisfied before the waste water is added to the bottles. Initial dissolved oxygen measurements (using the membrane electrode method) are taken on all the bottles.

The immediate oxygen demand can be satisfied by aerating the specimen for a 10 to 15 min period before making dilutions of the material.

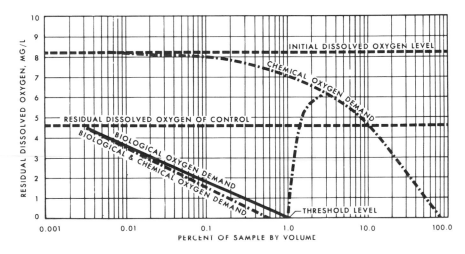

FIG. 1—*Example data plot.*

If the waste water exerts an organic chemical oxygen demand (such as a free radical reaction, which is a slow reaction), it is necessary to set up a duplicate test eliminating the biological culture. An organic chemical oxygen demand is determined empirically by plotting the data. The results will be similar to those shown in Fig. 1. If biological organisms are present in the waste water, the specimen should be sterilized by autoclaving for the determination of the chemical oxygen demand.

The bottles are incubated at 20° C (68° F) for a period of three days, at which time a final dissolved oxygen measurement is made on the bottles. The residual dissolved oxygen is plotted on semilog paper against the percent by volume of the specimen, as shown in Figs. 1 and 2.

Figure 2 contains the plots of two different waste waters, both of which exhibit a microbiological inhibitory effect. The two plots demonstrate the difference between a waste water which exerts a biological oxygen demand and one that does not.

If a supplementary organic was not included in the test procedure (Fig. 2), there would have been no significant depletion in any of the BOD bottles, and the results would have been improperly interpreted as inhibition at the lowest concentration.

Figure 1 is presented to demonstrate the type of results that may be expected if the waste water does exert a chemical oxygen demand. The chemical oxygen demand curve can be defined by repeating the tests with a duplicate test and eliminating the biological culture.

Figure 1 is the plot of data from a waste water which exhibits microbiological inhibition, has a chemical oxygen demand, and contains biodegradable organics.

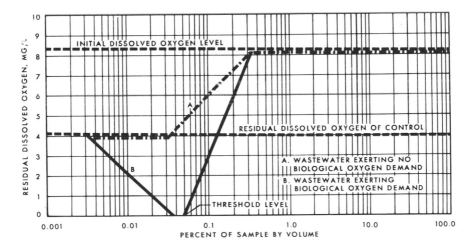

FIG. 2—*Example data plot.*

The test procedure can be performed utilizing higher concentrations of biomass, if a specimen of mixed liquor from an activated sludge or aerated lagoon system is readily available. If higher concentrations of biomass are utilized in the procedure, a much shorter incubation time is required, as short as 2 to 4 h. This modification of the procedure is applicable when a biological treatment process is in operation and the analyst is interested in evaluating the acute effects of an additional waste water on the treatment system.

Discussion

The Microbiological Inhibition Test Procedure can be a useful tool in evaluating the possible deleterious effects a waste water or specific compound may have on a biological treatment system. If the test results indicate that the waste water above a certain concentration is inhibitory, an attempt can be made to acclimate the biological culture by feeding the waste water to the culture at a dosage below the threshold level. The test can then be repeated to determine if the "acclimated" culture is more tolerant to the waste water.

The limitation of this procedure is that the concentration of viable biomass is not quantitatively defined and is less than what is normally found in a biological treatment process.

The effects of inhibitory compounds can, at times, be overcome by increasing the concentration of viable organisms in the system. Consequently, the results of a test procedure that employs a relatively low level of biomass must be interpreted by an individual with a thorough understanding of the subject.

References

[1] Thimann, K. V., *The Life of Bacteria,* MacMillan, New York, pp. 759–783.
[2] "Standard Methods for Examination of Water and Wastewater," 13th ed, American Public Health Association, New York, pp. 490–491.

T. W. Beak,[1] *T. C. Griffing,*[1] *and A. G. Appleby*[1]

Use of Artificial Substrate Samplers to Assess Water Pollution

REFERENCE: Beak, T. W., Griffing, T. C., and Appleby, A. G., "Use of Artificial Substrate Samplers to Assess Water Pollution," *Biological Methods for the Assessment of Water Quality, ASTM STP 528,* American Society for Testing and Materials, 1973, pp. 227–241.

ABSTRACT: The benthic macro-invertebrate fauna and the benthic micro- and macrophytic flora are important parts of the aquatic ecosystem for measurement of the impact of pollution. Artificial substrate samplers provide a means of sampling in many locations where other samplers are not effective. The historical development and use of artificial substrate samplers is discussed, including the major types of apparatus developed. Three main macroinvertebrate samplers, the rock-filled basket, the multi-plate sampler, and the steel tray (Beak) type, are discussed and evaluated critically in light of practical and theoretical considerations. The results obtained with these samplers are compared to the results obtained by other methods, including Surber sampler, dip net, and Petersen grab. Artificial substrate samplers have proven that they obtain an equally diverse fauna with less variability between samples. Periphyton samplers usually consist of glass or plastic plates, with differing methods of suspension. Marine intertidal and subtidal communities may be sampled by fiberglass plates bolted to rocks or building blocks. It is concluded that artificial substrate samplers are an effective method of biological monitoring and evaluation of water pollution.

KEYWORDS: samplers, water pollution, environmental surveys, artificial substrates, invertebrates, periphyton

It is now widely accepted in scientific circles of many disciplines that the degree to which a part of the aqueous environment is polluted can be evaluated by study of the benthic macroinvertebrate fauna, or the micro- and macroflora, or both. The quality of the evaluation depends to a large extent on the effectiveness of sampling, particularly the ability of the investi-

[1] Chairman of the Board, senior biologist, and biologist, respectively, T. W. Beak Consultants Limited, Rexdale, Ontario, Canada.

gator to collect comparable samples at different times and from different locations. The use of artificial substrates permits effective sampling in many locations which can not be effectively sampled by other means. This paper includes a review of the development of the use of artificial substrate sampling devices, a review of the types which have been used, a comparison of some of the different types of devices, and a comparison with other types of sampling.

Ordinarily, when sampling with mechanical grabs or with net-type samplers the investigator attempts to obtain organisms from some standard unit of natural substrate (square meter or cubic meter). The development of artificial substrate samplers undoubtedly grew out of the realization that all situations are not readily adaptable to these methods and also out of attempts to refine and quantify the units of measure. It is not surprising, therefore, that the development of artificial substrate techniques closely parallels the development of aquatic biology as a quantitative discipline.

By definition, "artificial substrate sampler" means that category of field equipment which is assembled on land and is placed in an aquatic environment where it mimics certain features of native habitats. It is suitable for colonization by sessile aquatic organisms and can be readily retrieved after an appropriate exposure time to provide a representative sample of native communities.

Artificial substrates have been employed in rivers and streams, and to a lesser extent in lakes and marine situations. The group of organisms which has received the greatest amount of attention with this method has been the macro-benthos of fresh water (particularly insect larvae, snails, free living flatworms, amphipods, isopods, oligochaete worms, bryozoans, hydroids and sponges). Communities of periphyton algae, fungi and bacteria have also been successfully studied with artificial substrates. These techniques have more recently been employed in the study of rocky intertidal and subtidal communities.

Historical Development of Artificial Substrates

The use of artificial substrates for sampling macroinvertebrates dates back to Moon[1],[2] and for periphyton to Butcher[2] in Europe. In North America the earliest references were Wene and Wickliff[3] for macroinvertebrates, and Patrick et al[4] for periphyton. One of the present authors (Beak) used them in the late fifties, but the reports of use did not reach the general literature.

Moon's sampling devices were canvas sacking and string mesh attached

---

[2] The italic numbers in brackets refer to the list of references appended to this paper.

to an iron frame to form a shallow bag, and filled with indigenous stones. They were used in littoral areas of Lake Windermere, England. Mundie[5], also in England, described an asbestos-cement plate which was used in sampling the sloping sides of reservoirs. It had a special cover to prevent loss of organisms during recovery.

Wene and Wickliff[3] used a "brush box" type of artificial substrate, which consisted of a cube of wire mesh hardware cloth filled with natural rubble. Scott[6] used a similar type of sampler suspended in the water column. Similar devices have been employed by Henson[7] and Dickson et al[8], who filled their samplers with 2-in. diameter limestone chips and grass.

Mason et al[9] reported the use of cylindrical commercial barbecue baskets filled with limestone rocks (Fig. 1). This type of artificial substrate sampler has proven very popular, and has since been used by many investigators including Anderson and Mason[10], Kreis and Smith[11], Mason et al[12,13], Crowe[14], Fullner[15], Prins and Black[16] and Jacobi[17]. This sampler was also described in the current American Public Health Association "Standard Methods"[18]. Some modifications which have been introduced by these authors include the replacement of rocks by concrete, styrofoam, and wood spheres[17], the use of porcelain spheres[13], and the use of a synthetic webbing to fill the baskets[16]. A method for suspending sets of these samplers in the euphotic zone of large reservoirs was developed by Kreis and Smith[11].

Hester and Dendy[19] developed a multi-plate substrate made from tempered hardboard, with alternate layers of 3-in. squares and 1-in. squares secured on a long ring bolt (Fig. 2). Similar samplers have been used by Arthur and Horning[20], and by Fullner[15], who added extra spacers to provide a variety of different-sized spaces between plates. This type of artificial substrate sampler is also described in "Standard Methods" and is

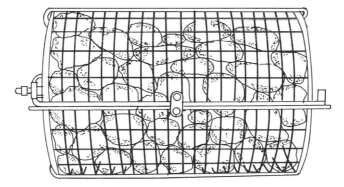

FIG. 1—*Rock-filled barbecue basket type of artificial substrate sampler.*

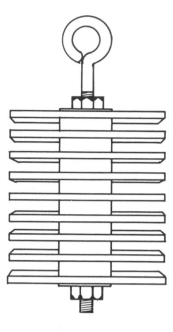

FIG. 2—*Hester-Dendy multi-plate artificial substrate sampler.*

commercially available. Mason et al[*13*] modified this basic design by using porcelain plates.

Some other types of substrates reported in the literature include those of Hilsenhoff[*21*], who used galvanized iron cylinders with inner layers of expanded metal mesh set on a peg through a patio slab, and Bull[*22*] who used collapsible wire bait traps holding gravel and surrounded by a fine mesh net bag. Yongue and Cairns[*23*] have used hexahedrals of polyurethane foam to sample protozoans. In Europe, Besch et al[*24*] and Besch and Hofmann[*25*] have reported the use of flat polyethylene plates suspended vertically in the water.

For periphyton, Butcher's method of using microscope slides held in photographic plate frames pegged to the substrate was used in a number of studies in the United Kingdom from 1930 onward. Patrick et al[*4*] described the "Catherwood Diatometer," which has racks of glass slides held in a float. Grzenda and Brehmer[*26*], used plexiglass plates attached to a horizontal cross bar supported by a vertical post driven into the stream bottom. Waters[*27*] used concrete cylinders placed on their sides in riffles to collect periphyton, and Kevern et al[*28*] used plexiglass plates placed on the stream bottom or suspended vertically to avoid siltation. Armstrong et al[*29*] used short sections of glass tubing held in arrays of test tube clamps at various depths to sample seston and periphyton. Arthur and Horning[20] have used the top plate of a Hester-Dendy sampler for chlorophyll 'a' determinations. An excellent review of methods for sampling and analyzing periphyton communities has been compiled by Sladeckova[30].

Critical Evaluation of Types of Samplers

It was obvious from this brief historical review that different authors have devised and tested a variety of artificial substrates and have reported at least some success with each of them. In order to evaluate the different types, it was necessary to review the requirements which an artificial substrate should meet.

First, a distinction must be made between the use of artificial substrates to measure detailed biological parameters and their use to assess water pollution. For the former, it is often essential that natural bottom conditions be duplicated as closely as possible. To assess water pollution, exact duplication of natural conditions is of less importance than ability to obtain replicate samples at different times and at different locations.

A simple case arises in assessing the effect of a single waste discharge on a river, where the physical bottom conditions are significantly different at various sampling stations in the vicinity of the discharge. Merely comparing the macro-invertebrate fauna without regard to location may make it difficult to evaluate differences due to the pollution and those due to the bottom. If, however, an artificial substrate is used in both locations, the variation due to the differences in bottom are eliminated. In this case, it is clear that the prime purpose of the substrate is not to duplicate bottom conditions, but rather to present conditions that are ecologically as nearly identical as possible at both locations. For reproducibility a substrate is required which represents the same spatial dimensions of surface area or volume.

Second, the artificial substrate should represent a sufficiently complex habitat to ensure that the biological community to be sampled will be reasonably well represented. Once again, it is less essential to attempt to duplicate the native habitat than it is to provide a habitat demonstrably suitable for colonization by both pollution tolerant and pollution sensitive assemblages of organisms.

Retrievability is also an important consideration. Since the samplers must be left in place for periods up to a month or more, they should not be excessively prone to loss by vandalism, passing boats, current, or current borne debris. Further, they should be relatively easy to handle in field situations and preferably not require excessive anchorage.

Fourth, the artificial substrates should be of suitable design to prevent loss of organisms during the retrieval process either by current, dessication, or from animals simply crawling out of the sampler.

Finally, for an adequate pollution assessment, replicated samples from a number of sampling stations are required, usually on several occasions during a year. Therefore it is also important that the substrates be constructed of fairly common but rugged materials, not be prohibitively expensive to fabricate, be as readily repairable in the field as possible, and still be applicable in a number of different field situations.

For sampling benthic invertebrates, the authors have found that a simple 16-in. diameter circular iron tray with sides 1-in. high and containing two discs of expanded metal lying in the tray meets these criteria nicely (Fig. 3). These flat samplers mimic the essential features of a rubble bottom by providing a large and stable surface area exposed to drifting particles and colonization by periphyton and benthos, yet, with a variety of areas variably protected from maximum water velocities. Some silt and organic sediments can accumulate below the wire mesh adding further ecological complexity. The expanded metal, because of its construction, gives a uniform distribution of boundary spaces available for colonization. This has been demonstrated to be essential for benthic invertebrates, particularly in flowing water[31,32]. It is likely that the number of these spaces, rather than the stream bottom surface area, is the spatial limiting factor in population densities and species diversity. The substrates are more uniform than equal areas of natural gravel or rock bottom, yet ecologically complex enough for

FIG. 3—*Beak tray type of artificial substrate sampler.*

colonization by diverse benthic communities. The plates are rugged; they pack conveniently for transport and, because of their weight and low profile in currents, do not require anchoring except in very fast rivers. Recovery is effected using a cover which fits over the tray so that no contents are lost (Fig. 4). The whole unit is dismantled in the field, and the contents washed through tubs with fine mesh wire screening (Fig. 5). Over many years of experience, the authors have found the population is adequate for statistical calculations and they have had good uniformity. These trays were developed by Beak from Mundie's design.

The barbecue basket-type of substrate with various types of filler is favored by several authors. It has the advantage of offering a fairly large volume of substrate and therefore collects a large number of individuals. It can be expected that if space is a limiting factor, the numbers of individuals would be related to the number of voids in the fillings. For this reason it is desirable that the filling should be standardized as to shape and size of the units, at least in any samples which are to be used for compara-

FIG. 4—*Cover used to retrieve tray sampler.*

FIG. 5—*Retrieving tray type sampler.*

tive purposes. It seems, for the same reason, that artificial filling units, such as concrete, styrofoam, wood or porcelain spheres, would be preferable to natural stones which would be more variable. There is greater difficulty in recovering this type of sampler without loss of animals in large, deep, and fast rivers, such as the Fraser River in British Columbia, where use of a retrieval net is not practical and where surface floats are quickly dispatched by debris. Apart from this, and the fact that appreciable field cleaning time is required, the basket sampler with uniform filler appears to be a reliable tool.

The other type of sampler in common use is the Hester and Dendy multi-plate sampler, consisting of eight 3-in. squares of tempered hardboard alternating with 1-in. squares, so that the spacing is the thickness of a sheet of hardboard. Presumably, the space between the larger squares acts in the same way as voids in gravel, providing suitable spaces for most benthic organisms. Multi-plate samplers have been fairly widely used and reports indicate that they collect a broad spectrum of species with a fairly high population density. They have the advantage of being inexpensive, light, and easily portable. The whole apparatus can be put into a plastic bag or jar and preserved for transport to the laboratory.

Crowe[14] compared barbecue baskets filled with 2 to 4 inch stones with steel trays of the Beak type. In 61 percent of samples, both samplers collected the same groups of animals with the same percentage composition, but the baskets collected a significantly higher population density, and she concluded they were therefore more effective. Actually, the minimization of variability was probably more important in pollution monitoring than was absolute population density.

Dickson et al[8] compared results at two stations using cubic foot baskets made of ½-in. mesh hardware cloth and filled with limestone chips and grass. They reported on variation in number of species and number of taxa and concluded that 4 to 6 samples would be required to establish with 95 percent confidence that the number of taxa was within 25 percent of true value, and four samples at one station and 21 at the other to produce the same data for number of specimens. Only one or two samples were necessary to produce this data for a diversity index ($\bar{d}$ of Ref 33) or for sequential comparison index[34].

Fullner[15] compared barbecue baskets filled with rocks with modified Hester-Dendy samplers. He found good correspondence in number of genera with both, and collected a wide variety of organisms. The Hester-Dendy sampler collected significantly more individuals and more per sample, but fewer per square foot area. He favored the multi-plate sampler because of small size and ease of handling.

Mason et al[13] reported Hester-Dendy samplers compared favorably with limestone filled baskets of similar surface areas in terms of abundance and diversity of fauna collected.

The Hilsenhoff cylinder[21] was similar in type to the barbecue basket of Mason et al, and results indicated that it collected similar samples.

From this review it appeared that the Beak trays, the barbecue basket with suitable filler, and the Hester-Dendy plates would all sample the available macro-invertebrate fauna in a manner suitable for evaluation of water pollution. The choice depends to some extent on the nature of the environment at the location, the personal preference of the investigator, and types of data calculations and statistical tests to be applied. The Hester-Dendy plate sampler has the advantage of lightness and ease of handling. The filled barbecue basket has the advantage that it collects large numbers of individuals, but it is awkward to store and transport and unless care is taken to use uniform filler, an undesirably large variability might be introduced between samplers. There may also be some problems with recovery. The Beak plates are probably best in large, deep, and fast river situations, but generally collect somewhat fewer individuals per square foot of river bottom. However, this does not appear to be significant in comparing samples from two or more stations using similar substrates for water pollution evaluation.

Comparison of Artificial Substrate with Other Methods for Benthic Macroinvertebrate Sampling

Consideration should be given to what each different sampling method measures. So far as benthic macroinvertebrates are concerned, area of stream bottom is not related to number of micro-habitats. For example, within a short distance in any rocky or gravel stream, one square foot of stream bottom may be entirely occupied by one rock, while in another it will be occupied by thousands of small stones. The number of habitats for macro-invertebrates will vary greatly between these two situations and both the number of individuals and number of species is likely to reflect this variation. In the case of an artificial substrate of the aforementioned type, provided uniform filler is used, the availability of suitable niches is likely to be much more consistent between the samplers. For this reason it is not necessarily meaningful to compare the results from artificial substrates, mechanical grab, or net-type samplers, for either numbers of individuals or species diversity. A more important parameter for water pollution measurement is variability between samples, and this can be compared.

Dickson et al[8], reported that four artificial substrate samples were needed at one station and 21 at another for 95 percent confidence for numbers of specimens, whereas Needham and Usinger[35] found 72 Surber samples were required. Hilsenhoff[21] sampled 20 locations including many types of stream habitat, and collected 91 genera with his artificial substrate samplers and 69 genera with a dip net. Many groups were much more abundant in artificial substrate samples than in dip net samples. Jacobi[17] compared his barbecue baskets filled with concrete, styrofoam, and wood spheres to a Surber sampler. He found no significant artificial substrate preference by the taxa encountered for his three substrate types. Also, 11 of 16 taxa were common to Surber and substrate samplers. Production estimates from his results also agreed well between Surber and substrates. Anderson and Mason[10] compared results of rock-filled barbecue baskets and Petersen grab and recorded a larger number and variety of immature insects on the artificial substrates. The Petersen grab did better only with burrowing forms such as *Chironomus* and *Hexagenia*.

On several occasions the present authors have had the opportunity of comparing the effectiveness of their substrate samplers with Surber samples and dip net collections taken at the same time. The comparisons have always been favorable from a pollution assessment vantage even though the absolute abundances seldom agree. The representation of respectable numbers of pollution tolerant and pollution sensitive taxa, their relative abundances, and the species diversity have been comparable in results from both types of samplers. Identical conclusions about the status of the aquatic environments in question have been drawn from both sets of data in each case. A substantially larger number of Surber and dip net samples has been required to achieve similar levels of statistical confidence, once again reflecting the variability of the physical structure in the stream bottom. The use of net-type samplers such as the Surber is obviously restricted to shallow streams or wadable sections of larger rivers, thus further restricting meaningful comparisons.

The present authors have used the Beak tray in 41 major surveys, many of which involved several separate sample collections at multiple stations within one overall study period. The number of samples collected in these surveys exceded one thousand. In most cases the plates have been used only at locations such as rocky or gravel bottom rivers or lakes in which Ponar or Petersen grabs were unsuitable. They have been used in preference to Surber and other similar net or grab samplers because of the reduced variability between samples.

Because of the variability of the aquatic habitat, the authors would recommend that several different types of substrates, including Beak type trays, barbecue baskets, and Hester-Dendy multi-plates, should be standardized. Care should be taken that there is uniformity of container and filler within each group and, as far as possible, the same type of substrate should be used at all stations in a single study area, particularly for water pollution evaluations.

Periphyton Samplers

The periphyton samplers are much more uniform than those for macro-invertebrates. Usually, they consist of plates of some material held in a frame. Some workers have preferred to use standard microscope slides because of universal availability and easy manipulation, especially under a microscope. Other workers have used plexiglass plates, because they offer a larger area and are less fragile.

The principle differences in periphyton samplers are in methods of suspension. Butcher[2] used photographic plates pegged to the bottom. These were restricted to wadable streams and the horizontal slides were often covered with silt. Patrick[4] and others have used different flotation devices for suspending the plates in mid-water either horizontally or vertically. The latter avoid much siltation but may receive less light, which may or may not be a factor.

There is little evidence to indicate that glass or plexiglass are selective with regard to attached algae. This is probably not too important, provided similar plates are used under similar conditions at the stations under comparison.

Periphyton is a valuable supplement to benthic macroinvertebrate samples, especially where questions of eutrophication or organic wastes are involved. The authors do not favor use of periphyton alone for assessment of water pollution. Patrick[4] has demonstrated that, provided the samples are analyzed by highly trained algologists, they can be used for accurate pollution evaluation. Over many years experience, the authors have found the macroinvertebrates to be a more valuable group for this purpose, enabling reliable evaluation to be achieved more rapidly and with a less intensive input of highly-skilled specialists.

Intertidal Plates

In marine and estuarine environments artificial substrate samplers have demonstrated significant value in assessments of pollution. Studies have been made of pollutional effects on the survival of spat fall, growth and development of larvae, survival of adult forms of attached intertidal and subtidal invertebrates, and production of attached algae.

The design of these marine samplers is similar to that of periphyton samplers, consisting of square fiberglass plates 15 cm by 15 cm by 2 mm thick (Fig. 6). The plates have been found to be most effectively installed by attaching them in a vertical orientation with nylon bolts to the face of concrete building blocks or to natural rock substrates. The building blocks can be placed at desired depths in the subtidal or intertidal zones either resting on natural substances or suspended by ropes from cliffs or floats.

The fiberglass has proven to be readily colonizable by diverse algal and

FIG. 6—*Marine intertidal plate sampler, bolted on concrete block.*

invertebrate communities. Depending upon the study design, the plates may be left in place for varying lengths of time. One common deployment is in ongoing monitoring programs to provide additional data compatible with zooplankton samples, water chemistry data, intertidal and benthic population data, and algal production data. In such cases, the plates are replaced monthly and sometimes in a sequence of overlapping exposure times. Such programs allow not only the identification and counting of sessile animal species but also measurements of survival and growth rates. Attached algal communities are often analyzed for species composition and diversity as well as standing crop, biomass, growth rates, and pigment concentrations.

As with any other artificial substrate sampler, the essential benefit derived here is uniformity of sampling which allows statistical comparison among stations or times. Because of the extreme variability in the composition of intertidal and subtidal communities and the remarkable seasonal influences on variations in spat fall and growth, the authors do not recommend that these types of substrates be used without the aid of other biological data in evaluating marine pollution.

Conclusions

Experience of a large number of investigators including the authors, has shown that artificial substrates are an effective method of biological sampling for evaluation of water pollution. Suitable substrates are available for benthic invertebrate, periphyton, and attached marine organisms.

For purposes of evaluating water pollution it is not essential that the substrates collect a fauna or flora identical to the naturally occurring one, provided it is broadly representative, has low variability, and is reproducible in both time and space. In the case of substrates with filling material, uniformity of this material is important.

In the case of gravel and rocky bottoms, unit area of stream bottom is not necessarily related to available space for benthic invertebrates. Artificial substrates therefore give more reproducible results than direct sampling of stream bottoms.

It is desirable to standardize one particular type of sampler, as local conditions and preference of workers vary. It is essential that the acceptable types meet certain requirements of reproducibility, variability and retrievability. It is recommended that plates, baskets, or multi-plates are suitable for benthic invertebrates. Some form of glass, plastic, or fiberglass plate is most suitable for periphyton and marine organisms.

References

[1] Moon, H. P., *International Revue der gesamten Hydrobiologie und Hydrographie*, Vol. 32, 1935, pp. 319–333.

[2] Butcher, R. W., *Journal of the Institute of Sewage Purification*, Vol. 2, 1946, pp. 92–102.

[3] Wene, G. and Wickliff, E. L., *California Entomology*, Vol. 72, 1940, pp. 131–135.

[4] Patrick, R., Hohn, M. H., and Wallace, J. H., "A New Method for Determining the Pattern of the Diatom Flora," *Notulae Naturae*, Vol. 259, 1959.

[5] Mundie, J. H., *Journal of Animal Ecology*, Vol. 25, 1956, pp. 429–432.

[6] Scott, D. C., *Sewage and Industrial Wastes*, Vol. 30, No. 9, 1958, p. 1169.

[7] Hensen, E. B., *Turtox News*, Vol. 43, No. 12, 1965, p. 209.

[8] Dickson, K. L., Cairns, J. Jr., and Arnold, J. C., *Transactions of the American Fisheries Society*, Vol. 100, No. 3, 1971, pp. 553–559.

[9] Mason, W. T., Jr., Anderson, J. B., and Morrison, G. E., *The Progressive Fish-Culturist*, Vol. 29, No. 2, 1967, p. 74.

[10] Anderson, J. B. and Mason, W. T., Jr., *Journal of the Water Pollution Control Federation*, Vol. 40, No. 2, pp. 252–259.

[11] Kreis, R. D. and Smith, R. L., *The Progressive Fish-Culturist*, Vol. 32, No. 3, 1970, pp. 182–183.

[12] Mason, W. T., Jr., Anderson, J. B., Kreis, R. D., and Johnson, W. C., *Journal of the Water Pollution Control Federation*, Vol. 42, No. 8, 1970, pp. R315–328.

[13] Mason, W. T., Jr., Weber, C. I., Lewis, P. A., and Julian, E. C., "Factors Affecting the Performance of Basket or Multi-Plate Macro-invertebrate Samplers," paper presented at 35th Annual Meeting of The American Society of Limnology and Oceanography, Florida State University, 19–22 March, 1972.

[14] Crowe, J. M. E., "The Use of Two Types of Artificial Substrates to Sample the Macro-invertebrates of the Rat River, 1970," paper presented at 19th Annual Meeting of the Midwest Benthological Society, Notre Dame University, 24–26 March, 1971.

[15] Fullner, R. W., *Journal of the Water Pollution Control Federation*, Vol. 43, No. 3, 1971, pp. 494–499.

[16] Prins, R. and Black, W., in *Reservoir Fisheries and Limnology*, G. E. Hall, Ed., American Fisheries Society Special Publication 8, 1971, pp. 203–208.

[17] Jacobi, G. Z., *Transactions of the American Fisheries Society*, Vol. 100, No. 1, pp. 136–138.

[18] *Standard Methods for the Examination of Water and Wastewater*, American Public Health Association, 13th ed, 1971.

[19] Hester, F. E. and Dendy, J. S., *Transactions of the American Fisheries Society*, Vol. 91, No. 4, 1962, pp. 420–421.

[20] Arthur, J. W. and Horning, W. B., *American Midland Naturalist*, Vol. 82, No. 1, 1969, pp. 83–99.

[21] Hilsenhoff, W. L., *Limnology and Oceanography*, Vol. 14, No. 3, 1969, pp. 465–471.

[22] Bull, C. J., *The Progressive Fish-Culturist*, Vol. 30, No. 2, 1968, pp. 119–120.

[23] Yongue, W. H., Jr. and Cairns, J., Jr., "Colonization and Succession of Fresh Water Protozoans in Polyurethane Foam Suspended in a Small Pond in North Carolina," *Notulae Naturae*, Vol. 443, 1971.

[24] Besch, W., Hofmann, W., and Ellenberger, W., *Annals de Limnologie*, Vol. 3, No. 2, 1967, pp. 331–367.

[25] Besch, W. and Hofmann, W., *Annals de Limnologie*, Vol. 4, No. 2, 1968, pp. 235–263.

[26] Grzenda, A. R. and Brehmer, M. L., *Limnology and Oceanography*, Vol. 5, No. 2, 1960, pp. 190–194.

[27] Waters, T. F., *Limnology and Oceanography*, Vol. 6, No. 4, 1961, pp. 486–488.

[28] Kevern, N. R., Wilhm, J. L., and Van Dyne, G. M., *Limnology and Oceanography*, Vol. 11, No. 4, 1966, pp. 499–502.

[29] Armstrong, R., Goldman, C. R., and Fujita, D. K., *Limnology and Oceanography,* Vol. 16, No. 1, 1971, pp. 137–139.

[30] Sladeckova, A., *Botanical Review,* Vol. 28, No. 2, 1962, pp. 286–350.

[31] Percival, E. and Whitehead, H., *Journal of Ecology,* Vol. 17, 1929, pp. 282–314.

[32] Sprules, W. M., "An Ecological Investigation of Stream Insects in Algonquin Park, Ontario," University of Toronto Studies, Biological Series, No. 56, 1947, pp. 1–81.

[33] Wilhm, J. L. and Dorris, T. C., *BioScience,* Vol. 18, No. 6, 1968, pp. 477–481.

[34] Cairns, J., Jr., Albaugh, D. W., Busey, F., and Chanay, M. D., *Journal of the Water Pollution Control Federation,* Vol. 40, No. 9, 1968, pp. 1607–1615.

[35] Needham, P. R. and Usinger, R. L., *Hilgardia,* Vol. 24, 1956, pp. 383–409.

R. M. Gerhold [1]

Mobile Bioassay Laboratories

REFERENCE: Gerhold, R. M., **"Mobile Bioassay Laboratories,"** *Biological Methods for the Assessment of Water Quality, ASTM STP 528,* American Society for Testing and Materials, 1973, pp. 242–256.

ABSTRACT: Mobile laboratories with flow-through systems utilize actual receiving waters with their unique physical, chemical, and biological characteristics which are known to influence the toxicity of environmental contaminants. Mobile bioassay laboratories have definite advantages over fixed laboratories with reference to data collection for enforcement of water-quality standards, for pest-control studies, and for pollution-engineering and research. Such laboratories may also be used to investigate the tainting of edible aquatic organisms.

A survey of mobile bioassay equipment was provided, with a listing of informational sources.

Greater use can be made of the mobile bioassay concept in research applied to pollution abatement than has been previously done. The equipment should be designed for maximum versatility consistent with the objectives of the study and with the budgetary limitations. In many instances, mobile or semi-permanent streamside or floating laboratories can be used to gain basic understanding of the environmental factors affecting the growth, development, reproduction, and behavior of aquatic organisms. This information is needed to better understand the long-term effects of pollutants on these organisms.

KEY WORDS: bioassay, laboratories, mobile equipment, portable equipment, environmental tests, toxicology, design, aquatic biology, fisheries, toxicity, water quality, pollution abatement, water pollution

The purpose of this report is to focus attention on some of the recent and current uses of mobile bioassay laboratories for the benefit of potential designers and users of such research facilities, to show advantages of mobile-lab bioassays as compared to fixed-lab bioassays, to define potential applications of these bioassays, and to indicate design problems.

---

[1] Section head, Environmental Toxicology, Industrial Bio-Test Laboratories, Inc., Northbrook, Ill. 60062.

. . . it is in nature that we wish the substances to be harmless; it is to nature that we must finally turn in our studies.[*1*, p. 214] [2]

Historical Background

The mobile laboratory is not a new concept. Such laboratories are currently in wide use by universities, industries, and governments as tools for environmental monitoring of physical and chemical air and water-quality characteristics[*2–4*]. Experience with these and with some of the mobile biological laboratories devoted to limnological[*5*] and desert research studies[*6*] provides guidance for the design of mobile laboratories for use in biomonitoring or toxicity bioassays.

Mobile biological laboratories have been both aquatic and terrestrial. Among the earliest types were the floating laboratories operated for river research during the periods 1896 to 1927, 1908 to 1930, and 1931 to 1951 by the Illinois Natural History Survey and its predecessor, the Illinois State Laboratory for Natural History[*7*]. Historically, floating laboratories have been larger and more permanent than those on wheels because of the magnitude or complexity of the studies. Many studies have been oriented toward basic research, including those of thermal effects of fixed-point sources of waste heat. Design problems related to self-contained power sources and remote operation in ocean or estuarine waters have been discussed for floating laboratories mounted on a 12½ by 38 ft scow[*7*], a 98½ ft barge[*8*], and a converted 32 by 110 ft WWII LSM[*9*]. Table 1 is a nonexhaustive compilation of existing and recently active units and is a source guide for individuals needing more detailed information.

Mobile laboratory bioassays have been conducted in which the species studied varied from pathogenic viruses[*10*] to humans[*11,12*]. The paper by Cox[*11*] is of particular interest for its details and discussion of design problems. Facilities for conducting mobile bioassays have varied in size from the "hip-pocket" category[*10*] and the hospital cart[*13*] to the converted house trailer[*14,15*], the motorized home[*16*], and the tractor trailer or van[*11*]. (See also unreferenced listings in Table 1.)

Justification for Mobile Bioassay Laboratories

Permanent laboratories cannot be built economically at each site of current or potential pollution at which bioassay information is needed. The many physical and chemical variables within receiving waters that affect toxicological evaluations are either continuously or intermittently changing and are difficult to simulate in artificial laboratory systems. Additionally, single or composite samples of the aquatic environment can-

---

[2] The italic numbers in brackets refer to the list of references appended to this paper.

TABLE 1—*A Compilation of Mobile Laboratories.*

Organization	Contact	Construction	Study Type[a]	Organisms Studied	Ref.[c]
		Facilities Used Primarily for Bioassays			
Central Institute for the Deaf	J. R. Cox	tractor trailer	R	humans	11
U.S. Bureau, Sport Fisheries & Wildlife Michigan Lamprey Control Operations	W. Gaylord	house trailer, 18 ft	Pe	lamprey larvae, rainbow trout	14
College of Dentistry, University Ky.	R. S. Fulghum	hospital cart	R	anaerobic bacteria	13
U.S. Army Chem. Corps. Biol. Lab. Ft. Detrick, Md.	W. R. Griffith	. . .	R	humans, animals, bacteria	12
Department Biol. Sciences, Stanford Univ.	H. A. Mooney	Dodge motor home 6.4 m, Model 210	R	plants	16
U.S. Dept. of Commerce, Nat'l Oceanic & Atmospheric Admin., Nat'l Marine Fisheries Service	G. R. Snyder	(1) "Van" (2) barge, 32 × 110 ft	R	dungeness crabs salmonid fish	b 9
Department Plant Pathology, University of California, Berkeley, Calif.	C. E. Yarwood	none: hand carried	R	seedling mung beans	10
Bureau of Water Management, Water Resources Commission, Michigan Department Natural Resources	M. Wuerthele	house trailer, 20 ft	E	fathead minnows	15
Oklahoma Oil Refiner's Waste Control Council & Oklahoma St. U., Stillwater	T. C. Dorris S. Burks	house trailer, 30 ft	R, Po	fish	b
American Petroleum Institute and Battelle Northwest Laboratory	W. Templeton	tractor trailers	R	fish, invertebrates	b
U.S. Environmental Protection Agency, Office of Water Programs, Wheeling, W. Va.	H. R. Preston	tractor trailer	R, Po	fathead minnows	b
U.S. Environmental Protection Agency Field Investigations Center, Cincinnati, Ohio	A. Lucas T. Bradech	self-propelled cab and chassis, 22 ft	E	fathead minnows	b
U.S. Environmental Protection Agency Div. Surveillance & Analysis, Region IV, Athens, Ga.	W. Peltiere	house trailer, 19 ft	E	fish, invertebrates, algae	b

TABLE 1—*Continued.*

Organization	Contact	Construction	Study Type [a]	Organisms Studied	Ref [c]
California State Water Pollution Control Laboratory, Nimbus Fish Hatchery, Sacramento, Calif.	R. Hansen, F. Kopperdahl, D. Wilson	house trailer	E	king salmon	[b]
Facilities Not Specifically Used for Bioassays					
Mobil Chem. Co., Agri-Division	F. Yelenik	motorized home, 21 ft	A, W		2
Orange Co. Health Dept., Calif.	H. W. Brydon	trailer, 19 ft	R	flies, poultry	31
Department of Zoology & Institute of Fisheries Research, Univ. of N.C.	M. R. Carriker	houseboat, 12½ × 30 ft	R	estuarine molluscs	7
Gulf Research & Development Co.	T. J. Puzniak	(1) motorized "van," Dodge chassis	Po. A	...	4
		(2) tractor trailer, 28 ft	Po. W	...	4
Limnological Research Center, University of Minnesota	R. O. Megard, J. Shapiro	truck-mounted camper	R	...	5
Fisheries Research Institute, College of Fisheries, Univ. Washington, Seattle	L. S. Smith	WW II LSM, 98½ ft	R	salmon	8
Desert Research Institute, Univ. of Nevada	F. Went	(1) house trailer, 16 ft	R	various organisms	6
		(2) house trailer, 29 ft	R	various organisms	6
Traveler's Research Corporation	J. E. Yocum	small open 2-wheel trailer	R, A	...	3

[a] R = Research, E = Enforcement, Po = Pollution Control, Pe = Pest Control, A = Air Monitoring, W = Water Chemistry.
[b] Personal communication.
[c] Numbers refer to the list of references appended to this paper.

not duplicate naturally fluctuating hydrological conditions. The factors most often cited which influence toxicity of components in the aquatic environment are pH (which can influence the molecular form, and hence the toxicity, of many compounds), the calcium and magnesium hardness (a moderating factor in the toxicity of heavy metals), the concentrations of dissolved gases (especially oxygen), and temperature (which, when above or below physiological thresholds, induces stresses that influence the organism's susceptibility to toxicants). Other important considerations are the shifting nutrient loads of various waters and the dependent populations of organisms of various types which can influence the susceptibility of organisms to toxicants. Natural waters upstream from waste outfalls contain "background" toxicants that can affect the acclimation of organisms to conditions within their environment[1]. These and other changing, interrelated, and often imprecisely known factors dictate the design both of in-the-environment studies and of continuous-flow bioassay equipment to best simulate the aquatic community's total environment. The on-site aquatic bioassay thus offers a practical and economical way to answer questions about the toxic conditions of natural aquatic systems, to establish a scientific criterion for regulatory standards, and to collect the data necessary to enforce these standards. It also provides a means for municipalities or industries to evaluate the effectiveness of abatement efforts and provides chemical, sanitary, and industrial engineers with appropriate stream criteria for the design or modification of treatment systems and waste outfalls.

Applications

General

Facilities for on-site mobile bioassays can be justified in any biological study in which field measurements are required from various locations at relatively frequent time intervals. The use of mobile bioassay procedures to evaluate biological problems of water pollution and aquatic toxicity are described below.

Research

The control of important physical, chemical, and biological variables is essential for any well-designed investigation. A mobile unit can support both the investigators and the appropriate instruments to best control these variables at on-site locations.

Providing data from which regulatory standards for receiving waters will be developed is a challenging and difficult task for the aquatic biologist. Standards for toxic materials have often been based on median toxicity limits (TLm) determined in acute, usually four-day, toxicity tests. Even the use of "application factors" (some fraction of the TLm) may not provide for levels that will be safe for prolonged exposure periods to some organisms important to the maintenance of the total endemic aquatic community. Information is needed on the effects of pollutants on biotic populations and communities as well as on the growth, development, and reproduction of individual organisms. Determination of biologically-derived "application factors" requires sophisticated on-site bioassays; and mobile units, as well as semi-permanent installations,[17-20] will undoubtedly be important in the acquisition of such factors.

Enforcement

Regulatory standards imply procedures designed to ensure compliance. A commonly applied procedure is litigation, with the associated presentation of evidence. Several federal and state regulatory agencies presently use mobile bioassay laboratories to collect data for such evidence (see "E" designations, Table 1). The most active of these agencies to date is the Michigan Department of Natural Resources[15]. Most of the agencies are planning to increase usage of mobile facilities, based on field testing of prototype units during the past three years. The U.S. Environmental Protection Agency is planning mobile bioassay facilities for each region.[3]

If an industrial or municipal facility in Michigan is suspected of introducing toxic wastes into a stream, that facility is invited by the state to provide both access to the waste outfall and space to locate an 8 by 20 ft mobile bioassay laboratory. The facility is also requested to supply electric power to the mobile laboratory to operate the necessary lights, heaters, continuous-flow automatic chemical monitors, pumps, filters, air conditioners, and other associated equipment.

Those facilities which wish to be considered cooperative usually agree to the above approach. The state then constructs a temporary wooden weir box and installs the necessary instruments and automatic samplers to monitor both the discharge flow and the receiving stream flow. Submersible pumps placed both upstream of (namely, outside the influence of the discharge) and in or near the discharge weir box circulate the two waters through separate flexible hoses (and filtering units if necessary) into head reservoirs inside the mobile laboratory. Fathead minnows or other suitable higher organisms are acclimated for one week in cages placed upstream from the discharge and are then exposed for 96 h in the mobile laboratory (in duplicate, one-liter plastic chambers) to stream water containing various proportions of the discharge. Separate head tanks

---

[3] Personal communication with A. Lucas, Environmental Protection Agency, Cincinnati, Ohio.

and a unique series of capillary tubes allow precise mixing of the upstream and discharge waters to provide the desired dilutions of the discharge water. Data from these 96-h exposures are related, through arbitrary application factors, to the measured discharge flows and the expected ten-year low flows of the stream. The normal on-site study time of two weeks allows for repeat exposures.

Many enforcement officials consider the tainting of edible fish, molluscs, or crustaceans as a valid concern for enforcement procedures. Tainting is also of concern to the petroleum refining industry[21] and to the paper industry[22]. Tainting studies can provide a practical, sensitive index to the efficiency of the removal of organic compounds in industrial or municipal waste treatment procedures. Many materials that can affect tastes or odors are absorbed rapidly through the gills of aquatic organisms. A major portion of tainting of some organisms with certain chemicals is quickly lost when the organisms are exposed to uncontaminated waters. This reversal increases the value of these studies for the monitoring of accidental spills. Exposure chambers housed in mobile units and supplied continuously with waters from above and below potential sources of contamination could provide data on the tainting potential of the wastes. Criteria for locating caged specimens within the receiving-water body for specified exposure periods could also be established from these data. Since it would probably be quite difficult to assemble a highly trained taste panel at the site of a mobile field lab in operation, live specimens can be shipped to the taste-testing laboratory. If live-shipping is not feasible, specimens may be frozen prior to shipment.

Pest Control

One of the best examples of the practical application of mobile laboratory bioassay data is the successful chemical control of the sea lamprey in the upper Great Lakes[14]. The havoc once inflicted on fisheries by this non-native pest and its subsequent control have been well documented [23–25]. This control has permitted the establishment of a multimillion dollar sport fishery that has economically revitalized several communities in the upper Great Lakes region.

The ongoing lamprey-control bioassay program is conducted in customized 18-ft house trailers. The toxicity of the selective larvicide 3-trifluoromethyl-4-nitrophenol (TFM) is evaluated using stream waters in static, 20-h acute toxicity bioassays on hatchery-reared fingerling rainbow trout and on lamprey larvae collected from the stream to be treated. Since it was found that the toxicity of TFM was temperature-dependent, stream water was pumped continuously into the trailer to water baths within which the assay chambers were placed. Toxicity data from these bioassays permit selection of dosages of TFM that kill lamprey larvae for significant lengths of the stream, but kill few gamefish. The design problems in the development of this bioassay procedure were formidable since as many as 20 workers had to be supported in the field. Power, food, and fish-holding facilities had to be self-contained and highly portable.

Other pest-control problems, such as rough-fish control using rotenone or antimycin, may be studied using streamside or mobile bioassay units[26].

Engineering

Aquatic biologists will be called upon to furnish engineers with necessary information as water-quality criteria are established and updated and as enforcement of standards is implemented by regulatory agencies. The mobile bioassay laboratory will be important in furnishing the chemical engineer with precise and timely information on the effects of planned or implemented process changes that may affect effluents and, hence, the receiving waters. Data collected from mobile bioassay studies will aid the hydraulic or sanitary engineer in the evaluation of existing waste treatment procedures, in the design of new waste treatment systems and in the design of waste outfalls so as to take maximum advantage of a stream's assimilatory capacity. The engineer, for example, may be expected to measure and predict accurately flow velocities and turbulence factors, but he cannot be expected to determine the thermal preference or the physiological requirements of benthic invertebrates. The on-site bioassay can be used to provide management personnel with timely data on the effectiveness of abatement expenditures: Was the investment justified by a significant stream improvement? Will similar expenditures at other sites be equally effective?

Design Problems

General

The concept of mobility for biological research implies three characteristics: on-site operation, self-containment, and compactness. For the budget-conscious designer, all these considerations offer a formidable challenge if the unit is to be multi-mission oriented. Investigations that are lengthy or located at great distances from the base laboratory will require greater self-containment characteristics. The greater the scope of the projects undertaken, the greater will be the manpower, space, and logistical support requirements.

Research Objectives

The determination of the general hazard of potential aquatic toxicants implies long-term studies of growth, development, behavior, and reproduction. Coupling this type of investigation with multi-species evaluations and biological community assessments will require lengthy studies at any one site. Research problems of this type might best be solved by a small team of biologists stationed in a modest permanent or semi-permanent stream-side laboratory[17].

On the other hand, missions directed toward determination of acute toxicity from point sources of contamination, the tainting of edible species, or pest-control problems using one or two species will reduce the complexity of the study design to a degree that mobile facilities may be effectively employed.

Equipment

References 5 through 9 and 14 through 17 describe various structural, space, and equipment specifications. Some of the problems and alternative solutions are described in the following.

Size—Mobile laboratories have varied in size from the "hip-pocket" category consisting of several petri dishes, filter pads, and a pair of forceps carried by a single researcher[10] to floating vessels with lengths in excess of 100 ft[9]. There are many tractor trailer and mobile home manufacturers who design custom facilities. For those institutions with adequate budgets and clearly defined missions, the trailer customizer can be of great assistance. For others, the availability of money and mechanicians for the project will govern both the size of the unit and the ability to perform major equipment modifications when missions change. The ability to locate close to shorelines is important. A small trailer or camper truck can gain closer access to sites than can tractor trailers. However, tractor trailers may offer greater rigidity and road clearance which may be important in certain applications.

A multi-species testing capability should be the goal of every designer.

> . . . knowledge of the effects of water quality changes on any single level of organization of life is really of little value unless it can be related to knowledge of the effect on the other levels.[1, p. 391]

The need for multi-species evaluations is also stressed in *Standard Methods* [27, pp. 574–575]. However, multi-species capabilities will require larger laboratory units, increased electrical power needs (for lights, pumps, heater/coolers, etc.), greater holding capacities, and a greater requirement for analytical and observational tools.

Strength—The designer of a mobile unit requiring large tank volumes for holding specimens should consult with the unit's manufacturer for gross weight-limit specifications to ensure that the anticipated load will not exceed the unit's ability either to support it *in situ* or to carry it (if holding in-transit is required or if the unit is to be used to haul dilution water or waste water to the site of bioassay).

If a semitrailer or van is modified for use as a mobile bioassay laboratory, it would be unwise to cut window openings, since experience indicates that these windows are easily broken due to the vibrations and stresses encountered during highway travel.

Traction—The question of joint or separate traction for wheeled assay units is one to consider carefully. Joint traction, in which the transporting unit is nonseparable from the laboratory unit (namely, such as a unitized delivery truck), is probably quite adequate for limited scope, minimal equipment bioassays. However, a strong case can be made for the added flexibility achieved by separate traction units, in which a pickup truck is used to carry or pull the laboratory unit[6]. A separate traction unit can provide for many auxiliary needs at the site of operation, such as serving as a carrier for supplies, boats and fish transport containers, or as a platform for auxiliary power generators. It is desirable to separate generating equipment from the bioassay housing because the noise, vibrations, and odors produced can cause considerable stress both on many assay species and the investigators. The Michigan Department of Natural Resources (Bureau of Water Management, Water Resources Commission) plans to expand enforcement bioassays by employing a truck-mounted camper unit which combines several favorable features of joint and separate traction. Once at the site of operation, the camper unit is established on dry ground and leveled with jacks. The ¾ ton pickup truck is then freed for auxiliary chores (personal communication; see also Ref 5).

Energy—Unit designs that incorporate electrical outlet jacks on the exterior of the bioassay housing unit are most flexible. When studies are performed close to an available line-power source, an appropriately sized cable can be used to connect the unit to the source. Went[6] used 60 A 3-wire cables 660 m in length to transmit power to a mobile unit with practically no voltage losses. When a line-power source is unavailable, a portable generator (mounted either on a truck, the bioassay unit, or a two-wheel trailer) can be used to provide power. Gasoline-fueled generators are often employed for short-term or infrequent operations, but diesel- or propane-fueled units have proved more reliable for continuous long-term maintenance-free use. The Michigan lamprey control program currently uses a 10-kilowatt propane-fueled generator, mounted on a two-wheel trailer, and equipped with a six-day supply of fuel in cylinders. This generator supplied the electrical requirements of the bioassay unit, a 36-ft cook trailer, and a 40-ft sleeper trailer in support of as many as 16 individuals.

Information on the design, availability, installation, and efficiency of heating and air conditioning units is readily available from trailer manufacturers. Both propane- and electrically-powered units are available, and many are both compact and efficient for use in extreme weather conditions.

Insulation that is adequate under the majority of severe weather conditions can be provided by 2 in. of polyurethane foam. However, severe cold weather presents formidable problems in preventing the freezing of water lines. In some cases this problem may be solved either by increasing flow rates, by wrapping hoses with special heating wires, or both. Overall electrical power requirements will be increased in either case.

Instrumentation—Many types of instruments (aside from the usual dissolved oxygen or pH meter, colorimeter, fluorometer, etc.) that may be of special interest to aquatic biologists and to physiologists may be adapted for continuous-flow on-site studies in compact laboratories. Three such instruments will be cited that are proving to be valuable in monitoring the subtle effects of pollutants on fish. With some modifications, these instruments should also be valuable in studies of the larger invertebrates.

1. The Flowing Water Respiratory Chamber or Swim Tunnel[28], which provides extremely reliable determinations of respiration rates on small- to medium-size organisms;

2. The Electrode Chamber[29], which monitors electronically the rate and magnitude of breathing and other movements of freely-moving aquatic animals; and

3. The Light-Beam-Interruption Counter[30], which indicates the movements and general position of fish in aquaria.

All of these instruments lend themselves to continuous recording, analog-digital conversion, mini-computers, and teleprinting devices.

Accommodations—The scope of facilities necessary to accommodate the requisite needs of the research workers depends on the study site, the length of the study, and the number of people involved. Requirements for sleeping quarters, self-contained food services, and sanitary facilities will be greater for extended operations in remote areas. For these operations, multi-trailer caravans will be required[6]. The experiences of the U. S. Bureau of Sport Fisheries and Wildlife in their lamprey control operations should be of value in guiding others for estimates of facility requirements[14]. For short-term operations near communities, investigators may best be accommodated with local food and housing through commercial sources.

Static versus Continuous Flow—Valuable information can be gained from certain acute static bioassays, as shown by the lamprey control programs[14,23–25]. Although pollution incidents characterized by single or infrequent occurrences may require only static bioassays, the greatest potential for mobile bioassay laboratories is with flow-through bioassays. Although water temperature and continuous aeration can be controlled for some static bioassays, flow-through exposure chambers provide both this control and the greatly added benefit of closer simulation of all stream factors.

Access to Waterways—An ideal study site for a point-source discharge combines several features: a roadway close to the water's edge for the mobile unit, close proximity to the discharge outfall, stream velocity and flow patterns such that dilution water obtained a short distance upstream from the outfall never includes portions of the discharge water, and the nearby availability of electric power. In practice, this ideal combination is seldom found. For example, although other characteristics may be favorable, stream access may not be closely available. The mobile unit's pumps must then be equipped with flexible conduits long enough to reach the stream, and the facility's hosing and water lifting (pumping) capabilities may be seriously taxed, depending on distances and elevations.

Therefore, the designer must consider alternative solutions. One alternative is to haul either upstream or discharge water (the choice being dependent on the differential accessibility of the two) to the mobile unit rather than pumping both. In either event, the assays will be continuous, but one component will be supplied to the flow-through exposure chambers continuously from a batch rather than being pumped directly from the stream. If both options are available, the choice should be to use a continuous supply of dilution water, with discharge water being supplied from a transported container filled with a representative sample. This option should best simulate the biologically important water chemistry and temperature characteristics of the stream.

Dilution Apparatus—A bioassay is the determination of the relative strength of a substance by comparing its effect on a test organism with that of a standard preparation. The mechanical diluter by which the "substance" (waste or toxicant) and the "standard preparation" (uncontaminated receiving water) are proportioned continuously together is a critical component of all continuous-flow toxicity bioassays and is essential if dose-response data are required. One basic requirement for diluters is that they be relatively maintenance-free for extended periods. Another important feature is a "fail-safe" feature (that is, if the diluent supply fails, the toxicant supply will be automatically shut off). For certain studies, automatic aeration devices and alarms should be coupled with the fail-safe feature. Finally, a diluter for use in a mobile laboratory should be both rugged and compact. A brief listing of several types of diluters which likely can be adapted for use in mobile units is as follows:

1. The Mount-Type "Proportional" Diluter[31]—Extremely accurate; useful with highly toxic wastes; incorporates fail-safe features; maintenance free; wide range of possible dilution factors; requires no external power

source; can be adapted to various total flow rates; not available commercially.

2. Peristaltic Electric Metering Pumps—Depending on the manufacturer, a wide range of sizes, flows, and accuracies are available; requires periodic calibration and tube replacement.

3. The Michigan Diluter[15]—Simple design; wide range of flows and dilutions possible; requires no external power source; inflows must be filtered; capillary tubes and "head" govern flow rates; capillaries require frequent cleaning; no "fail-safe" feature; not available commercially.

4. Flow-Proportioning Devices[32]—Simple device; suitable for relatively nontoxic industrial effluents and relatively high flows; design of fail-safe features not published, but probably could be devised; relatively maintenance free; requires no external power source; questionable accuracy over long periods.

5. The Oregon Diluter[33]—Very simple design; requires no external power source; incorporates some features of both the Michigan Diluter and the Mount "Proportional" Diluter and probably requires less maintenance than either; fail-safe feature can be incorporated for most applications.

Conclusions

Although some current use is being made of several types of mobile bioassay laboratories, the full potential for their use in on-site environmental investigations has yet to be realized.

The most practical present applications of mobile bioassay units are in applied research areas as aids for engineering design, in investigations to determine water-quality criteria, in enforcement of water-quality standards, and in aquatic pest-control studies.

Ideally, the design of mobile bioassay laboratories should be guided primarily by the mission of the sponsor and secondarily by considerations of economy and flexibility.

References

[1] Warren, C. E., *Biology and Water Pollution Control*, W. B. Saunders, Philadelphia, 1971, p. 214.
[2] "Mobil Takes Action to Prevent Pollution," *Farm Chemicals*, Vol. 131, No. 3, March 1968, p. 34.
[3] Yocum, J. E., Clink, W. L., and Coke, W. A., *Journal of the Air Pollution Control Association*, Vol. 21, No. 5, 1971, pp. 251–259.
[4] Puzniak, T. J., Benusa, W. F., and Condron, J. A., *Proceedings*, 16th Annual Symposium of the Instrument Society of America, Pittsburgh, Pa., Vol. 8, 25–27. May 1970, pp. V4/1–V4/5.
[5] Megard, R. O. and Shapiro, J., *Limnology and Oceanography*, Vol. 11, No. 3, July 1966, pp. 420–422.
[6] Went, F., *Bioscience*, Vol. 18, No. 4, April 1968, pp. 293–297.

[7] Carriker, M. R., "Use of a Mobile Laboratory for Ecological Estuarine Research," *Estuarine Bulletin*, Vol. 6, Nos. 1 and 2, 1961, pp. 9–16.

[8] Smith, L., *Laboratory Practice*, Vol. 19, No. 7, July 1970, pp. 709–712.

[9] Snyder, G. R., Blahm, T. H., and McConnell, R. J., "Floating Laboratory for Study of Aquatic Organisms and Their Environment," United States Department of Commerce, National Oceanic and Atmospheric Administration, National Marine Fisheries Service, Circular 356, Seattle, May 1971.

[10] Yarwood, C. E., *Plant Disease Reporter*, Vol. 48, No. 1, Jan. 1964, pp. 24, 25.

[11] Cox, J. R., *Noise Control*, Vol. 3, No. 92, 1957, pp. 44–48.

[12] Griffith, W. R., *American Review of Respiratory Diseases*, Vol. 89, No. 2, 1964, pp. 240–249.

[13] Fulghum, R. S., *Applied Microbiology*, Vol. 21, No. 4, April 1971, pp. 769, 770.

[14] Howell, J. H. and Marquette, W. M., "Use of Mobile Bioassay Equipment in the Chemical Control of Sea Lamprey," Special Scientific Report—Fisheries No. 418, USDI, Fish and Wildlife Service, Washington, D. C., April 1962.

[15] Wuerthele, M., "Description of Michigan's Continuous Flow Bioassay Trailer Laboratory," presented at the Division of Water, Air and Waste Chemistry, American Chemical Society, Washington, D. C., 13–15 Sept. 1971.

[16] Mooney, H. A., Dunn, E. L., Harrison, A. T., Morrow, P. A., Bartholomew, B., and Hays, R. L., *Photosynthetica*, Vol. 5, No. 2, 1971, pp. 128–132.

[17] Stober, Q. J., "A Small Bioassay Laboratory Designed for Experimental Thermal Effects Evaluations," Fisheries Research Institute, College of Fisheries, University of Washington, Seattle, Circular 72–1, Jan. 1972.

[18] Henderson, C. and Pickering, Q. H., *Journal of the American Water Works Association*, Vol. 55, June 1963, pp. 715–720.

[19] Cairns, J. Jr., "Don't Be Half-Safe—The Current Revolution in Bioassay Techniques," Purdue University Engineering Extension Series, No. 121, 21st Industrial Waste Conference Proceedings, 1966, pp. 559–567.

[20] Sparks, R. E., Cairns, J. Jr., and Waller, W. T., "Using Fish As Sensors In Industrial Plants to Prevent Pollution In Streams," 35th Annual Meeting, American Society of Limnology and Oceanography, Inc., Florida State University, Tallahassee, 19–22 March 1972.

[21] Krishnaswami, S. K. and Kupchanko, E. E., *Journal of the Water Pollution Control Federation*, Vol. 41, Research Supplement, May 1969, pp. R189–R196.

[22] Shumway, D. L. and Chadwick, G. C., *Water Research*, Vol. 5, 1971, pp. 997–1003.

[23] Dees, L. T., "Sea Lamprey," Fishery Leaflet 580, USDI, Fish and Wildlife Service, Washington, D. C., Aug. 1965.

[24] McVeigh, E. J., "Showdown in the Great Lakes," Dow Diamond, June 1958.

[25] Howell, J. N., "The Life Cycle of the Sea Lamprey and a Toxicological Approach to its Control," *Phylogeny of Immunity*, University of Florida Press, 1966.

[26] Gilderhus, P. A., "Exposure Times Necessary for Antimycin and Rotenone to Eliminate Certain Freshwater Fish," *Journal of the Fisheries Research Board of Canada*, Vol. 29, No. 2, Feb. 1972.

[27] *Standard Methods for the Examination of Water and Wastewater*, American Public Health Association, American Water Works Association, and Water Pollution Control Federation, 13th ed., 1971.

[28] O'Hara, J., *Water Research*, Vol. 5, 1971, pp. 143–145.

[29] Spoor, W. A., Neiheisel, T. W., and Drummond, R. A., *Transactions*, American Fisheries Society, Vol. 100, No. 1, Jan. 1971, pp. 22–28.

[30] Cairns, J. Jr., Sparks, R. E., and Waller, W. T., "The Design of A Continuous Flow Biological Early Warning System For Industrial Use," presented at the 27th Purdue University Industrial Waste Conference, 2–4 May 1972.

[31] Mount, D. I. and Brungs, W. A., *Water Research,* Pergamon Press, Vol. 1, 1967, pp. 21–29.
[32] Jackson, H. W. and Brungs, W. A., *Proceedings,* 21st Purdue Industrial Waste Conference, Part I, Vol. 50, No. 2, March 1967, pp. 117–124.
[33] Chadwick, G. C., unpublished, "Diluter Diagram," Oak Creek Laboratories, Department of Fisheries and Wildlife, Oregon State University, Corvallis, Ore., Nov. 1971.
[34] Brydon, H. W., *Mosquito News,* Vol. 25, No. 2, 1965, pp. 160–164.